THE EXPLOSION OF SCIENCE

The Physical Universe

485 illustrations, including 143 in full color
and 144 in two colors

MEREDITH PRESS   NEW YORK

The

THE EXPLOSION OF SCIENCE

Physical

Edited by

SIR BERNARD LOVELL AND TOM MARGERISON

Universe

Texts by

COLIN BAYLEY   T. F. GASKELL   M. A. JASWON

SIR BERNARD LOVELL   TOM MARGERISON

P. T. MATTHEWS   G. D. MUIR   G. J. WHITROW

Designed and produced by THAMES AND HUDSON

MANAGING EDITOR: Max Parrish OBE, MA

EDITORIAL AND RESEARCH: Stephen England MA;
Ruth Gardiner BA

ART EDITOR: Tony Birks DFA, MA

DRAWINGS IN COLOR: Laszlo Acs; Gordon Cramp;
David Cox; Gordon Davies; Barry Evans; Clive
Tunnicliffe

PROCESS WORK: Schwitter Ltd Zurich

Set in Lutetia and Brede vette Antieke and printed in
Holland by Meijer Wormerveer N.V.
Bound by Van Rijmenam N.V. The Hague, Holland

Copyright © 1967 by Thames and Hudson London

Published in the United States of America
by Meredith Press, Des Moines and New York, 1967
Library of Congress Catalog Card Number: 67–12219

FOREWORD

It is always difficult to understand the age in which one lives. The trivial things swamp the significant in the mere process of living. And the most significant of all often pass unnoticed in the contemporary scene. But one thing at least is obvious about the twentieth century: historians will see it as a clear-cut period of revolution, much more sharp and stormy than earlier periods of change like the age of exploration, or even the industrial revolution.

We are living in what has been called the explosion of science, a period in which our rate of accumulating knowledge about the world and universe around us is galloping ahead more than 100 times as quickly as at the turn of the century. And with growing knowledge comes a growing ability to apply it. All around us new knowledge is being applied, sometimes well, often badly, to transform the way in which we live.

The reality of this explosion is not difficult to discover, qualitatively or quantitatively. Less than 40 years ago two young scientists at Cambridge University, using equipment they had made themselves out of part of a petrol pump, built the world's first particle accelerator and succeeded in splitting the atomic nucleus. Little more than 40 years before that the atom was regarded as the ultimate indivisible particle of matter. Today every major country has its own nuclear reactors, many of them generating electricity and feeding it undramatically to our homes. Military men take for granted the power of the nuclear missile. Scientists struggle to sort out the behaviour of the once indivisible nucleus and understand the strange symmetries of a hundred or more subnuclear 'particles'.

Or take the case of space research. Ten years ago one diminutive Sputnik bleeped its way across the skies, signalling back to earth the conditions it found on this first trip beyond the atmosphere. Today orbital space flight by teams of two or three men are almost commonplace. Spacecraft land on the moon and send back photographs of its surface. And it is now almost certain that within a few years man will set foot on the moon.

In quantitative terms it is a little more difficult to assess the explosion. The simplest way is to count the number of scientific papers published each year, or the quantity of literature in scientific libraries. Or one can assess the number of scientists working in laboratories, or the number graduating from universities. Or, perhaps most difficult, one can estimate the number of significant scientific discoveries made each year.

Whatever the method the result is almost the same. Scientific activities are doubling every 10 years, or, in other words, 90 per cent of all scientists and research workers who have ever existed are alive and working today. Meanwhile the growth of all other human activities is progressing at a much slower pace, doubling about every 40 years.

Clearly, in due course, the scientific explosion must burn itself out. It cannot continue for ever increasing at a rate which is faster than the population increase of the world! As the number of scientists increases—and there could be 2,000,000 by the end of this century—their efficiency will decrease, largely because communication will be insufficiently good to prevent them duplicating each other's work. But long before then the social implications of so much science will be enormous.

And science itself will change—indeed, it has already changed. The old disciplines ranging from mathematics to sociology have been dismembered and rearranged to make new subjects like radio-astronomy and molecular biology. For the non-professional scientist, and particularly the non-mathematician, it must all seem very confusing.

This book is an attempt to describe for him what is happening in the physical sciences now and what are the implications of these advances. Many of the ideas are complex, and difficult to make clear without the use of mathematics. However, we have tried. The book has been arranged so that the fundamental ideas—which are relatively few in number—are described in the text part of the chapters, while the profusion of applications is indicated in the illustrated sections which follow each chapter.

In bringing these two elements together, the editors have found their task greatly lightened by the co-operation and expert advice of the authors, who have answered queries, guided the picture research and given invaluable help with the diagrams and captions. The final responsibility, however, for the choice and arrangement of the pictures, and for the captions, belongs to the publishers.

THE EDITORS

CONTENTS

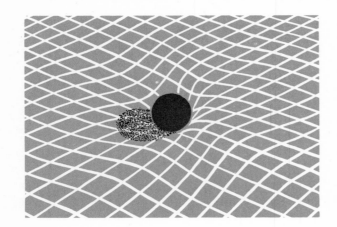
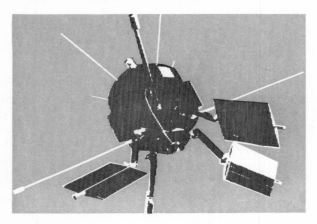

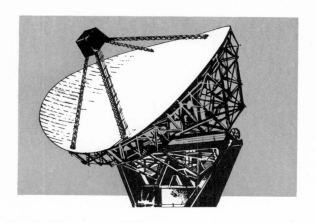
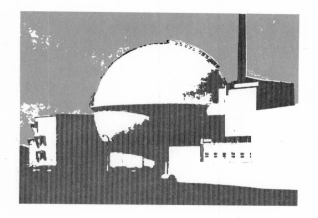
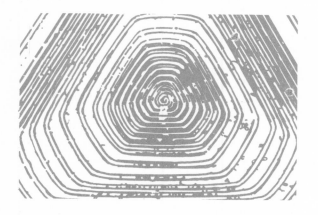

Acknowledgments

The editors and publishers are grateful for the continual help generously given by scholars, learned bodies and industrial organizations all over the world, in particular:

Atomic Power Constructions Ltd (Mr. H. Harding); Prof. L. F. Bates; British Drug Houses Ltd; British Petroleum Co. Ltd; Brookhaven National Laboratory; Centre d'études météorologiques spatiales; CERN—European Organization for Nuclear Research (M. Anthoine); CIBA; Crystal Structures Ltd (Dr. Nora Wooster); E. I. du Pont de Nemours & Co; A. Gallenkamp & Co. Ltd; Dr. Karl Gentil; High Altitude Observatory, Boulder, Colo.; Hughes Aircraft Co; Imperial Chemical Industries; International Business Machines; Howard J. Lobb & Partners (Mr. J. Dunoway); Dr. Kurt Mendelssohn, FRS; Mount Wilson and Palomar Observatories (Mr. Wm. C. Miller); Prof. Erwin W. Mueller; Mullard Ltd (Mr. E. J. Brazier); National Aeronautics and Space Administration; National Institute of Oceanography; Novosti Press Agency (APN) Moscow; Nuffield Radio Astronomy Laboratories, Jodrell Bank; Prof. C. F. Powell, FRS; Republic Observatory, Johannesburg (Dr. W. S. Finsen); Royal Astronomical Society; Dr. K. H. Ruddock; Rutherford High Energy Laboratory; Sacramento Peak Observatory Air Force Cambridge Research Laboratories; Schulsternwarte Rodewisch; Shell Chemicals Ltd; Prof. S. Tolansky, FRS; U. K. Atomic Energy Authority (Mrs. M. Evans); United States Information Services, London (Mr. Terence W. Franklin); U. S. Naval Observatory, Flagstaff, Arizona; Dr. James A. Van Allen; Vatican Observatory (Fr. D. J. K. O'Connell, SJ); Vereinigte Glanzstoff Fabriken AG; Dr. F. A. Ward; Academician N. L. Zenkevich.

1   Time and the shape of space

G. J. Whitrow

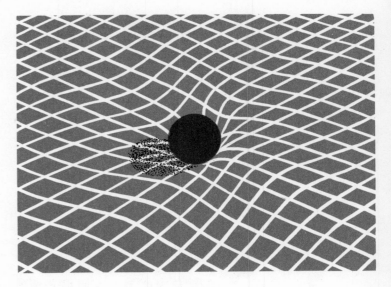

Time and the shape of space

One of the outstanding features of scientific investigation is the part played by measurement. So important is this that often a particular subject may be said to have ceased being a question for general speculation and have become a science only when effective methods of measurement were first successfully introduced into its study. The reason is that measurement fills a peculiar dual role. On the one hand, it provides an enormous wealth of detailed information which is not only valuable in itself but often leads us to ask questions and formulate problems which would never occur to us otherwise. On the other hand, measurement often yields the crucial tests which scientific theories and hypotheses must submit to and pass if they are to survive. Indeed, the practical success of scientific method is largely due to the fact that measurement provides a powerful method for deciding between rival theories. If imaginative curiosity and speculation are the life-blood of science, submission to the test of measurement may be said to be its infallible rule of health. Many a hypothesis which seemed qualitatively plausible and even brilliant when originally formulated has soon withered away when examined in the fierce light of quantitative investigation. Conversely, detailed quantitative corroboration can enormously increase the confidence which we feel in a particular theory.

A famous and easily understood example of the power of the quantitative approach to a scientific problem is provided by William Harvey's discovery of the circulation of the blood, in the first part of the 17th century. Harvey began by assuming that there is some analogy between the action of the heart and its one-way valves and that of a pump. This meant that he thought of the ebb and flow of the blood in essentially mechanical terms, as if it were a problem of hydraulics. Most of the observations which guided his thought had in fact been made by his predecessors, but he was the first to exploit the idea that the flow of blood in the body proceeds continuously in the same direction all the time. He argued as follows.

Suppose the left ventricle of the heart holds only two ounces and that with each beat this amount is forced into the aorta but, so as to be on the safe side in our assumptions, let us assume that only a quarter of this is sent into the artery. In half an hour the heart normally makes considerably more than a thousand beats. Therefore, in that interval of time there is poured through it more than five hundred ounces of blood—a greater quantity than is to be found in the whole body. Harvey therefore concluded that the blood must move, as it were, in a circle and return to the heart.

The force of this argument is essentially quantitative. It is an outstanding example of how an adequate explanation of a natural process was discovered by invoking considerations of this kind. Harvey's work was the starting point of the modern science of physiology, and has been aptly described by a leading historian of science, the late Charles Singer, as the first milestone on the road to the rationalization of biological thought.

This momentous investigation involved only the very crudest measurements of time and weight and a little elementary arithmetic. If we turn now to one of the latest achievements of modern science and technology, the successful launching and return of a man in a capsule designed for orbiting the earth, we find that the measurements and calculations involved are of such complexity that they require the full resources of the latest electronic computers. Indeed, so obvious does it now seem to us that measurement is an essential part of science that it needs a considerable effort of mind to imagine how men regarded the world in the days when this habit of thought was not cultivated.

The two fundamental concepts in which this habit first developed were time and space. Any attempt to understand the foundations and general nature of modern science must include some account of these concepts and of their measurement. Indeed, the comparative failure of ancient science, primarily cultivated by the Greeks and those influenced by them, was due to the severe restrictions imposed on their investigations by the limitations of their ideas of space and time and of their instruments of measurement.

Galileo feels his pulse

One of the peculiarities of modern civilization is our acute consciousness of time. Lewis Mumford claims that the clock more than any other artifact is the key-machine of the modern industrial age. By its essential nature, 'it dissociated time from human events and helped create the belief in an independent world of mathematically measurable sequences: the special world of science'. Conversely, primitive people seem to have little sense of time and tend to live in a continual present. This is still the case with races such as the Australian aborigines. Although aboriginal children are, broadly speaking, of similar mental capacity to white children, they find it extremely difficult to tell the time by a clock, and they cannot easily relate the time on a clock to the time of day. The reason presumably is that their lives, unlike ours, are not dominated by time.

Nevertheless, all primitive peoples have some idea of time and some method of reckoning based on astronomical observations. The Australian aborigine will fix the time for a proposed action by placing a stone in, say, the fork of a tree so that the sun will strike it at the agreed hour.

Generally, in primitive societies and in most ancient civilizations change was not conceived as a continuous process spread out in time but as discontinuous and abrupt. The principal changes in nature were regarded as sudden but inevitable occurrences in a cycle with a definite rhythm. Consequently, highly elaborate calendars went with extremely crude methods for measuring short intervals of time. As late as the end of the 16th century, Galileo used his pulse-beat to discover the regularity of the swinging pendulum.

One of the important differences between ancient and modern methods of measuring time is that in the former the day was not divided into twenty-four hours of equal duration. Instead, it was customary to divide the periods of daylight and darkness separately into twelve hours each. The length of these 'temporal' hours varied during the course of the year, although in the latitudes of the ancient Mediterranean civilizations the variations are much less than they would be in more northerly latitudes. This difference between ancient and modern hours is not just of antiquarian interest, for it illustrates vividly that the idea of measurement in terms of fixed and uniform units, which we nowadays take for granted, developed comparatively recently. Before modern developments in artificial illumination, day and night were sharply distinct, and most human activities were confined to the former.

The first approach to a continuous process for measuring time which could operate both by day and by night was the invention of the water-clock. Early Egyptian water-clocks were usually cone-shaped stone vessels from which water was allowed to escape through a hole near the bottom, the time being indicated by the level of the water within them. Water-clocks or 'clepsydrae' were used by the Greeks and Romans. In these, to secure a uniform flow of water the pressure head was kept constant, and 'temporal' hours were indicated by varying either the rate of flow or the scale of hours according to the season of the year. In late antiquity these water-clocks were often complicated and ingenious in their operation.

From rough time to 'good' time

The crucial importance of the invention of the mechanical clock was due not so much to its accuracy, great as this eventually became, as to its dependence on a periodic instead of a continuous process. For this dependence on a mechanical motion which repeats itself over and over again led to a more precise concept of a unit of time. Despite attempts by astronomers in antiquity to introduce the hour of constant length, it was not generally adopted until the 14th century with the advent of the striking clock.

The origins of the invention of the mechanical clock are shrouded in mystery The first mechanical clocks of which we have reliable information were public clocks, the earliest being set up in Milan in 1335. Recent researches have shown that a possible precursor of the mechanical escapement of these medieval European clocks may have been a device described in a Chinese text written by Su Sung about the year 1090. This was an elaborate water-clock powered by a water-wheel which advanced in a step-by-step motion. Water was poured into a series of cups which emptied (or escaped) every quarter of an hour when the weight of water was sufficient to tilt a steelyard. The mechanism was then unlocked until the arrival of the next cup below the water stream, when it was locked again. An astronomical check on

fig 1

timekeeping was made by a sighting tube pointed to a selected star. The timekeeping was governed mainly by the flow of water rather than by the escapement action itself, and so it may perhaps be regarded as a rather remote first link between the timekeeping properties of a steady flow of liquid and those of mechanically produced oscillations.

Indeed the fundamental difference between a water-clock and a mechanical clock is that, in the latter, timekeeping is entirely governed by a periodic mechanical motion. The type of motion employed in the earliest mechanical clocks, known as the 'verge' escapement—probably from the Latin *virga* (a rod, or twig)—was one in which a heavy bar or 'foliot', pivoted near its centre, was pushed first one way and then the other by a toothed wheel which advanced through the space of one tooth for each double oscillation of the bar. The wheel was driven by a weight suspended from a drum. Since the bar had no natural period of its own, the rate of the clock was mainly controlled by the driving weight and was greatly affected by variations in friction of the driving mechanism. The accuracy was very low and clocks could not be relied on to keep time more closely than to about a quarter of an hour a day at best, and an error of an hour was not unusual. Until the middle of the 17th century mechanical clocks usually had but one hand and the dial was divided only into hours and quarters. The earliest clocks had no dials, and time was recorded purely by the striking mechanism. This is reflected in our word 'clock' which is derived from the French word *cloche*, meaning a bell.

The swinging pendulum

The development of modern science based on the idea of mathematically measurable sequences was for a long time hampered by the lack of any accurate mechanism for measuring small intervals of time. Thus, in his famous experiments on the rate of fall of bodies rolling down an inclined

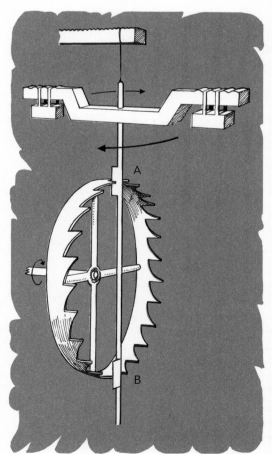

The first mechanical clocks of the 14th-16th centuries were driven by the pull of a weight falling under gravity. Such a pull, unchecked, would 'run away' as the weight gained speed, so the verge escapement was devised to govern it. The weight, through geared wheels (not shown), turns the toothed wheel (left). A vertical bar (the 'verge') carries projections A and B, at right angles to one another, which engage the teeth alternately. A, engaged, is pushed by the tooth and sets the verge and its heavy cross-bar turning. This causes B to engage and stops the wheel (tick). Now the pressure of the wheel on B brings the cross-bar to a halt and starts it swinging the other way, when B is released and A engages, stopping the wheel (tock). The wheel is thus released in a tick-tock movement and, working back through the geared wheels, controls the dial or striking mechanism accordingly. The clock is regulated by moving the weights on the cross-bar inwards (faster) or outwards. (1)

p 22
(2)

p 22
(3)

plane, Galileo measured time by weighing the quantity of water which emerged as a thin jet from a vessel with a small hole in it. For this and other reasons, it is not surprising that he obtained a value for the constant of acceleration that was less than half the correct amount. Nevertheless, a new era in the history of time measurement was due to Galileo's discovery that the time of swing of a simple pendulum depends only on its length, provided the arc of swing is small. To obtain a satisfactory timekeeper the pendulum had to be combined with clockwork to keep it swinging and to count the number of swings. In his old age, Galileo (who died in 1642) worked on this problem with his son Vicenzio and left drawings of a pendulum clock with an original form of escapement.

The first to construct a successful pendulum clock was the Dutch scientist Christiaan Huygens, whose original model was made in 1656. In the following year a patent was granted to Salomon Coster at the Hague to make clocks to Huygens's design. Huygens's achievement was a landmark in the history of timekeeping, because the pendulum has a definite period of swing of its own, and so gives a fairly precise repeatable unit of time. Pendulum clocks soon spread to most countries. Huygens himself succeeded in determining with reasonable accuracy the value of gravitational acceleration on the earth's surface. The next step in time measurement was the invention of a new type of escapement. Huygens's clock incorporated the verge type,

fig 2

The anchor escapement was an improvement of the late 17th century. The long pendulum (above) is suspended by a flat steel spring, its swing transmitted by a crutch to a fluked 'anchor' which engages a toothed wheel. As the pendulum swings forward, fluke A engages, stopping the wheel (tick). As the pendulum swings back, fluke A releases the wheel (which, turned by the driving weights, gives an impulse to the pendulum at the same time) and B engages (tock). The pendulum thus governs the wheel and through its geared wheels (not shown) the dial. Each swing one way takes one second and moves the wheel half the space of a tooth. With 30 teeth, the wheel revolves once in 60 seconds. (3)

fig 3

but about 1670 the anchor type was invented, probably by the London clockmaker William Clement. The great advantage of this escapement is that only a small angle of swing is required.

The earth is not accurate enough

p 22
(4)

Pendulum clocks, and likewise watches and chronometers controlled by springs, are machines for the uniform division of time. Throughout history the ultimate standard of time has been astronomical and the hour, minute and second have been defined as fractions of the period of one rotation of the earth on its axis. The earth is a solid body surrounded by water and air, and its time of rotation varies slightly from one season to another. It is also being slowed down very gradually by tidal friction. Moreover, even when all known and predictable irregularities in the earth's rate of rotation are taken into account, there remain small changes, the causes of which are not yet fully understood and for which corrections cannot be predicted. Recently, astronomers have introduced more accurately reproducible definitions of the hour, minute and second based on the period of the earth's revolution around the sun. Nevertheless, it is desirable to have some more fundamental standard of time than any based on the motion of our planet.

One such unit is the natural period of characteristic electromagnetic waves produced by a vibrating atom or molecule. These electromagnetic waves, due to particular modes of vibration, are of very precise frequency and form sharp 'lines' in the spectrum. Optical spectral lines (such as the well-known yellow light produced by sodium atoms) are unsuitable for use as a standard of time since no method is available for measuring their frequency (the number of

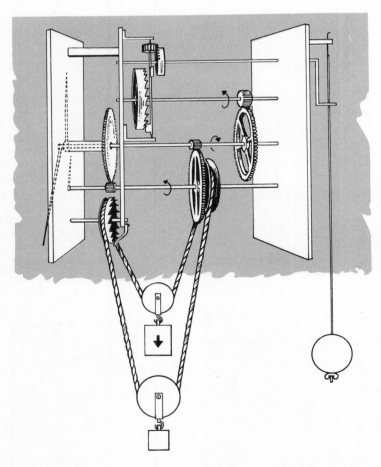

Although Galileo was the first to discover the regularity of the pendulum's swing, and worked out how this could be used to control clockwork, Christiaan Huygens was the first (in 1656) to build a clock with a pendulum. His drawing, expanded above, shows clearly the verge escapement (top centre) and the way the to and fro swing of the pendulum keeps it to a tick-tock movement. The large geared wheel on the right drives a hand which rotates once in five minutes, working through the axle of that on the left. The large wheel below centre drives a small hand which marks the minutes anticlockwise, and is also geared to the wheel left centre which drives the hour hand. To wind, the lighter weight is pulled down, the ratchet and pawl (below left) lock on the rope and the force of the weight-difference is thrown on the gear wheels. (2)

oscillations a second) directly. They are, however, used as a standard of length since the wavelength of light can be measured directly.

The discovery that certain atoms also produce discrete radio frequencies which can be measured directly led to the development of the caesium atomic clock, or, more correctly, the caesium frequency standard. The extreme accuracy of this clock is due to the fact that the fundamental properties of the atom are independent of external factors (temperature etc.), except magnetic fields.

p 22-3
(5)

The choice of caesium was made because its atoms happen to vibrate in such a way that they produce radio waves of definite frequency: about 9200 megacycles per second, corresponding to a wavelength of about 3 cms. This is within the range of wavelengths used for radar, and electronic techniques for handling these frequencies are well advanced.

p 21
(1)

The particular kind of vibration used in the caesium clock is unusual. A caesium atom has a fairly heavy nucleus, surrounded by a number of shells, like the skins of an onion, each filled with electrons. The outermost shell has only a single electron, which spins like a top. The nucleus, too, is spinning. There are two possibilities: the electron may spin in the same direction as the nucleus; or in the opposite direction. By supplying a little energy the electron can be persuaded to change the direction in which it is spinning. And when, some time later, it changes back again the energy given up is released as a burst of radio waves at 9200 megacycles a second.

fig 4

The clock consists of a small radio transmitter which is tuned in to match the frequency of the caesium atoms. The oscillating magnetic field produced by the transmitter makes the caesium atoms resonate when the frequency is correct, just as a singer can make a wine-glass vibrate and even shatter by singing into it at its natural frequency. The magnetic field can be tuned to the atomic vibrations with extreme sharpness. The tuning can be made to an accuracy of one part in a hundred thousand million, which corresponds to a clock error of only one second in 3000 years. This is wholly independent of astronomical determination of time and is reproducible with an accuracy considerably greater than the best which has been obtained from astronomical observations. It may be expected that in future the second will be defined in terms of the natural period of the atom, rather than in terms of the movement of heavenly bodies.

Unlike other standards of measurement, notably length, time can be broadcast and so made available at any place where there is a radio receiver. During recent years there has been a general tendency to regard time measurements as more fundamental than space measurements and to use them as a means of determining the latter, as in radar. Provided that the velocity of radio waves in empty space (which is the same as that of light) is known with sufficient accuracy, the time taken by a radio signal to travel to a distant object and be reflected back can be used to measure the distance of that object. The measurement of base-lines for map-making is now done in this way, using an instrument called a tellurometer. This method has actually been used in recent years to check the distance of the planet Venus, and there is little doubt that before long it will supersede older methods for accurate determination of the scale of the solar system.

The general rules of Euclid's world

Previously the theoretical basis of all spatial measurement was the idea of the rigid measuring rod, that is of the non-deformable ruler graduated by equal spacings between marks or notches. From the philosophical point of view, it has often been argued that length measurement by means of such a ruler is fundamental because it is the only type of measurement which does not involve reference to other types of physical magnitude. Despite its superficial plausibility, this statement is not strictly true, for any actual measurement of length necessarily involves some implicit reference to the time at which it is made. Furthermore, the actual control in practice of a standard yardstick or metre rod is a difficult problem, involving the most delicate regulation of temperature.

In surveying, direct measurement of length is confined to that of base-lines and most measurements are of angles. Distances are then computed by trigonometrical calculations and therefore depend on the laws of geometry. Indeed, the word *geometry* is derived from Greek terms signifying 'earth measurement', and the subject was originally developed by the Egyptians and others for the purposes of surveying, though it was also studied in connection with religious ritual (altar construction, etc.). The subsequent transformation of the empirical art of mensuration into a theoretical science, in which general rules were deduced by logical

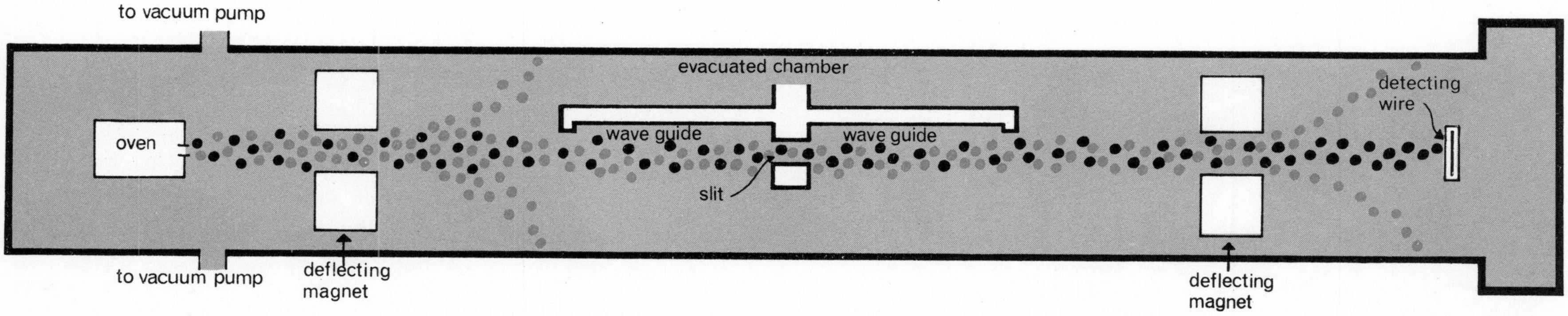

In the caesium atomic clock a beam of caesium atoms is employed. In some of the atoms the single electron in the outermost shell spins on its axis in the same direction as the spin of the nucleus itself, in others it spins in the opposite direction. Radio waves of the right frequency will change the spin from one way to the other. The beam passes through a magnetic field which deflects atoms with unwanted states of spin and allows suitable atoms to proceed. The moving beam is next crossed at right angles by radio waves at a frequency of 9192 million cycles per second (within the radar range) and some of the electrons flip over from

one spin to the other. Then the beam passes through a second magnetic field which allows those electrons to pass which have changed their spin but deflects the others. Finally the straight beam strikes a wire in which it produces a current, its strength proportional to the number of atoms which reach the wire. The number of electrons which flip over (and therefore reach the wire) is at a maximum when the frequency is precisely that to which the atoms naturally respond. The current is made to double back and maintain the radio frequency at the maximum effect—the 'clock' is self-adjusting. (4)

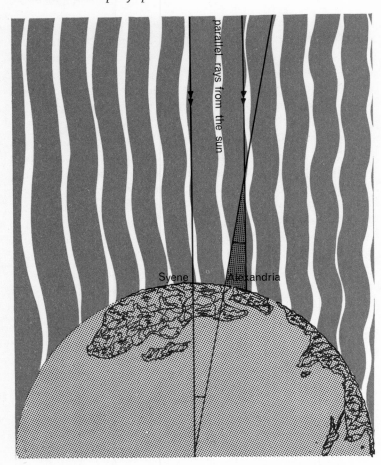

At noon at Syene (Aswan on the Nile), at the summer solstice, the sun cast no shadow of an upright post—it was directly overhead. On the same date, at Alexandria, 500 miles to the north and roughly on the same meridian, Eratosthenes found that the shadow made an angle with the vertical equal to one-fiftieth of four right angles. The two angles in the drawing are equal, therefore 500 miles is one-fiftieth of the circumference of the earth. 25,000 miles, though a lucky shot by such methods, is impressively accurate. (5)

argument from initial axioms and definitions, was one of the greatest achievements of the ancient Greeks. It was a unique contribution to which no other nation aspired.

Typical of this development was the famous theorem named after Pythagoras. Particular examples had long been known of right-angled triangles in which the square of the length of the side opposite the right angle is equal to the sum of the squares of the two sides enclosing that angle. The Greeks showed that this is a general rule applicable to any triangle whatsoever containing a right angle. They showed that this followed from the initial axioms of geometry. Similarly, they found that the sum of the angles of any triangle is equal to two right angles, and that the lengths of

all the sides of any triangle can be calculated if we know the length of one side (the base) and the angles between the base and the other two sides. From this theoretical science later nations, including the medieval Hindus and Arabs, developed the metrical science of trigonometry used in modern surveying.

Although the Greeks were alone among nations of antiquity in developing geometry as a deductive science they did not confine their attention entirely to theory but made some remarkable applications. For example, Eratosthenes, a younger contemporary of Archimedes who lived in the third century BC, obtained a very good estimate of the size *fig 5* of the earth. Observing that at noon at Syene, at the summer solstice, the sun cast no shadow of an upright post, while at Alexandria (taken to be on the same meridian) the sun's rays were inclined to the vertical at an angle equal to one-fiftieth of four right angles, he deduced that the circumference of the earth must be fifty times the known distance between the two towns, which is very nearly correct.

A generation earlier a less successful, but more remark-*fig 6* able, attempt was made by Aristarchus to determine the sizes and distances of the sun and moon. His treatise on this subject is the oldest surviving specimen of Greek geometry with a trigonometrical object. Assuming that the moon shines by reflected light from the sun, he argued that when the moon appears to us halved, the line dividing the bright and dark portions is in the direction of our eye. The effect of this is that at this time the centres of the sun, moon and earth form a triangle which has a right angle at the centre of the moon. Aristarchus assigned the value 87 degrees to the angle subtended at the earth at this time by the sun and moon, and deduced that the distance of the sun is about twenty times that of the moon. Unfortunately, the value of this ratio is very sensitive to the accuracy of the value assigned to the angle in question. The correct value is about 89 degrees 50 minutes, and the sun is therefore about four hundred times as far away as the moon.

Aristarchus was a better mathematician than observer, and from the standpoint of theory his work could not be improved upon today. Underlying his argument was the implicit assumption that the theorems of geometry can be applied just as well to the heavens as to the earth. The extension of this hypothesis to cover physical laws in general was the great achievement of the scientific revolution of the 17th century, culminating in Newton's theory of universal gravitation. This theory was, in fact, dependent on the idea of homogeneous universal space, subject to the rules of Euclid's geometry. The influence of a centre of gravi-

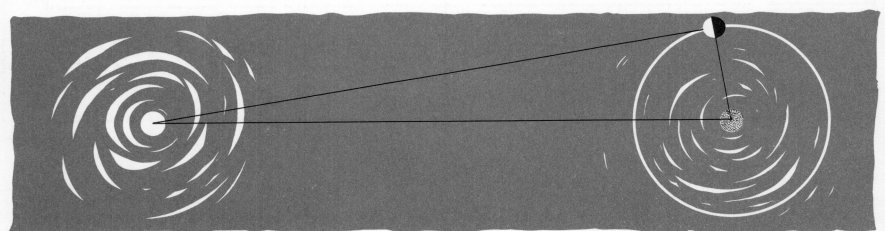

When the moon is exactly half light and half dark, argued Aristarchus, the line of division points to the centre of the earth, and the triangle with the sun is right-angled. By measuring the angle at the earth he could calculate how much

further away the sun is than the moon. His theory and mathematics were correct, but the angle is difficult to measure, and an error of nearly 3° was sufficient to throw his answer widely out. (6)

tational force was visualized as spreading out equally in all directions and hence over a succession of concentric spherical surfaces. Since in Euclid's geometry the surface of a sphere is proportional to the square of its radius, or distance from the centre, the idea arose that the intensity of gravitational force at any point is inversely proportional to the square of the distance from the centre of attraction.

The new geometries of today

The remarkable success of Newton's theory in accounting for the observed motions of the planets led the philosopher Immanuel Kant, in the latter part of the 18th century, to argue that the ideas of space and time on which it was based are necessities of thought. In particular, he claimed that geometry, or the science of space, is a direct consequence of the way in which our minds work.

When Kant wrote, geometry was still the unique system expounded by Euclid, but in the early 19th century it was found that there are other logically possible forms of geometry. To explain briefly how this came about, we must consider a difficulty which had long been felt concerning the foundations of Euclid's geometry. The initial axioms were all accepted as self-evident truths, except one. This was the famous axiom concerning parallel lines: through any given point in space one and only one straight line can be drawn parallel to a given straight line, so that however far the two lines are extended in either direction they will never meet. Numerous attempts had been made to derive this property from the other more cogent axioms of geometry. Despite the lack of success of these efforts, it required a tremendous revolution in human thought to accept these defeats as evidence that it might be possible to devise logically consistent systems of geometry to which the parallel axiom does not apply.

Replacing Euclid's axiom by the assumption that an infinite number of parallels to a given line can be drawn through any point, Lobachevsky in Russia discovered a system of geometry which is quite distinct from that of Euclid. It is known nowadays as hyperbolic geometry. In this geometry, as in Euclid's, space extends infinitely in all directions, but the sum of the angles of a triangle is less than two right angles, the difference depending on the size of the triangle, being insignificant for small triangles.

Later another geometry was invented in which Euclid's axiom was replaced by the assumption that there are no parallel lines. As parallel lines can be extended to infinity without meeting, it is not surprising that their absence implies that space is not infinite in extent. This type of space is finite but has no edge or boundary. A plane in this geometry is just like the surface of a sphere in Euclid's geometry. In this so-called spherical geometry the sum of the angles of a triangle exceeds two right angles, the difference again depending on the size of the triangle, being insignificant for small triangles.

Despite their differences, Euclidean, hyperbolic and spherical geometry have much in common. They each imply that space is homogeneous and isotropic—that is, geometrically the same at all points and in all directions. Moreover, the differences between these geometries diminish the smaller the regions considered. Thus, the fact that on earth, and even within the solar system, Euclidean geometry appears to work so well can no longer be taken as evidence that physical space is necessarily Euclidean, as Newton and Kant believed. It was suggested in the last century that the

G. J. Whitrow

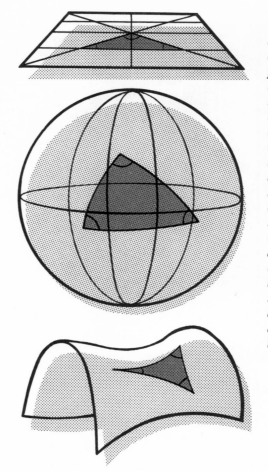

The Euclidean geometry of our schooldays applied to figures that can be drawn on a flat plane. But if such figures are drawn on curved surfaces—a sphere, for instance, or a saddle shape—many of Euclid's theorems no longer hold. On a flat plane, the sum of the angles in a triangle is equal to two right angles: on the surface of a sphere it is greater than two right angles, on a saddle surface less. The shortest distance between two points on a flat plane is what we know as a straight line; confined to the surface of a sphere it is curved and runs along circles with their centres at the centre of the sphere ('great circles', such as lines of longitude or the equator); on a saddle-shape the shortest distance curves the opposite way. All great circles intersect, so there are no parallel lines in spherical geometry. (7)

fig 9

fig 7

fig 7

geometry of physical space could be determined, at least in principle, by measuring the sides and angles of triangles formed by various stars.

Now, although this is not yet a feasible operation, one can at least imagine it being performed. A famous French mathematician and philosopher of science at the turn of the present century, Henri Poincaré, argued, however, that the measurements involved would not, in fact, settle the problem in the simple way previously imagined. They would provide us with information about the light travelling between the stars, but the light rays concerned need not be geometrical straight lines, as had been automatically assumed by those who originally discussed the experiment. Poincaré believed that, in principle, we could either regard them as such and then measure the sides and angles to determine the geometry, or we could assume that the geometry is Euclidean (or some other form) and then determine whether or not the rays are straight lines.

The different logically permissible types of geometry are not confined to those that are homogeneous and isotropic, for the German mathematician Riemann, in the middle of the last century, and others since, have discovered more general types. Poincaré claimed that we can use any geometry we like to represent physical space, although we may find it more convenient to use one, say Euclidean, rather than another. His argument was based on the assumption that, in principle, we are free to adopt any scale of measurement whatsoever, however distorted it may appear to someone engaged in practical mensuration, for example, a surveyor. A somewhat similar situation arises when we try to map the earth's surface. We can, if we wish, represent this on a plane, as in Mercator's projection, but despite its convenience such a map is a definite distortion of the object it is meant to represent. Similarly, the choice of a particular geometry for the universe may involve a serious distortion in the representation of physical objects: e.g. if the universe is infinite in extent and we try to map it in a spherical space which, although unbounded, is only of finite total volume.

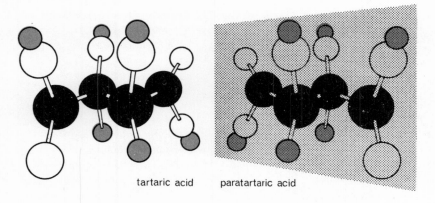

tartaric acid   paratartaric acid

'Congruent but not superposable': Pasteur showed that the atoms in tartaric and paratartaric acids are arranged in three dimensions as in the drawing above; carbon (black), hydrogen (coloured) and oxygen. The geometrical arrangements are 'equal in all respects', and one is the mirror image of the other, but you cannot however you turn them fit one on top of the other. (8)

A left glove on a right hand?

Such distortions do not affect those properties of the universe and its contents which are independent of measurement and are unaffected by continuous deformation. The best known of these 'topological' properties, as they are called, is dimensionality. There is a fundamental distinction between spaces of different dimensions. Instead of the dimensionality of physical space being a matter of choice, it is an intrinsic characteristic of the universe. All our experience goes to show that physical space is three-dimensional, and should be represented by a three-dimensional geometry. The universe would be a very different place if space had a different number of dimensions.

For example, it is impossible to put a left glove on to a right hand so as to obtain a perfect fit even when both hands and both gloves are congruent, that is of precisely the same size and shape. But if space had four dimensions it would be possible to put a left glove successfully on to the right hand, and vice versa, by rotating the glove in the fourth dimension. This example shows that not all solid bodies that are congruent are superposable. This restriction on what is geometrically possible in the natural world has far-reaching consequences. The famous French scientist Louis Pasteur first made his name by showing that the only difference between tartaric and paratartaric acid, which are of the same chemical composition, is that the spatial arrangements of the atoms in their molecules are congruent but not superposable: one is the mirror image of the other.

One of the most important consequences of the three-dimensional character of space is its influence on the geometry of the laws of nature. For example, as we have previously noted, it is due to this property of space that gravitational force varies inversely as the square of the distance from the attracting body. More generally, any physical effect which is propagated equally in all directions from a localized source will spread over successive concentric spherical surfaces as it diffuses outwards. In Euclidean geometry, the area of such a surface varies as the square of the radius or distance from the centre, *if, and only if, the number of spatial dimensions is three.* If physical space had, say, four dimensions, we should expect to find the inverse cube law, rather than the inverse square law, playing a central part in physics. This would have very different consequences. For example, a planet would not move in a closed path about the sun but in a spiral, and so would

fig 8

fig 9

either eventually fall into the sun or move ever farther away from it. In either case, the continued existence of terrestrial life would soon become impossible.

Not only gravitational force, but also electrostatic and magnetic forces and the intensity of any source of light or radiation all vary inversely as the square of the distance. This common feature of phenomena which otherwise differ widely in their nature occurs because physical space has three dimensions.

Poincaré's belief in our complete freedom of choice of the geometry of physical space has given rise to much discussion and controversy. At least it should be modified so as to refer only to metrical properties and not to topological features. It is, however, generally agreed that in practice we cannot entirely separate physical geometry from physical objects. The physical objects employed for spatial measurement are usually either solid bodies or electromagnetic signals, notably light and radio. As previously mentioned, electromagnetic signalling techniques are tending to replace old-fashioned ruler-based measurements. The further we depart from the scale of everyday life, whether on the astronomical scale or on the atomic and nuclear scales, the more inappropriate becomes the rigid measuring rod. Instead of using measuring rods and triangulation from a measured base-line (and this too normally depends on the hypothesis of the rectilinear propagation of light) we rely on electromagnetic signals. The time of transit of a signal is taken as a measure of distance traversed, the velocity of light being a universal factor converting times into lengths.

A speed limit in the universe

The inadequacy of the rigid measuring rod is not entirely a question of practical convenience. There is a deep theoretical reason why we can no longer accept the classical idea of

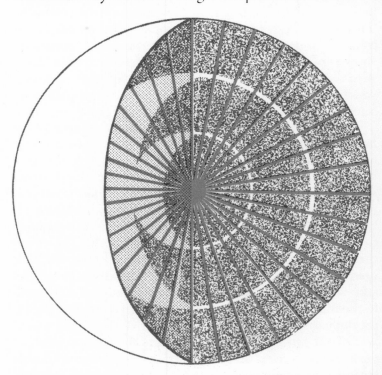

If a burst of light, or any of its family of waves (or the influence of a field of force such as that of gravitation) radiates out from one point in all directions, it will 'thin out'—its intensity will decrease—in an expanding sphere. The surface of the sphere, when its radius is r, is $4\pi r^2$ and the area the radiation covers will increase as the square of the distance it travels. The intensity of the radiation at any point on the surface will therefore decrease as the square of the distance. If the universe were four-dimensional instead of three-dimensional this well-established law would not hold. (9)

p 21 (1)

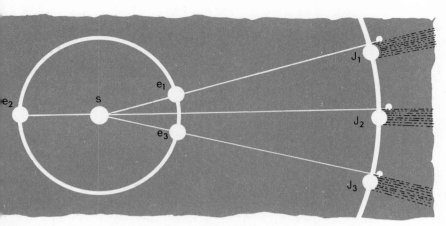

The velocity of light was first determined in 1676 by Ole Roemer, who examined the apparent times taken for Jupiter's nearest moon to travel round the planet. He found that the times varied according to the position of the earth in its own orbit round the sun, and he argued that when the earth was farther from Jupiter, light took longer to travel between them. He therefore recorded the precise time when he saw the moon disappear into Jupiter's shadow, when the planets were in the three positions shown above—which have the advantage that the number of orbits which the moon makes between J_1 and J_2 is exactly the same as the number between J_2 and J_3. A simple calculation then shows that the time differences between J_1 and J_2 (denoted by T_1) and between J_2 and J_3 (denoted by T_2) obey the formula $T_1 - T_2 = 4r/c$ where r is the mean radius of the earth's orbit and c the velocity of light. (10)

a perfectly rigid body as a legitimate scientific concept. In principle, any disturbance must be transmitted through such a body instantaneously. For example, if we tap one part of it so that that part begins to move, then immediately all other parts of the body must begin to move in exactly the same way; otherwise, the body would change its shape and so would cease to be rigid. Consequently, the existence of rigid bodies—in the strict sense—implies the possibility of communicating effects (or, as we tend to say nowadays, 'information') with infinite velocity. This, however, is incompatible with the theory of relativity which Einstein based on the assumption that there are no instantaneously transmitted effects in nature. He assumed that no effects are transmitted more rapidly than electromagnetic signals in empty space. These travel with the velocity of light. Einstein's theory assumes that this is the maximum speed at which information can be communicated by any form of signal.

p 24 (8)

The fact that light always travels with a finite speed was first discovered astronomically from careful study of Jupiter's eclipses of its principal moons, which did not take place at exactly the regular intervals predicted. The Danish astronomer Roemer discovered in 1676 that the observed irregularities in these eclipses depended on the distance of the earth from Jupiter, the total variation of which is equal to the diameter of the earth's orbit about the sun. He found that the eclipses were observed earlier when Jupiter was near the earth and later when Jupiter was farther away. He suggested that this time-difference in the eclipses was equal to the time which light takes to traverse the earth's orbit. In this way he obtained a value for the velocity of light which was of the right order of magnitude. The correct value is very nearly 300,000 kilometres (186,000 miles) per second.

fig 10

Since the velocity of light is finite, it follows that all our observations of distant events are associated with some time-lag. This means that the universe as we observe it at a given instant cannot be regarded as a picture of the universe as it is at a given moment of time, for the more distant an object the greater the time-lag between it and ourselves. Moreover, the universe as seen at a given epoch depends on the loca-

fig 11

p 24 (7)

tion of the observer, so that the apparent temporal order of events, no less than their spatial perspective, depends on who is observing them. Today we may see a solar flare and a nova (stellar explosion), but the former happened just over eight minutes ago, whereas thousands of years may have elapsed since the latter.

If the velocity of light were infinite, events which we perceive as apparently simultaneous would also appear to be simultaneous to observers in other places and we should therefore be justified in regarding them as objectively simultaneous. In other words, we should believe—as in fact many generally believed until the present century—that there is a universal time. But, since light travels with a finite velocity and we have no reason to think that any signal can travel more rapidly, the concept of an objective time-order independent of the observer is, in principle, open to question.

The invariable velocity of light

That the classical ideas of universal time and universal simultaneity must be rejected was first clearly realized by Einstein, who was puzzled by the following difficulty. It is essential that a ray or wave of light be in motion relative to all possible observers. But, since the velocity of light is finite, we could imagine an observer chasing a light-wave with the same velocity. According to classical ideas of measurement, to this observer the light-wave concerned would be at relative rest. The more Einstein thought about this conclusion, the more convinced he became of its impossibility. Finally, in 1905 he realized that to prevent such a situation arising, the traditional ideas of space and time must be modified so as to take due account of the peculiar nature of the velocity of light. Some idea of the crucial importance of this velocity had been revealed in the eighteen-sixties when Clerk Maxwell first realized that light must be a form of electromagnetic radiation because electromagnetic waves travel in empty space with the same speed. But the full significance of this velocity only became clear through the work of Einstein.

The need for some revision of the classical ideas of measurement was accentuated by a famous optical experiment first performed in 1887 by two American physicists,

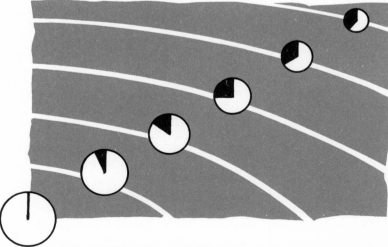

The effect of the discovery that light does not travel instantaneously can be seen by imagining a series of clocks stretching out into space, each synchronized with our own clock. They would all read different times when observed from the earth. Light which left the furthest at 7 o'clock, the next in order at 8, 9, 10 and 11 would reach us when our clock read noon. But the speed of light is so great that for two clocks to register a difference of one hour they would have to be 669,600,000 miles apart. (11)

A. A. Michelson and E. W. Morley. They found that, to a high degree of accuracy, the time taken by a ray of light to travel a given distance is independent of direction. Now, if the earth were stationary in space, there would be nothing surprising about this result. But, since the earth is in motion about the sun and the sun moves relatively to the other stars, Michelson and Morley expected that the time taken by light to travel to and fro along an arm of their apparatus would vary slightly with direction, depending on how the earth was moving. Indeed, their object was to determine the earth's motion with respect to the hypothetical ether associated with the wave-theory of light. One interpretation of the unexpected result of their experiment, suggested a few years later by the Irish physicist Fitzgerald, was that the length of the arm of their apparatus varied with the direction in which it was pointing by just the amount required to counteract the presumed variation in the velocity of light along the arm. This hypothesis was, of course, in direct conflict with the idea of the rigid body and its application to spatial measurement.

Einstein's method was very different. Although he had little to say about rigid bodies, the effect of his work was to eliminate them. He began by considering the concept of

fig 12

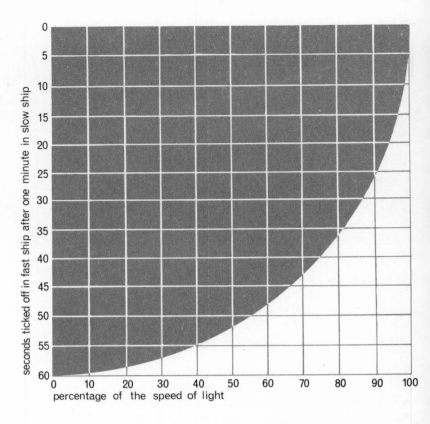

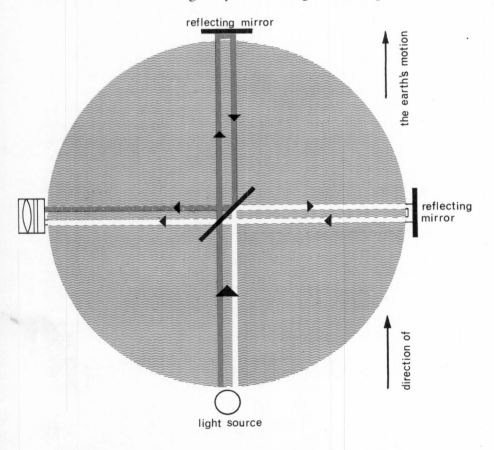

'The most important experiment-that-didn't-work in the history of science', as Asimov describes it, was performed in 1887 by Michelson and Morley. If light were a wave-motion in an all-pervading and stationary 'ether', they argued, an 'ether-wind' should flow past the moving earth. Also light travelling up-wind and back should take longer than light travelling across-stream and back. To detect this time-difference the scientists directed a beam of light on to a half-silvered glass plate: part of it was reflected at right angles, part (above, in colour) passed straight through. Both beams were then reflected back to the plate and from it into a telescope, the total distance travelled by the beams being exactly the same. An observer at the telescope then saw a series of light and dark interference fringes, light where the two streams of waves were 'in step', dark where they were 'out of step'. If the whole apparatus were rotated, any difference in time taken over the two paths would be extremely sensitively registered by a movement of the fringes. With refinements of great skill, including multiple reflections to lengthen the paths travelled and a mercury bath in which to float the apparatus (and so lessen vibration) no difference in time was detected. It was only by Einstein's theory that this result was completely explained. (12)*

Imagine two space ships travelling at steady speeds in the same straight line, the second faster than the first by a velocity v. According to an observer on the first ship, a clock on the second ship would seem to run slow by the formula of Special Relativity: time on clock in second ship = time assigned to this clock by observer on first ship × $\sqrt{(1-v^2/c^2)}$, where c is the velocity of light. The effect of this, for different speeds v, is shown on the graph above. When v = 0 and the ships are moving at the same speed, the two times agree, but the discrepancy becomes greater and greater as we consider larger and larger speeds v. The discrepancy is most marked for speeds v close to the speed of light. In the limit, if the second ship could travel at the speed of light, its clock would seem to stand still to the observer in the first ship. (13)

time and the velocity of light. In his view, the Michelson-Morley experiment was evidence supporting the conclusion which he had come to on other grounds that the velocity of light is the same in all directions and for all observers in uniform motion. This conclusion conflicted with the traditional ideas of space and time and reinforced his criticism of these concepts. In particular, he rejected the commonsense idea of universal simultaneity. He believed that only events at the same place can be intrinsically simultaneous. Otherwise, the idea of two events being simultaneous depends on the rules of measurement which we decide to adopt. Originally confining his attention to observers in uniform relative motion, Einstein decided that

(i) the laws of nature can be expressed in the same mathematical form by each observer;

(ii) each observer assigns the same constant value c to the velocity of light.

p 24·5 (9)

The first condition is called the Principle of Relativity, and the theory based on these two principles when confined to observers in uniform relative motion is called the Special Theory of Relativity.

When rods seem to contract and clocks to run slow

Although Einstein abandoned the classical concept of universal time, he assumed that each observer possesses a unique standard of time for recording events occurring at himself, but he found that the above rules implied that a standard clock will appear to run slow when in motion relative to the observer. Nevertheless, there is complete symmetry between observers. If two observers, moving at uniform relative velocity v, look at each other's clock they will each think it is running slow in exactly the same way. Similarly, each will regard any solid body, such as a ruler, carried by the other as contracted in the direction of relative motion by just the amount imagined by Fitzgerald. But, whereas Fitzgerald believed that this is a real contraction, Einstein saw that it is only an apparent effect: for an observer at rest with respect to the body concerned no such effect would arise.

Similarly, the slowing-down of a moving clock is also only an apparent phenomenon, and there is no intrinsic change in its rate. The proportional apparent slowing down of the clock and contraction of the ruler can be shown to be $\sqrt{(1-v^2/c^2)}$, which is effectively unity for all velocities v arising in everyday life, since these are very small compared with the velocity of light, c, which amounts to about 186,000 miles a second. Indeed, even for a velocity v equal to that of the earth in its orbit round the sun, this factor differs from unity by only one part in 200 million. On the other hand, for a clock moving very nearly with the velocity of light the slowing-down factor can be extremely important, and in the limiting case of motion with the velocity of light itself the hands of the clock would appear to the observer to stand still.

p 25
(11)

fig 13

The bizarre effect of travelling there and back

Although the slowing-down of a uniformly moving clock is an apparent effect, a real effect would occur if a clock B moving uniformly away from the observer A is suddenly made to reverse its motion and return to A. In such a case, on return to A the clock B would be found to have run slow compared with a similarly constructed clock kept by A. The reason for this peculiar discrepancy between the two clocks which has given rise to vigorous controversy (the so-called 'clock paradox') is that the two clocks are not treated in the same way. The clock B must be constrained by special forces to make it reverse its motion, whereas no such forces need act on the clock kept by A.

The consequences of this difference in treatment could be bizarre in the extreme. For example, if a man were to travel in a space-rocket to the nearest star and back at a speed of one kilometre a second less than that of light, on his return to earth he would find us all nearly eight and a half years older, whereas he would have aged barely a week! Fantastic as this may seem, it is no more remarkable than the well-established prolongation of the life of organisms which have been kept in a state of suspended animation by means of artificial refrigeration.

p 26
(12)

For velocities close to that of light the apparent length (in its direction of motion) of a uniformly moving solid body is greatly diminished. In the limit, for a velocity indistinguishable from that of light, it would effectively vanish. Thus, both from the point of spatial measurement and temporal measurement the velocity of light plays the role of a limiting velocity. In Einstein's theory, no material body can move with the velocity of light and it is impossible to bring within its scope anything moving with a greater velocity.

One of the features of the theory is that velocities are not compounded by the ordinary law of addition. Instead they are compounded in such a way that the resultant of any number of velocities each of which is less than the velocity of light is itself less than the velocity of light. This means

p 27
(13)

p 24
(8-10)

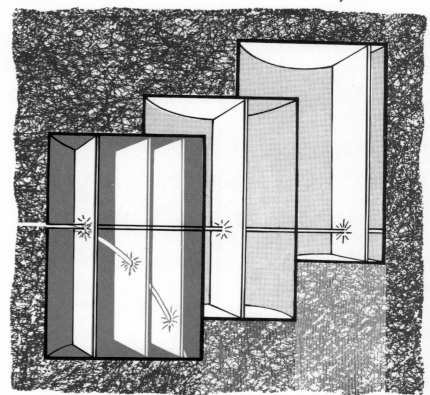

A 'bending' of light from remote stars when it passes the great mass of the sun was predicted by Einstein's General Theory. Consider a ship far out in space, beyond the effect of gravity, moving with a steadily increasing speed approaching that of light. A beam of light strikes horizontally across it, through fluorescent glass plates which reveal its path. The beam travels in fact in a straight line at a constant speed, but how does it seem to the spaceman? Since the ship is travelling upwards at an ever increasing speed, the spots of light on the glass will seem to him to approach the floor at an increasing rate: the light will seem to bend in a curve. Light rays should bend similarly, said Einstein, if the acceleration were due to a gravitational field. The effect is so small, however, that a field as strong as the sun's is necessary if the bending is to be measured, and photographs of starlight passing near the sun are possible only during a total eclipse. Several expeditions have been made, to set up telescopes in the narrow path of the shadow across the earth and where cloudless skies are likely. Bending is observed, to an extent which seems to support Einstein's prediction, but does not yet confirm it. (14)

that, if A is moving at half the velocity of light away from B and B is moving at the same velocity away from C, then A is not moving away from C with the velocity of light but with four-fifths of that velocity. Only for velocities which are comparable with that of light does Einstein's theory lead to results which differ significantly from the traditional addition law.

The most remarkable result in special relativity is Einstein's law of the equivalence of mass and energy. Since the energy of motion (kinetic energy) of a body depends on its mass and its velocity, it follows that, if the energy of a body is increased indefinitely by the continued application of a force, its mass must be increased too. If not, its velocity would ultimately exceed the velocity of light. Einstein found that corresponding to *any* increase in the energy of a body there is a corresponding increase in its mass. Mass and energy are thus different aspects of the same thing, the energy E associated with a mass M being given by $E = Mc^2$, where c is the velocity of light. (Owing to the magnitude of c, to a small mass there corresponds a fantastically large quantity of energy.) Einstein was thus led by his new theory of space and time measurement to formulate the revolutionary hypothesis that matter is a highly concentrated form of energy, a view that has been abundantly confirmed by modern work on nuclear fission. The enormous release of energy in these processes is due to the conversion of small amounts of mass into vast quantities of energy.

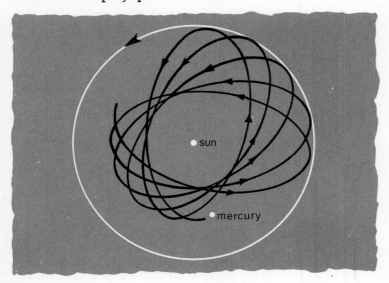

The planet Mercury moves round the sun faster than any other planet and in one of the most elliptical orbits. It never travels in the same ellipse twice, for its orbit rotates very slowly round the sun, 574 seconds of arc per century. The gravitational pull of the other planets accounts for 531 seconds of this, but the remaining 43 remained unexplained for many years. When Einstein, developing his General Theory (which is also a theory of gravitation) worked out the orbital rotation Mercury should have, he found it required just this 43 seconds extra. (15)

Space takes a new shape

In his general theory of relativity, Einstein went on to consider the effects of accelerated motion. He stipulated that the laws of nature must, in principle, be expressible in the same mathematical form for all possible hypothetical observers without restriction on their relative motion. He found it necessary, however, to abandon the principle of the invariability of the velocity of light and the assumption that the geometry of space is Euclidean. Instead, these two conditions, which hold in special relativity, were now interpreted as applying only at great distances from centres of gravitational force. In their neighbourhood special relativity is only approximately true.

Inside the solar system, the corrections which must be made to Newtonian gravitational effects when due account is taken of the principles of general relativity are all small. They include a slight 'bending' (or departure from straight line motion) of light-rays from remote stars as these rays pass near the sun. This effect (which amounts to less than 2 seconds of arc at most) has been measured with varying

fig 14

degrees of success at eclipses of the sun since 1919. Another effect predicted by Einstein is the slowing down of clocks in a gravitational field. As a result, atoms at the surface of the sun should send out their vibrations at a slightly slower rate (by two parts in a million) than corresponding atoms on the surface of the earth. This minute effect has recently been confirmed observationally.

p 28
(14-16)

p 28
(17, 18)

fig 15

The most searching test of general relativity arises in connection with planetary motions. Einstein found that he could account for a small discrepancy between the observed motion of the planet Mercury and its motion as predicted by Newton's theory. This achievement is particularly striking in view of the smallness of the discrepancy involved —less than a minute of arc per century. Recently, fairly good agreement has been reached in the case of a similar discrepancy in the motion of the earth, although the corresponding residual motion is less than a tenth of that in the case of Mercury. Further tests of general relativity may be expected from detailed analysis of the motions of artificial satellites.

Einstein's special theory of relativity marked the first great breach in the classical concept of time. It also undermined the concept of the rigid body on which the classical theory of space measurement was based. His general theory of relativity revealed the limitations of traditional geometry and Euclidean space and was the first major attempt to introduce other types of geometry into physical science. Gravitational force was replaced by the sophisticated geometrical concept of spatial curvature, which does not arise in Euclidean space. Thus space, time and measurement became more closely linked with the physical objects under investigation than in classical physics.

This tendency became even more pronounced with the rise of the modern quantum theory of atoms and molecules: analysis of the interaction between the things being measured and the things with which they are measured has led to a further limitation on the range of application of unmodified classical physics. For, whereas relativity made it clear that our traditional ideas of measurement break down for rapidly moving objects, quantum theory has shown that these ideas also do not apply to extremely small objects. Nevertheless, neither theory can be used without appealing at some point to classical ideas and principles of measurement. For all their limitations, these still form the solid rock on which the elaborate structures of the most modern and sophisticated physical theories are ultimately based.

'If imaginative curiosity and speculation

are the life-blood of science, submission to the test of measurement may be said to be its infallible rule of health.' Measurement in this sense is not old in the history of the world, and it was not until men learned to apply the ruler and the clock systematically to natural phenomena that the physical sciences began their great leap forward. Today, neither satisfies the needs of the scientists; rulers change their length with changing temperature, clocks depend upon the daily and yearly motions of the earth – and the earth is not accurate enough. Science has turned to the vibrations of the atom for its clock and to time and the speed of light for its ruler.

How the radar operators have directed their waves to the surface of Venus is now well known. By timing the journey as the waves bounced back, they obtained an accurate check of the distance. By more sophisticated application to terrestrial measurement surveyors

have greatly increased both the precision and the speed of their work. Instruments such as the tellurometer (opposite) measure distances of up to 50 miles within 8 inches. But it is a measurement of *time*. Radio waves, of length 10 cms., are directed by one operator to another at a distance, in this case by the Ordnance Survey across the English Channel, and re-radiated back. They carry both the longer wave modulations required to compute the distance and also, by selection of a switch, speech for immediate communication. Modulated waves of a length (say) of 100 ft. pass to and fro. They will cover a certain number of times their length plus a fraction, and the time taken to cover this fraction is displayed on a cathode ray screen in thousand-millionths of a second. Such readings, from signals on several wavelengths, enable the operator to calculate the time taken by the waves for the double journey and therefore the distance. (1)

The first known clocks which could measure time continuously, day and night were the water-clocks of ancient Egypt. The cast above is of a clock from the Temple of Karnak, 1415–1380 BC. Water escaped from a hole near the bottom, time was registered by the level of the water inside. As the level fell, the flow grew less, and the vessels were made cone-shaped to keep the intervals even. (2)

The first moving mechanism known is described in a Chinese text written by Su Sung about AD 1090. In the model below, built from his description, water pours in a thin stream from the square vessel right centre, filling one of a series of cups at the ends of the spokes of the wheel. When the cup is full, originally in a quarter of an hour, the weight tilts the steelyard above, the wheel is released and the next cup moves into place. There is a suggestion of escapement action, but the clock was governed mainly by the flow of water. Time was checked by a sighting tube, directed at a star. (3)

The ingenious and elaborate mechanical clocks of today developed in Europe from the 14th century. Harrison's first marine chronometer of 1735 (below right) was driven by a mainspring, which can be seen low down on the left. The power from this, working through an intermeshed train of cogwheels, turned the hands of four dials, one each for seconds, minutes, hours and days. The movement was governed by the two pivoted rods on the right, weighted at each end and connected by coiled springs. These swung back and forth in opposite directions like double-ended pendulums, so that the pitch and roll of a ship could never affect the swing of both at once. Harrison's fourth chronometer erred by only five seconds between London and Jamaica. (4)

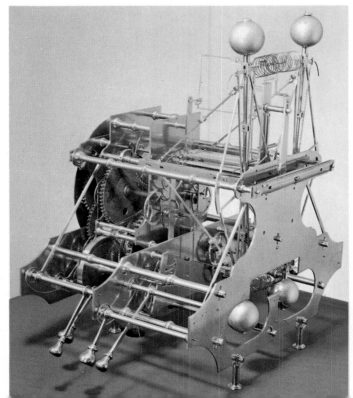

The tick of the atom is the standard by which the scientist controls his most accurate clocks today. The self-adjustment of the caesium clock, the theory of which has already been explained, is so fine that it will not gain or lose more than a second in 3000 years. This extreme accuracy is possible because the fundamental properties of the atom are not affected by external factors such as changes of temperature, but only by magnetic fields.

The photograph above shows the first caesium clock made. Caesium, at normal temperatures a silvery liquid, is heated to the gaseous state in an electric furnace at the left of a long evacuated tube enclosed in the rectangular box. The atoms enter the tube through a small hole and pass the first magnet immediately (first label) and proceed, in military order without collisions, to the centre (second labels) where the radio waves cross them at right angles. Next they pass between the poles of the second deflecting magnet (third label) and finally reach the detector at the end.

This caesium frequency standard, as it is more correctly named, establishes and maintains the radio waves at a frequency of extreme precision. The waves govern the frequency of oscillations from a quartz crystal, which in turn can be reduced to about 60 cycles per second and fed into an ordinary electric clock. (5)

The watch for daily use is not yet governed by vibrations within the atom, but modern electronics have been adapted to its construction. The *Accutron* (right) is controlled by the tuning fork which stretches from 6 to 12; its vibrations, at precisely 360 cycles per second, drive a conventional gear train which turns the hands. Power comes from the cell on the right, through a transistor circuit which changes its current into pulses and through electro-magnets within the cup-shaped ends of the fork (at 12) which maintain its vibrations. The circuit also keeps the amplitude of the vibrations within the necessary limits. Accuracy in normal use is one minute a month. (6)

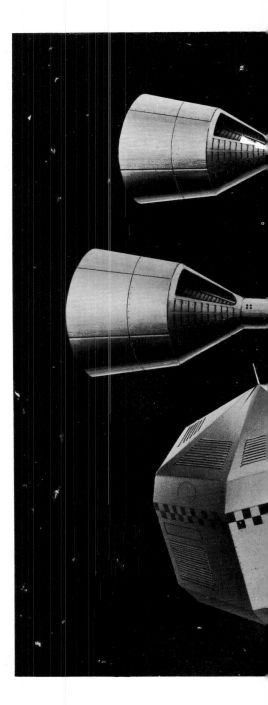

Einstein tackled such problems, to find **Einstein tackled such problems,** to find out what really happens when we make measurements of fast-moving objects by the light which comes from them. He arrived at two postulates. Provided that we are moving at a steady speed in a straight line: 1. The laws of nature will seem the same to us, wherever we are. 2. The speed of light will seem the same to us, wherever we are and whichever direction the light is coming from. With these in mind, examine the drawing below. Two

What happens if we measure time, not on earth, but out in space? Suppose Betelgeuse, the great star in Orion's right hand, were to explode on 17 March, 2000 (above). It takes 300 years for the light from the explosion to reach us on earth, and our date for the explosion would be 17 March 2300. But the light from the explosion would reach Aldebaran, in the constellation Taurus, in 250 years, and an observer on that star would say (if he used our calendar) the explosion occurred on 17 March 2250. If Aldebaran could signal the news to us, it would reach us in 53 years on 17 March 2303. The single event is not simultaneous to the three different places. (7)

Can anything travel faster than light? Suppose we are observers in a space station (below), with a defending ship orbiting near us. An enemy ship approaches it at a speed three-quarters that of light ($\frac{3}{4}$ c). The enemy fires a rocket at an extra speed of $\frac{1}{2}$ c. Is the rocket travelling at $1\frac{1}{4}$ c, faster than light? If so, we should *first* see our defending ship, hit by the rocket, exploding. Then we should see the rocket moving *backwards* until it reached the enemy. Is this possible? When V2 rockets were approaching London at a speed greater than that of sound, the inhabitants heard the explosion first, *followed* by the hiss of the rocket coming down. Does the same happen with light? (8)

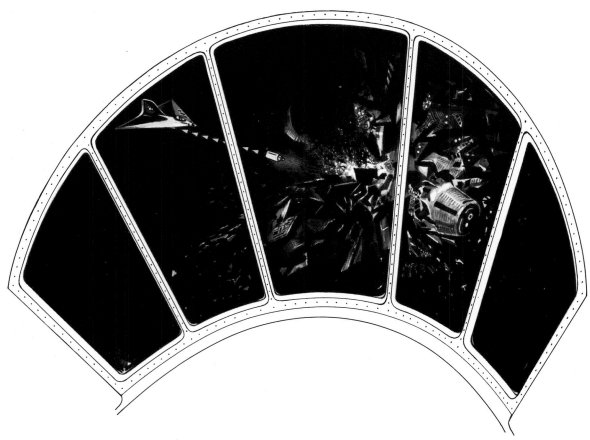

Results difficult to believe follow from this simple example, and need only the ancient theorem of Pythagoras to give them precision (right). If the ships are passing the station at v miles per second, in one second they will have moved on v miles. the velocity of light is c miles per second, the flash will have travelled c miles in the same time, *judged from the station*. But judged from the first ship, it will seem only to have travelled along the third side of the right-angled triangle or, from Pythagoras, $\sqrt{c^2 - v^2}$ miles. Measured by either station or ship, said Einstein, the speed of light is the same—which can only mean that in the ship, *time* passes more slowly. The ship's clock ticks more slowly than the station clock, exactly in the ratio of the distances the light seems to travel. This is the fundamental formula of Einstein's Special Theory of Relativity:

space ships are travelling parallel to each other at the same steady speed. They pass a space station. First, consider only the station and the ship nearest to it; they are out of sight of the earth and have no fixed basis to measure their speeds by. *They will not know which is moving.* All they can measure is the difference between their speeds; one of them indeed might be moving backwards. Speeds can only be measured relatively to something else. Now suppose that as

they pass the space station, the second ship flashes a light signal to the first. By the time the signal reaches the first ship, both will have moved on. Judged from the first ship, the flash will seem to have come straight across (if you don't believe this, imagine yourself watching a match struck at the other side of a moving railroad car). But judged from the station, which sees the ships moving past, the flash will seem to have crossed diagonally.

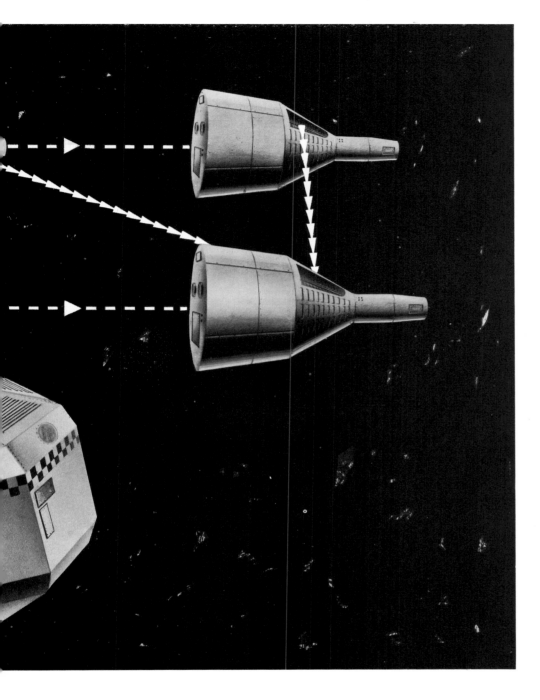

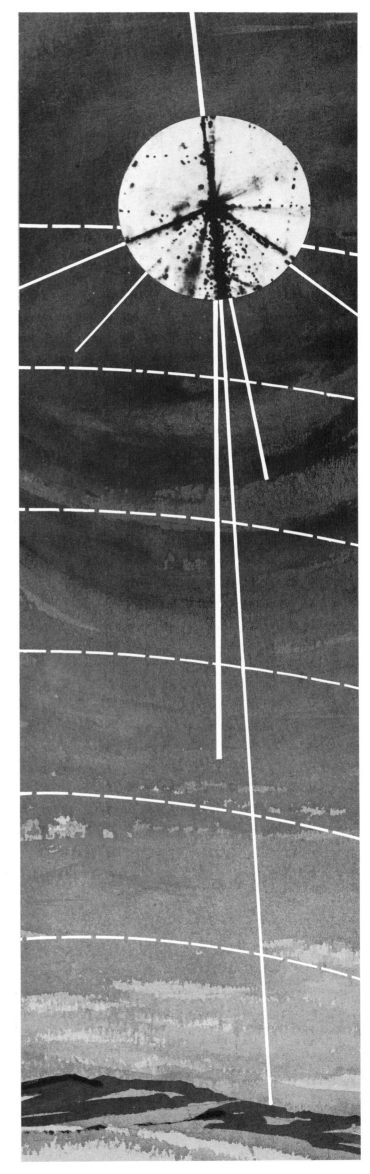

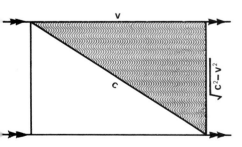

$$\frac{\text{Time by ship's clock}}{\text{Time by station clock}} = \frac{\sqrt{c^2 - v^2}}{c} = \sqrt{1 - \frac{v^2}{c^2}}$$

From this formula it is not difficult to deduce what happens to the attacking rocket (left). Its speed works out at only ten elevenths of the speed of light, and the space station will see events in their proper order. (9, 10)

The stretching of time is dramatically illustrated when protons in the cosmic rays collide with atoms high in the atmosphere. Their speed is so great that the nucleus is shattered and muons shoot down towards the earth, some at speeds almost that of light ($0.995c$). Now muons decay into other particles in 2.2×10^{-6} seconds, during which time they would travel just over half a kilometre. Yet six kilometres farther down, at the surface of the earth, muons are detected in considerable numbers. Why have they not decayed? At such high speeds time for the muons slows down, their 'clocks' tick at one-tenth the rate of ours. They decay in the same number of ticks, but travel ten times farther first. Careful measurements of this stretching of time agree favourably with that from the formula (left). (11)

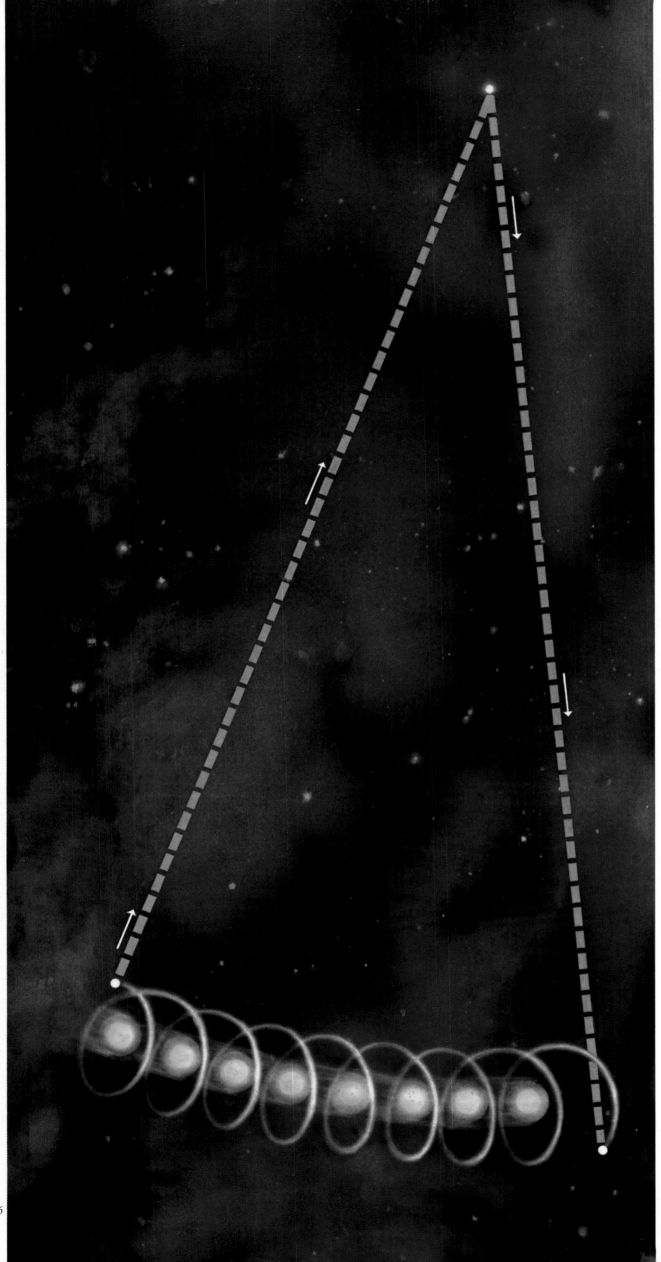

'Einstein is not difficult', said someone, 'only unbelievable.' Let us apply the formula for the stretching of time, arrived at on the previous page, to a journey into space. Suppose men could set out in a space ship for the nearest star, $4\frac{1}{4}$ light years away, at a speed one kilometre per second less than that of light. They would arrive back at the earth in a little over eight and a half years (the drawing on the left is not to scale). But what would have happened to the men in the ship? From the formula, clocks in the ship would have registered barely a week. *The men would be only seven days older.* As long as they were travelling at a steady speed, they would not be aware of this. Their clocks would tick more slowly, but they would not notice it—their own life processes would slow down at exactly the same rate, and so they would age more slowly. But nothing they saw would be contrary to *their* common sense.

Is this possible? We cannot test it directly, for we have no means of supplying the enormous energy required to approach the speed of light. Also it is argued that a steady speed in a straight line cannot be maintained all the time, the ship has to get up speed, to turn round, and to slow down to land, when the assumptions of Einstein's Special Theory would no longer apply to the ship. At these times, when they were under acceleration, the spacemen would know what was happening, and that strong forces were acting upon them. Nevertheless most scientists today believe that the deduction above is correct, though the argument goes on. (12)

The most astonishing formula in science, and one which has had bitter proof, is $E = Mc^2$. Einstein was led to it by arguments based on his Special Theory of Relativity. In it, c is the velocity of light and M the mass of a body (the 'quantity of matter' in it): what is E? Einstein was led by his theory to conclude that matter is a highly concentrated form of energy, and that if the whole of the mass M of a body could be converted into its equivalent energy, the result would be an energy E, equal to Mc^2. The square of c gives a figure so great (in square centimetres 900 million million million) that a very small mass would yield enormous energy—a railroad ticket contains enough to drive a large train several times round the world. It is not yet possible to release all the energy in a body: a fraction of it produces the now familiar mushroom clouds of which the photograph opposite is an example—an early military test, exploded from a balloon, over the Nevada desert. The brilliant streak is the edge of the luminous fireball, showing through the cloud. (13)

One part in 10 million million
was the precision necessary to measure the wavelength shift due to the earth's gravitational field—a greater accuracy than the atomic clock provides. Light moving one kilometre to the earth's surface should have its wavelength decreased (a 'blue shift') by this amount. How could it be measured? A means was found when Mössbauer discovered that certain radioactive crystals emitted gamma-rays at an extremely precise wavelength. Physicists in several countries tried the experiment: Pound and Rebka at Harvard passed the rays down a 74 ft. column of flowing helium. Pound (above) controlled the emission from an isotope of iron, moving up and down to produce an artificial shift in the wavelength by the Doppler effect. Rebka (below) counted the rays which passed through a thin film of the same isotope. If only the artificial shift was occurring, his count during the down movement should equal that for the up movement, but if gravity was adding its own shift, the counts would be unequal. Results showed a gravitational shift reasonably in accord with Einstein's prediction. (17, 18)

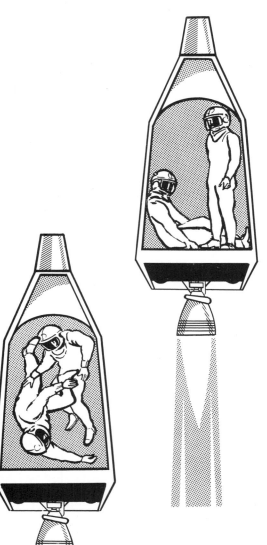

Long before man had orbited in space, Einstein imagined an observer 'inside a spacious chest resembling a room', so far removed from the earth or any heavenly bodies that gravitation did not exist for him. 'He must', said Einstein, 'fasten himself with strings to the floor, otherwise the slightest impact against the floor will cause him to rise slowly towards the ceiling of the room.' Edward White, above, floating outside spacecraft Gemini 4 in 1965, is experiencing just this weightlessness, for, although he is not beyond the effect of gravity, its force is neutralized by the centrifugal force of his rapid orbital motion.

Einstein pictured his 'chest' with its weightless man as moving with a steady speed in a straight line (far left). What would happen, he asked, if the chest were suddenly pulled upwards with a steadily increasing speed? In today's idiom, the space ship would catch up with the astronaut and he would remain, as long as the speed was increasing, standing or sitting on the floor (left). If the increase in speed were similar to that known on earth as due to gravity the astronaut might well conclude that he was suspended in a gravitational field. Without looking outside, *he could not decide otherwise*. From considerations like this, Einstein concluded that, out in space, the effects of gravitation and accelerated motion are equivalent and cannot be distinguished from one another.

It was this Principle of Equivalence which led Einstein to develop his General Theory of Relativity. One of its consequences is known as the 'gravitational red-shift': light escaping from a star with a strong gravitational field loses energy in the process and its wavelength increases—it becomes redder. Solar measurements now seem to confirm this; could a shift be measured which was due to the earth's field? (14, 15, 16)

2 The empire of the sun

T. F. Gaskell

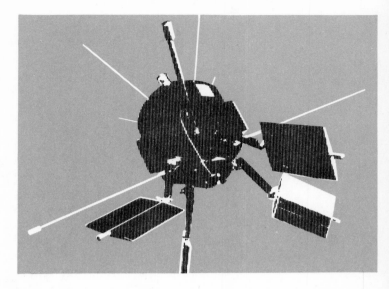

The empire of the sun

It was the belief in ancient Babylon that the universe was like a box, the earth being the flat floor of this box. During the centuries when man's knowledge and understanding of his environment have grown, first the earth, and then the sun have been relegated to minor positions in the universe. The earth is merely one of nine planets that move in nearly circular orbits round the sun, the sun is one star of millions that form a single galaxy, and there are many millions of galaxies in the universe.

Studies of the radioactivity of rocks indicate that the earth solidified about 4,500 million years ago, and it is probable that the group consisting of the sun and its satellites—the solar system—came into being only a short time before the earth was born. It is not certain how the solar system originated. Any explanation must take into account that most of the planets move in almost circular orbits in the same direction round the sun and in almost the same plane.

Pierre-Simon Laplace, a French mathematician and astronomer, put forward a brilliant theory in 1796 which was accepted for many years. He suggested that the solar system originated as a great whirling mass of gas larger in diameter than the orbit of the most distant planet. This disk gradually shrank, pulled together by the forces of gravity, and as it did so, span still more rapidly, just as an ice skater spins more quickly by drawing in his arms and legs. At various stages during this shrinking process, rings of gas and dust got left behind, and these contracted to form the different planets.

The theory failed for two reasons. First, observations showed that the sun rotates rather slowly, much more slowly than would be expected according to this theory. Secondly, the sun is now known to be made almost entirely of hydrogen, while the planets are made of much heavier

elements. It is difficult to see how they could come from the same rotating mass of gas.

Early in this century attention was turned to catastrophic processes to describe the birth of the solar system. Sir James Jeans suggested that at some time in the past another star passed so close to the sun that it raised gigantic tides, and pulled away lumps of sun-material which condensed into the primeval planets. Another British scientist, Sir Harold Jeffreys, suggested an actual collision which rubbed away the planet material. Both theories failed because calculations proved that the orbits of planets produced in this way could not be more than a few solar radii, and certainly not as much even as 80 solar radii, the distance of the nearest planet, Mercury, from the sun.

Nowadays the tendency is to favour theories bearing some resemblance to the Laplace nebular theory, but which assume that the source of materials from which the planets were formed was different from that of the sun. One such idea assumes that the sun once had a companion star at a very much later stage in evolution, which therefore contained heavy elements. This star became a supernova and blew up. The explosion allowed the greater part of the star to escape from the sun, but the remaining wisps gradually expanded to form a lenticular disk around the sun.

The cold dust and gas in the disk-shaped cloud would gradually aggregate by collision to form the planets, by a process rather like rolling a giant snowball. More recently the idea has been put forward that the disk may be a normal feature in the evolution of certain types of star, a result of the magnetic forces in the neighbourhood of the star. Modern theories seem to suggest that the solar system is probably not unique, and that other stars have planets revolving round them, although they are too far away to be

p 41

fig 1

fig 2

fig 3

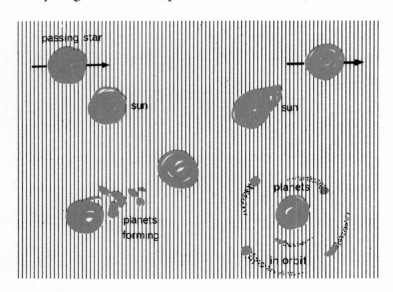

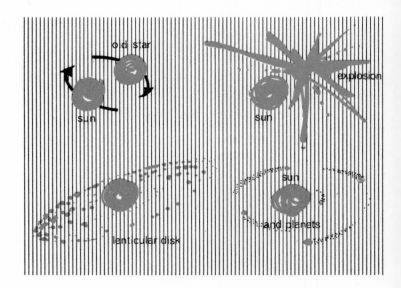

T. F. Gaskell

observed through the most powerful telescope. It is possible that if conditions on some other planet of another star are similar to those on earth, life may have emerged there, too.

A star of moderate size

The sun is a typical star, 864,000 miles in diameter or just over 100 times the diameter of the earth, but nevertheless of only moderate size compared with some other stars. The distance from the earth to the sun is about 93 million miles, yet the sun provides the primary source of energy for the earth. The amount of energy given out by the sun is immense. It amounts to the equivalent of 4 million tons of heat, light and ultra-violet waves a second, corresponding to a flow of 84,000 horsepower continuously through every square metre of its surface. This energy is produced by the fusion of hydrogen nuclei to form the heavier helium nuclei at the rate of 564 million tons of hydrogen a second. There is no fear of the sun's 'atomic power house' running down. It has been giving out energy at about the same rate for several thousand million years at least and yet only a few per cent of its supply of hydrogen has been used up. p 142

Apart from the steady flow of light and heat from the sun's surface, it emits, from time to time, bursts of electrically charged particles, X-rays and ultra-violet rays. Some of the emissions interact with the earth's atmosphere, causing the aurora and interfering with normal radio transmission. p 47 (13) p 46

The origin of these bursts has been shown to be connected with the appearance on the sun's disk of various special features, such as the dark patches called sunspots, described by Galileo in 1612, the jets of hot gas called prominences, and the occasional major outbursts known as solar flares. The disturbances which occur on the edge or 'limb' of the sun's disk are best observed during a solar eclipse. p 42-4 (2-8)

Solar flares produce the most dramatic effects on earth. The flare is a violent explosion which may eject jets of gas into space at hundreds of miles a second. The hydrogen gas in these jets is ionized, that is the hydrogen atoms have had their electrons stripped off, leaving the electrically charged nucleus. This fast-moving jet of electrified particles is thus equivalent to an electric current flowing through space, and produces a magnetic field. If one of these jets hits the earth, the fast-moving particles squash the earth's natural magnetic field, and cause violent auroral displays. p 45 p 46

The high-speed particles thrown out by the flare take about half an hour to reach the earth at a speed of around 50,000 miles a second. About 24 hours later the slower particles in the jet arrive, having travelled the 93 million miles at about 1000 miles a second. These, as we shall see, cause a number of different effects in the earth's atmosphere.

But before even the fastest particles arrive, the powerful electromagnetic waves produced by the flare reach the earth. Their journey takes 8 minutes at the velocity of light, 186,000 miles a second. Arriving at the same moment are a burst of reddish light, characteristic of the hydrogen gas, flashes of ultra-violet waves, and short radio waves of various wavelengths.

These are the exceptional outbursts of the sun. In addition there is a continual output of energy in the form of electromagnetic waves, mainly light and infra-red or heat waves, but including a fairly large proportion of ultra-violet and some radio waves. p 47 (13)

Part of the sun's output of energy, regular and irregular, reaches the neighbourhood of the earth. Part of it penetrates through the earth's atmosphere and reaches the surface in the form of sunlight: part is stopped by the atmosphere and the region of space above it.

The trap for the 'solar wind'

It is in this region that the electrically charged hydrogen atoms thrown out by disturbances on the sun, what is often called the 'solar wind', are trapped. The discovery was made by rocket and satellite experiments carried out in the past few years by Dr James Van Allen and confirmed by similar Russian measurements made with their Lunik I and other rockets. p 48 (15-17)

These experiments showed that the earth is surrounded by a girdle-like region starting a few hundred miles above the surface and extending 36,000 miles into space. The girdle is at its thickest and highest over the equator and tails away towards the poles, dipping down towards the atmosphere. At first there appeared to be two separate layers or belts of particles with a gap between them; now it appears more likely that there is only one, whose position and particle population change with time. p 45

It is believed that these charged particles are trapped in the magnetic field of the earth. The charged particles follow a corkscrew or helical path in the magnetic field, moving from pole to pole along the magnetic lines of force. As one of the particles moves towards a pole it finds a steadily increasing magnetic field which gradually reduces the pitch of the helix, until the particle is eventually moving back towards the equator. fig 4

This theory has been confirmed by the 'Argus' and 'Rain-

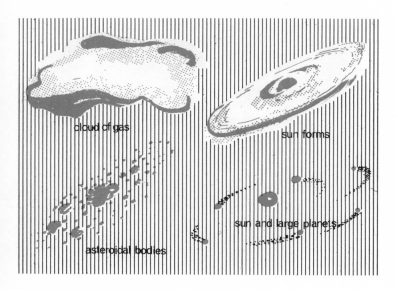

cloud of gas

sun forms

sun and large planets

asteroidal bodies

There have been many theories about the creation of the solar system. Sir James Jeans suggested a near-collision (far left), in which the mutual gravitational attraction of the sun with a passing star tore off lumps of material which then condensed into the planets. But the theory is not fully satisfactory and such an event in the universe is most unlikely. If the sun once had a companion, a much older star, which exploded into a nova (centre), a small part of the star material, captured by the sun, might have spread out into a lens-shaped disk round the sun, eventually condensing into planet-sized lumps by gravity and the collection of interstellar dust. Theories today seek to explain the formation of both the sun and the planets from interstellar matter. Giant turbulences in the hot and cold gases could form clouds of sufficient mass to start contraction under gravity (left), forming the sun and leaving a disk of cold gas and dust-grains rotating round it. Within the disk, collisions, gravitational attraction and the presence of dust-grains could result in coagulation of the heavier atoms into smaller and then larger bodies, and dispersion of the bulk of the lighter atoms. (1,2,3)

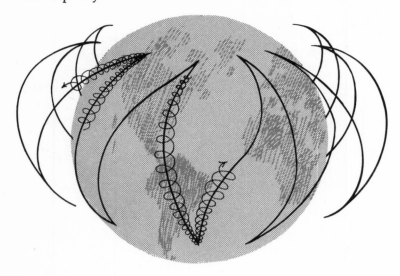

The stable inner zone of trapped particles which encircles the earth stretches from the upper atmosphere to 3200 miles out in space. It consists of protons and electrons spiralling at great speed along the lines of force of the earth's magnetic field. Towards the poles, where the lines converge and the field increases in strength, the pitch of the corkscrew path is steadily reduced until the particle is reflected and returns on its path. Protons and electrons travel in opposite directions; oscillating back and forth from hemisphere to hemisphere in a few seconds, the protons (left) drift from east to west, the electrons (right) from west to east round the rotating earth. Multiplied a million-million-fold, this pattern builds up the crescent-shaped inner zone. (4)

bow' nuclear bomb explosions in space carried out, against many scientists' wishes, by the United States. The charged particles released by the bomb followed helical paths along the magnetic lines of force, and produced an artificial radiation belt round the earth.

The discovery of the radiation belt round the earth provided a partial explanation for the aurora, the patterns of brilliant red, green and blue flames, curtains, rays and arcs seen in the polar sky during periods of solar activity. Study of the aurora during the International Geophysical Year showed that displays occurred simultaneously across the entire night sky in northern and southern hemispheres. The familiar glows occur at heights of 60 to 100 miles above the surface, in the upper layers of the atmosphere, and the flickering light is produced in much the same way as the red light from a neon sign: by the excitation of the atoms in a rarefied gas. Odd forms of aurorae may be as high as 600 miles.

It now appears that the excitation of the atoms of oxygen and nitrogen in the upper atmosphere is due to collision with charged hydrogen atoms from the sun. These charged particles are probably spilled out of the Van Allen radiation belt when a powerful outburst from the sun distorts the magnetic field. The particles then corkscrew down into the atmosphere without having reached a magnetic field strong enough to turn them back towards the equator. In fact, the radiation belt appears to behave as a kind of gas-bag. The solar wind fills the bag in great gusts so that from time to time it overflows at the edges, creating the aurora.

The activity of the sun, as judged by the behaviour of solar prominences, sunspots etc., exhibits an eleven-year cycle and the last period of least solar activity occurred in 1954. In order to investigate the behaviour of the environment of the earth during the following sunspot maximum period, the International Geophysical Year (IGY) was proposed and carried out in 1957–58. From this co-operative effort by over sixty nations emerged a great deal of valuable scientific data which has been collected and catalogued at World Data Centres and freely interchanged.

p 46

fig 5

p 45

p 114-5

fig 5

It has been realized that the value of the scientific data obtained during the IGY would be considerably enhanced were similar data to be obtained during the period when the sun's activity was next expected to be at a minimum. Accordingly, a special scientific effort was made in 1964 and 1965, using both techniques similar to those employed during the IGY and more refined techniques since developed.

Measurements concerning meteorology include some determinations using balloons and rockets to give a distribution with height. Continuous recording of the earth's magnetic field all over the earth show the regional changes that take place and help to determine the connection with changes in the charged belts of the ionosphere. The international years of the quiet sun are not so spectacular as the IGY years of great activity, but they are necessary to show the steady-state values of what is going on.

The shield and blanket of the earth

The earth's surface is completely immersed in a gaseous atmosphere, held by gravitational forces. The composition of the atmosphere varies with altitude. It appears that from 1500 to 6000 miles above the surface hydrogen is the main element present, while helium occupies the zone from 600 to 1500 miles' altitude. From 600 to 72 miles the atmosphere is mostly oxygen, with some nitrogen in the form of nitrous oxide. Below 72 miles the atmosphere gradually assumes the 78 per cent nitrogen, 21 per cent oxygen mixture that we breathe on earth. The odd one per cent is made up mainly of argon with traces of carbon dioxide, neon, helium, methane, krypton, nitrous oxide, hydrogen, ozone and xenon.

The atmosphere exerts a pressure of 14.7 pounds per square inch at the earth's surface and it is concentrated close to the earth by the earth's gravitational pull. At a height of 70 miles the pressure is only two millionths of a pound per square inch, while even at an altitude of 10 miles breathing is impossible without protective apparatus.

In the upper tenuous layers of the atmosphere, the energetic X- and ultra-violet radiation from the sun is absorbed by the atoms and molecules. The result is that electrons are stripped from the neutral atoms, and so, in these regions, the atmosphere contains large numbers of charged particles or ions. This region of the atmosphere is called the ionosphere. It consists of four layers named, from the bottom upwards, D, E, F_1 and F_2, between 50 and 250 miles above the surface, and has important scientific and technological consequences. The existence of the charged particle layer was suspected when in 1901, inexplicably, G. Marconi succeeded in transmitting a wireless signal across the Atlantic. Later Sir Edward Appleton in Britain and Dr Merle Tuve in the United States proved that the layer did exist and studied its properties. Their work showed how the ionosphere could be used as a 'mirror in the sky' to direct radio waves beyond the horizon.

The ionosphere is also responsible for the daily variations in the earth's magnetic field, which are caused by powerful currents flowing through it. These currents are particularly strong when the sun is disturbed and is emitting a greater quantity of X-rays than usual. The result is a 'magnetic storm' in which the earth's magnetic field is disturbed. At these times radio communication via the ionosphere is also upset. Sometimes communication becomes impossible; at others, radio waves of such high frequency that they are not normally reflected by the ionosphere are returned to earth.

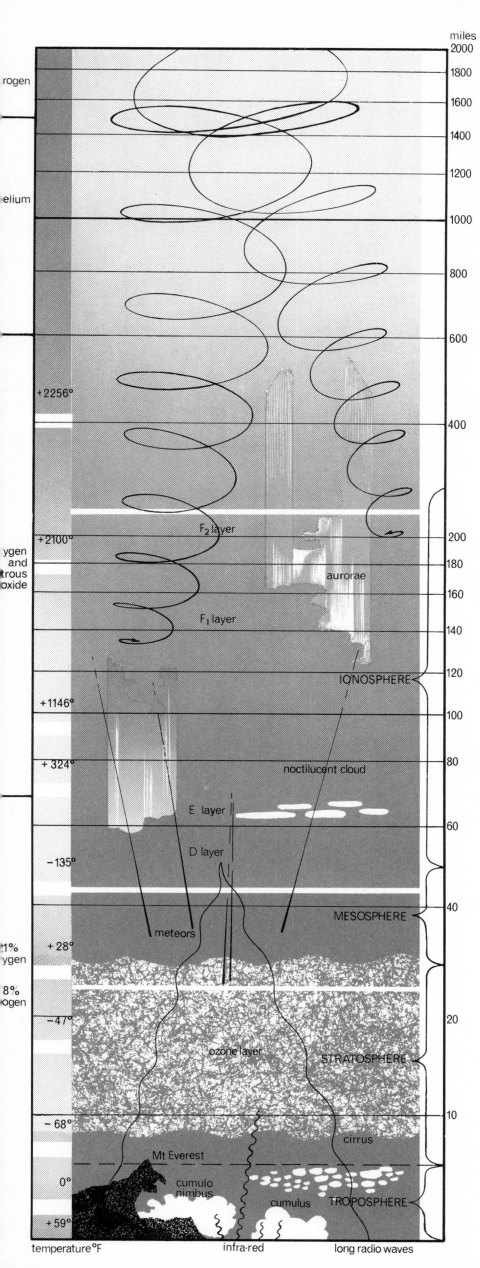

T. F. Gaskell

This is the explanation of the occasional reports that British television stations (which operate at frequencies too high to be reflected by the ionosphere under normal conditions, and which therefore cannot be received beyond 'line of sight') have been picked up in South Africa and elsewhere.

fig 5

Below the ionosphere, reaching down to an altitude of only 10 miles, the longest-wave ultra-violet radiation from the sun is absorbed by the atmosphere in a different way to build ozone molecules containing three oxygen atoms in place of the ordinary oxygen molecule with two atoms. This ozone layer, or at least the lower part of it, can be sampled by balloon, while the upper part is being investigated by instruments carried in a satellite. The effect of the ozone layer on the earth has still not been fully discovered. But both it and the ionosphere above it serve the purpose of protecting the earth's surface from the dangerous X-rays and ultra-violet radiation from the sun.

p 114-5

The atmosphere also acts as a protective blanket to the earth by absorbing the heat of the sun's rays and by retaining heat at night. The earth re-emits the energy it receives from the sun, but being a comparatively cool body it does so mainly in the infra-red region of the energy spectrum. Infra-red radiation is strongly absorbed by water vapour, carbon dioxide and ozone, and these cause the atmosphere to act in much the same way as the glass of a greenhouse. The heat from the sun, being short-wave radiation in the visible region of the spectrum, is transmitted, while the outgoing radiation is absorbed so that the heat is retained by the atmosphere.

As the atmosphere thins out with increasing height, so the temperature falls, until at a height of 6 to 10 miles a temperature of –68°F is reached. The temperature stays steady at this value for the next several miles' increase of altitude. This allows a convenient classification into the *troposphere* and *stratosphere*. The troposphere is that part of the atmosphere associated with the weather and winds. The stratosphere is much more regular and stratified, although modern probings with balloons, rockets and satellites, together with observations on the movement of fall-out from nuclear explosions, are showing that the stratosphere has a circulation of its own. In the stratosphere at an altitude of about 25 to 30 miles there is an increase of temperature to about 28°F. This is the top of the ozone layer, and the rise in temperature is due to the strong absorption of ultra-violet radiation from the sun and infra-red from the earth.

The circulation of the atmosphere is extremely complicated, but this does not mean that the problems involved cannot

The envelope of gas which, held by gravitation, accompanies the earth on its journey through space, weighs about four thousand million tons. It changes from the air we breathe, at a pressure of 14.7 lb. per square inch, to the near-vacuum of hydrogen beginning about 1500 miles up (left column). Its temperature (second column) at first falls to about −68°F, rises almost to freezing point and then drops steeply again. The rise is due to the conversion back to oxygen of the ozone formed by the longest ultra-violet rays from the sun, and also to the absorption, by the ozone, of heat rays from the earth.

The very high temperatures at great heights represent only the high speed of the gas molecules, so few that the unprotected skin, if it could be exposed, would not feel the effect as heat.

The atmosphere falls conveniently into regions: the troposphere, the wind and weather level, the more regular stratosphere and mesosphere, seat of the ozone, and the four layers of the ionosphere. It is here that ultra-violet and X-rays from the sun, which would be lethal if they reached the earth, use up their energy in splitting the neutral atmospheric atoms into charged particles (electrons and ions) which reflect long radio waves but absorb the short waves of television. (5)

33

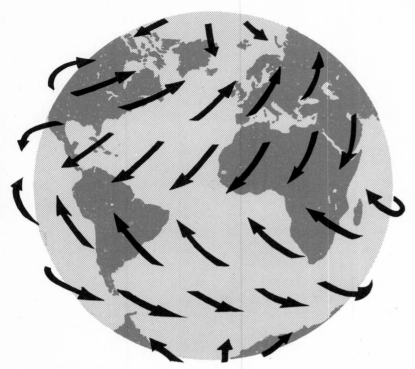

The winds vary continuously with changing local conditions, but an underlying general global pattern can be discerned. At the equator, the air, heated by the sun, rises, and is replaced by cooler air from the north (in the Northern Hemisphere). As this warms, it rises and returns at high altitudes to about 30° north. Similarly cold, dense air at the Pole flows south at ground level to about latitude 60°, rises and returns in the upper regions. Between the two, a counter-circulation operates, flowing north at surface levels, from the high pressure descending air at 30° to the low pressure rising air at 60°.

But the surface of the earth, and the atmosphere above it, is rotating from west to east at speeds varying from 1000 m.p.h. at the equator to zero at the Poles. Air starting south at 30°, and rotating at (say) 650 m.p.h., is rotating more slowly than the ground below it when it reaches the equator. It is left behind, seeming to flow from east to west. The two tendencies, a flow to the south and to the west, restrained by friction, produce a wind flowing south-west, the N.E. Trades. In the same way, air flowing from 30° to 60°, northwards, is rotating faster at 60° than the ground and seems to flow eastwards, the two combined producing the prevailing westerlies and, in the Southern Hemisphere, the Roaring Forties. (6)

be solved. A vast quantity of observation is needed, but it should be forthcoming now that satellites can be made to orbit the earth in any desired track. The difficulties of handling such a large volume of results can be overcome with the aid of computers, so that we are approaching an age when a full understanding of atmospheric circulation will be possible, and as a corollary to this, some form of long-range weather forecasting or even control of weather may be achieved.

p 48-9
(18, 19)

The pattern of wind and weather

In the lower parts of the atmosphere there are many small local eddies of the order of tens of miles across, and large depressions and anti-cyclones a thousand miles across. Underlying these important but transient features there is a general pattern of airflow which, near the ground, is familiar as an easterly wind belt between 30° N and 30° S (the north-east and south-east trade winds are the part of this system at the sea-surface), and belts of generally westerly winds between 30° N and 60° N and between 30° S and 60° S. This pattern is confused by the continent of Asia, which terminates the Indian Ocean to the north and so provides a different geographical picture to that of the Atlantic or Pacific Oceans. In July a clockwise air movement occurs over southern Asia and the Indian Ocean,

fig 6

p 50-1
(20, 22)

while in January there is an anti-clockwise circulation. This change in circulation accounts for the main climatic features of the area, and the wind patterns bear the familiar name of monsoons.

Two kinds of information are gathered concerning winds. Firstly wind speed and direction are recorded continuously at a network of meteorological stations all over the earth. These measurements are extended upwards into the atmosphere by observations (often made by radar) on free-floating balloons. By averaging over long periods of time, local effects such as thunderstorms and the larger depressions and 'highs' may be smoothed out to give the world pattern of winds. A similar result is obtained by measuring the pressure of the atmosphere at many places over the earth's surface, and deducing the direction of flow that the air must take in an effort to equalize the pressure. The general pattern of circulation as shown by these measurements agrees with what might be expected from a consideration of the rotation of the earth and the unequal heating from the sun at the equator and at the poles.

p 52
(24-7)

Superposed on these general circulatory movements of the atmosphere are the local whirls and eddies that are responsible for changes in the weather. The behaviour of these local features, the depressions and anti-cyclones, has been examined over a period of many years, so that short-range forecasts may be made of the air movement at a particular place. However, since a depression can develop, move or disappear in many different ways, the longer the forecast the more likely it is that the air movement will not behave as expected. Long-range forecasts based on similar patterns of weather in past years are sometimes successful for some months ahead, but can only be used when there are conspicuous features in the weather pattern which can be compared with the past. There is great hope that the continuous observation of clouds which has been started from the American weather satellites will help in elucidating more accurately the behaviour of depressions and anti-cyclones.

p 48-9
(18, 19)

300 million cubic miles of water

The steady trade and westerly winds blowing on the surface of the water produce a circulatory system in the oceans. The ocean currents are deflected by the barriers formed by the continents, and they are also affected, to some extent, by the earth's rotation. In the Atlantic there is a steady flow from east to west in the equatorial region, corresponding to the easterly trade winds. The top part of South America deflects the equatorial current to the Gulf of Mexico. Since water cannot, to any large extent, pile up in one place, an outward flow of warm water leaves the Gulf of Mexico to flow north along the American seaboard as the well-known Gulf Stream. After the Gulf Stream leaves the American coast it is helped along its journey to Europe by the westerly winds. Part of the Gulf Stream continues to beyond Iceland and Scandinavia, while the remainder makes a complete circuit to rejoin the North Equatorial current.

p 50-1
(21, 23)

In the southern Atlantic a similar pattern of currents is observed. The Brazil current shares the westward flow of the South Equatorial current with the Gulf Stream and therefore is not so large as the Gulf Stream. The cold Benguela current runs up the west coast of Africa to complete the circulation.

Since the wind pattern in the Pacific is similar to that in the Atlantic Ocean, the ocean current pattern also follows the same general trends. The North Equatorial current is

T. F. Gaskell

the largest in the world and runs for 9000 miles from Panama to the Philippines. It is turned to the north, but not with the strong funnelling effect that the Gulf of Mexico provides to produce the Gulf Stream. However, the Kuroshio current sweeps past Japan and right across the North Pacific Ocean, and spreads out and turns south in much the same way as the Gulf Stream. The South Pacific system of currents is more muddled because the South Equatorial current is broken up into energy-wasting eddies by the many islands in its path. The famous cold Humboldt current brings water from the Antarctic all the way up the western coast of South America.

p 50 (21) fig 8

The currents in the Indian Ocean change with the changing monsoon wind pattern, and the details of the water movement have not been worked out. However, the fact that the wind pattern does change should provide a means of learning more about the mechanism of wind moving the sea.

There are currents in the depths of the oceans as well as at the surface. The cold, relatively dense water of the Arctic and Antarctic regions sinks and flows towards the equator along the sea bed, helping to replace the surface water carried westwards by the equatorial currents. The salt content of sea water also affects the density and this again has an influence on the ocean currents. In the Mediterranean, for example, the high rate of evaporation makes the water abnormally salty and causes a deep current of salty water to slide over the sill of the Straits of Gibraltar into the Atlantic. A compensating surface current flows inwards through the Straits, a fact well-known to the earliest navigators.

The surface currents are measured directly by observing how much ships are set off course by the water movement. A stream of 1 knot will carry the ship 24 miles in a day, which is readily observable by fixing the ship's position with star sights. The ocean currents are so large in cross section that mixing with the surrounding water is not very rapid. Therefore currents maintain characteristic salinities and temperatures. It is quite easy for ships to keep in the Gulf Stream flow by watching the surface temperature. By following bodies of water labelled by salinity and temperature it is possible to track many of the currents. Salinity and temperature determine the pressure exerted by the water, and a pressure map over the ocean indicates which way the water will tend to move, in exactly the same way as the air barometric pressure allows winds to be calculated.

fig 7

The deep currents have been checked with floats called 'pingers' which can be set to ride at any desired depth below the surface. The floats are tracked by a ship at the surface, which listens for the sound signals (a series of 'pings') transmitted by the float. The ship checks its position with reference to a buoy anchored to the sea bed. The floats can be followed for several weeks. This is necessary to separate the backward and forward motion due to eddies from the general trend of the deep currents, which appear to be of the order of a few miles a day.

The sea occupies nearly three-quarters of the earth's surface and so the interaction with the atmosphere is most important to the climate of the world. In general the oceans exercise a moderating effect by absorbing excessive heat and providing beneficial winter warmth. The volume of the sea is very large, over 300 million cubic miles. The greater part of the oceans are about 2900 fathoms (three miles) deep, while there are several deep trenches about 25 miles across and nearly six miles deep. The deepest part of the ocean, 5940 fathoms (6³/₄ miles) discovered by H.M.S. *Challenger* in 1951, is in the Marianas Trench in the West Pacific. The

p 53 (29-30)

bathyscaphe *Trieste* has demonstrated that it is possible for observers to reach the deepest parts of the oceans, and it is probable that more will be learnt about the ocean deeps by such investigations.

A thin skin of rock

The earth's crust is the rocky skin which covers the whole surface of the earth and includes the upper layers of rock with which we are familiar on land. Although the crust is only a thin skin of rock 5 to 20 miles thick, compared with the 8000-mile diameter of the earth, it comprises all the topographical features that go to make the varied scenery of mountains, valleys and plains. All the geological changes that have taken place in the earth's history are concerned with changes in the earth's crust. Like the soil in a garden, it is the top layer of the earth that has been continually worked over by forces originating in the atmosphere, the sea and the inside of the earth.

The material that forms the continents probably settled at the surface of the once molten earth as a scum of light rock of a comparatively acidic nature. Beneath this lighter material, of which granite rock is typical, there is a lower part of the crust formed of more dense basalt type of rock. The main bulk of the earth beneath the thin skin of crust is formed of solid basic rock called the mantle, which extends downwards for about 2000 miles, and encloses the liquid core of the earth. The core is very dense and probably consists of a mixture of iron and nickel, together with a little silicon.

p 59 (42)

The crust is made up of three types of rock, the division into types being based on the methods of formation of the rock. Igneous rocks have solidified from molten material. We know something about their past history because we can see them being produced today by such massive volcanoes as those in Hawaii. Apart from the lava flows which solidify into flat sheets of rock, there are great plugs of material which have been squeezed out of underground melting-pots by the pressure which is developed when rock is melted. Sometimes molten rock is forced up in narrow fissures, to form vertical sheets of rock or dykes.

p 58

For most of the life of the earth the original igneous continental crust has been subjected to erosion, and the

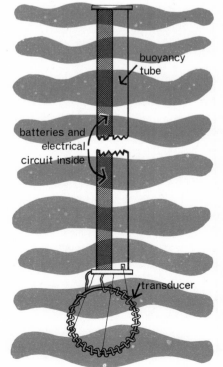

The direction and speed of the ocean currents at varying depths can be checked by means of the Swallow float, or 'pinger'. This consists of two aluminium tubes, sealed at the ends, and a ring-shaped transducer which converts electrical energy into sound signals ('pings') every few seconds. One tube contains dry batteries; the other is loaded with weights, the number of which can be varied to make the 'pinger' float along with the current at the desired depth. The 'pings' are picked up by hydrophones about 100 ft. apart on the ship, and, the ship's position being accurately known, the float's progress can be charted by cross-bearings. The 'pingers' cannot be recovered, but each new one can be followed for several weeks. (7)

buoyancy tube

batteries and electrical circuit inside

transducer

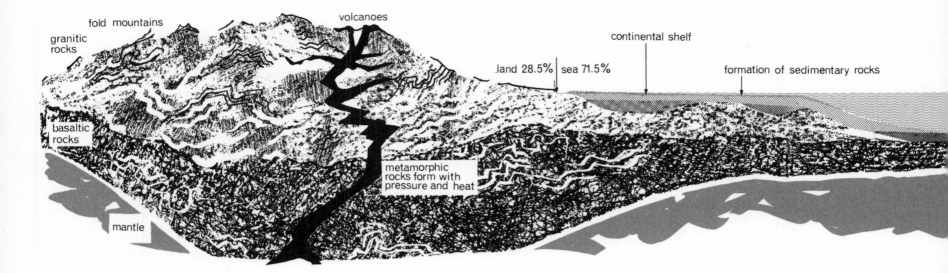

fold mountains

granitic rocks

volcanoes

continental shelf

land 28.5% sea 71.5%

formation of sedimentary rocks

basaltic rocks

metamorphic rocks form with pressure and heat

mantle

result of this wearing away of the original rock has been to form layers of sedimentary rocks. Erosion can be seen to be taking place all around us. Along the coast the force of the waves attacks and undermines cliffs, and the rock that falls into the sea is rapidly ground up by further wave action. In the mountains rain inexorably wears away the rock, and it is assisted by the penetration of the roots of plants and trees. Rivers carry boulders along with them to pound away more rock; the Grand Canyon is over a mile deep and several miles across and is still being eaten away by a fast flowing river. Alternate heating and cooling causes rocks to split. When ice forms in small cracks it exerts great forces because its volume is greater than the water from which it is formed. In high mountains snow compacts to produce glaciers, and these slowly moving rivers of ice grind away at the rock and reduce it to small particles.

p 54
(31)

p 54
(32)

p 55

There is a general downhill movement of the eroded rock, and although some of the soil is deposited by rivers when they reach the flat plains at the foot of the mountains, most of the debris finds its way eventually into the sea, where it gradually settles to the sea bed. Some of the finer particles are so slow in settling that they reach the deep oceans where they help to form the carpet which covers the original sea bed, but the bulk of the material washed off the continents forms layers of sedimentary rocks, such as clay, sandstone or limestone, around the fringes of the continents. This does not necessarily mean that the continents are continually growing outwards, because geological examination of the crustal rocks shows that continents tilt and the crust is deformed, so that what is land today was, in the past, a shallow sea or a vast lake. When a shallow depression forms, owing to forces in the interior of the earth, it automatically draws rivers towards it and then it gradually becomes filled with sediment.

fig 8

The changes that have been taking place in the crust revive the continents at intervals as well as making them sink under water. A small wrinkle in the earth's crust may take the form of a mountain range, so that what has been a shallow sea accumulating layer upon layer of sediment may millions of years later be thrust up to form mountains that in their turn are attacked and denuded by the forces of erosion. Usually there is a great deal of igneous activity associated with these phases of mountain building so that we find massive cores of igneous rock in such places as the Alps and the Rockies.

p 56
(34)

When the crust is wrinkled to form mountains, a local thickening of the crust takes place. The mountains have a root of continental rock to them, and this root is forced down into the more dense mantle rock. The amount of forcing down is normally just enough to let the mountain 'float' on the mantle just as an iceberg floats in the sea. We

The earth's crust under the continents extends on an average one-two-hundredth of the distance to the centre of the earth – a thin skin under slow but constant change. At first a scum on a molten earth perhaps, it still shows plenty of evidence, in its volcanoes and earthquakes, of the heat and pressure beneath, of the fiery origin of the granite and denser basalt of which much of it is composed, and of the forces which have buckled and thrust its mountains upwards. Throughout its history the surface, uniquely perhaps among the planets we know, has been torn by wind and rain and ice and the flowing rivers. The sediments these created were deposited again as rocks such as limestones and sandstones, buckled again under upheavals from below and metamorphosed by heat and pressure into shales and slates. The sediments stretch out as a shelf beneath the fringing seas, while the deeper ocean bed, below the deposits of millions of years, reveals igneous rock pierced and split by volcano and earthquake. The high mountains have deep roots forced down into the hard mantle below, upon which the whole crust 'floats', the join between them a clear-cut change in rock-type known as 'the Moho'. The undersea crust, much thinner than the land crust, will soon be pierced by the probes of scientists seeking to reveal what no man has yet seen—the mantle. (8)

know that this is so by measuring the gravitational attraction of the mountain. The attraction should be in excess of that on the flat parts of the continent because of the extra bulk of the mountain. In fact, the attraction is the same over the mountain as on the plains, owing to the compensation of the extra mass by the deficiency of heavy mantle which is pushed away by the light root of the mountain. That this explanation of the observed facts is the right one has been shown by determining the depth of the mountain root by observations on the waves sent out by earthquakes and by man-made explosions.

The forces that are associated with mountain-building, and the high temperatures of the igneous rocks that intrude into the sediments, alter the original form of the rock to make the third main class—the metamorphic rocks. For example, clay is compressed to form shale and slate, while the solution effect of hot vapours beneath the ground causes local concentrations of valuable materials, and deposits them as veins of ores. A similar concentration sometimes occurs during the formation of sedimentary rocks. If an inland sea gradually dries up owing to evaporation being greater than the supply of water from rivers, the chemicals contained in the water are precipitated like 'fur' in a kettle. Since materials have different solubilities, the least soluble compounds separate out first, and distinct layers of such useful products as salt, potassium iodide, phosphates, etc. are produced.

The debris from animal and plant life, both on land and sea, is added to that eroded from the mountains. Coal is formed from vegetable matter accumulated in swamps, while oil appears to be the result of the decay of marine organisms in shallow seas. It is possible that part of the oil comes from the waxy hydrocarbons associated with plants, and the reason for its close association with marine sedi-

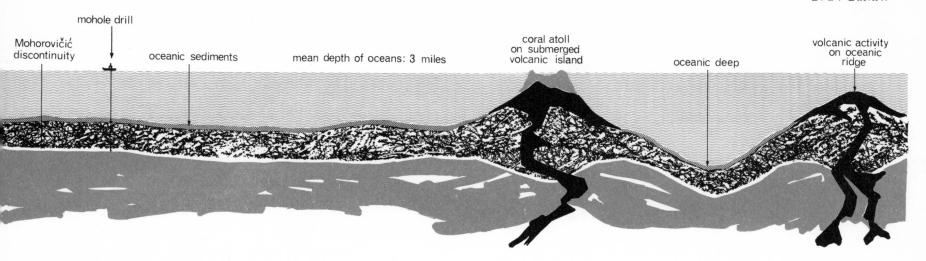

T. F. Gaskell

Mohorovičić
discontinuity | mohole drill | oceanic sediments | mean depth of oceans: 3 miles | coral atoll on submerged volcanic island | oceanic deep | volcanic activity on oceanic ridge

ments may be that it is in shallow marine conditions that the most important rocks for storing oil—limestones and sandstones—are formed.

p 56
(35-6)

fig 10

Wandering continents

The crust is continuous all over the earth, but beneath the deep oceans it is only a few miles thick, instead of the 20–25 miles under the continents. This is because the lighter granitic layer, and the sediments that have been derived from it by the continual re-working process of erosion and deposition, are missing. This is what we should expect if the separation into continents and oceans took place at an early stage of the earth's history, because there is very little erosion below three miles of sea.

fig 8

The fact that the crust is thinner under oceans than under continents, together with the preponderance of ocean compared with land area, encourages a new way of visualizing the earth—as a simple oceanic crustal structure with large 'rafts' of light continental rock superimposed in certain places. On this picture the floors of the ocean are permanent, in the sense that they have never been raised up to form dry land. Although the great thicknesses of sedimentary rock which can be measured on the continents exceed in some cases the depth of the oceans, all these sediments have the characteristics of shallow-water deposits. They were, therefore, laid down when the continental blocks were tilted to provide shallow seas such as the North Sea, or when changes in the inside of the earth caused a wrinkling of the crustal rocks that formed a local depression. Such a depression is apparent in the Persian Gulf; layers of rock many miles thick have been formed by the sediment deposits which have kept pace with the slow sinking over millions of years.

There is a certain amount of evidence in favour of the hypothesis that the continents can move bodily sideways as well as suffering tilts and flexures. The similarity in shape of the continents on the two sides of the Atlantic Ocean, for example, can be adduced as a natural result of the splitting apart of an original continent to form the Americas on the one hand and Europe and Africa on the other. Similar movements are postulated for Antarctica, Australia and India and some details of the geology do lend weight to the 'wandering continent' theory. It is possible that the measurement of 'fossil magnetism' in old rocks may allow a definite conclusion to be reached. When rocks are being formed they become magnetized in the direction of the earth's magnetic field. If the continents have moved, then the direction of magnetization of old rocks laid down before the movement

fig 9

took place will be different from that observed for recent rocks. The position is made more difficult by the fact that the earth's magnetic poles have also moved. The magnetic measurements are difficult to make, but the accumulation of results is tending to support some form of continental movement.

On this basis the Atlantic is a comparatively new ocean formed by the separation of the Americas from Europe and Africa. Yet the rock structure of its sea bed is similar to that

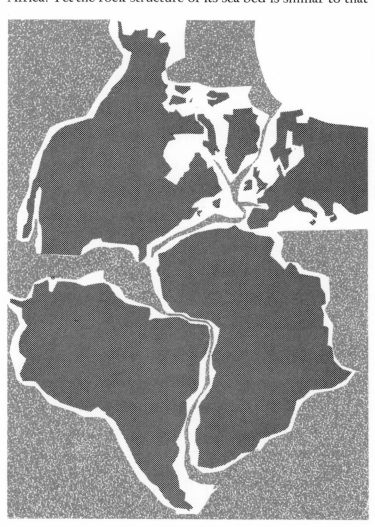

If the continents are fitted together, like a gigantic jigsaw puzzle, along the 2000-metre contour of the continental shelf, the fit is too good to be coincidental. It is thought that the Americas, Europe and Africa could once have been one great land mass, which slowly tore apart, possibly driven by convection currents in the plastic layer of the mantle. Naturally the process is too slow to be observed, but supporters of this 'continental drift' theory consider the San Andreas fault in California, Africa's Great Rift Valley and the Chilean strip of South America to be places where the splitting process is still going on. 'Fossil' magnetism in old rocks also tends to support this view: if the continents have moved, the old magnetic direction will be different from that of today. (9)

37

of the Pacific, and quite unlike that of the continents, although there are minor points of difference which support a different geological history. For example, the floor of the Pacific Ocean is not strong enough to support the load of volcanic islands such as Hawaii, which erupt from the sea-bed, and then sink until the root of the island is supported by being floated in the underlying mantle. The thick layers (some 5000 feet deep) of coral, which can grow only close to the surface, discovered on atolls like Bikini or Funafuti, give a measure of the amount of sinking that has taken place since the volcanic island core of the atoll first appeared. Islands such as Bermuda in the Atlantic show only a few hundred feet thickness of coral in their surrounding reefs, so that for some reason they have not followed the Pacific regime of sinking. In the Indian Ocean the same is true of islands like Aldabra or the Seychelles. It is possible that the Seychelles plateau may be a fragment of a continent left behind when India parted company with Africa and Madagascar.

A sideways movement of the continents is not hard to accept when the rift valley system of Africa and the Red Sea is viewed on a map. The splits, running roughly north-south, make it appear that fresh segments of Africa are ready to move off to follow Madagascar and India. Sideways movements have also been demonstrated in the Pacific. In California the San Andreas fault shows a sideways tearing of hundreds of miles, and in Chile movement in the same direction is taking place. It is as if the whole of the land bordering the Pacific Ocean is rotating clockwise around the ocean floor. Although the continents are demonstrably splitting and tearing, the mechanisms by which these processes take place are not fully understood. However, they are connected with the inside of the earth and with the heat production that is going on there.

The thickness of the earth's crust was first measured by

fig 8

fig 10

p 57

p 59
(42)

Prof. A. Mohorovičić, who successfully interpreted the behaviour of seismic waves sent out from nearby earthquakes as indicating that the crustal rocks were underlain by some other rock material at a depth of about 20 miles. The clear-cut change in rock type that was shown by the earthquake waves is in fact the boundary between the crust and the mantle, and it is called the Mohorovičić discontinuity, or the Moho for short. The recording of controlled explosions such as quarry blasts has allowed greater precision in determinations of crustal thickness than was possible from earthquakes. In a similar way observations made with underwater explosions have shown that the crust beneath the deep oceans is only a few miles thick. Apart from demonstrating that the crustal structure beneath the oceans is essentially different from that on land, the oceanographic experiments have suggested a practical possibility for investigating further the interior of the earth. Holes have been drilled on land to depths of about five miles, so the few miles of crustal rock underlying the oceans is within the range of modern drilling equipment. This means that a sample of the mantle rock could be obtained and the *Mohole Project* is actively pursuing this aim.

At the melting point of rock

The mantle rock forms about three-quarters of the earth, since it extends downwards for nearly 2000 miles—halfway to the centre of the earth. While guesses have been made of the chemical and petrological composition of the mantle, and while it is probably a basic rock similar to dunites or harzburgites which have been extruded from somewhere inside the earth, there is no certainty in the identification, because of the amount of mixing that takes place when molten rock is forced to the earth's surface, and also because

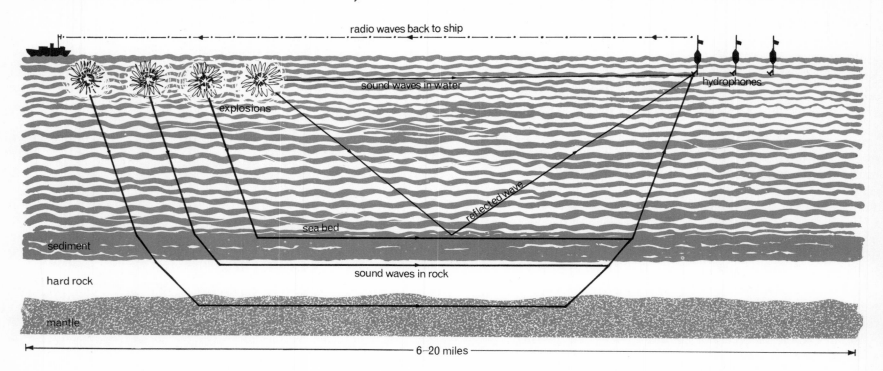

The denser matter is, the faster sound waves travel through it. If a depth charge is exploded in water, sound waves travelling directly from it could be expected to be the first to reach a distant hydrophone—earlier for instance than those reflected from the sea bottom. But if more charges are exploded, successively farther away, a time comes when the first wave to reach the hydrophone is one which has penetrated the sea bed, travelled more quickly through the rock beneath, and been refracted up again. If the horizontal distance is great enough, the time saved in the fast layer more than makes up for the time lost in travelling

down and up again. At a still greater distance, waves which have travelled through a still deeper and denser rock layer will be the first to arrive. If the times between the direct 'clunks' of the explosion on the ship's bottom and the first signals from the hydrophone are plotted against the distance between shot and detector, a measure of the depth of the layers and of the velocity of sound in the layers (a clue to the nature of the rock) can be obtained. In practice, the charges in this refraction method are exploded about 900 feet down, and a string of hydrophones, half a mile apart, give several sets of measurements. (10)

of an unknown amount of differentiation of molten material which may take place in the underground melting-pot.

Knowledge of the relative abundance of chemical elements in the earth is needed to check theories of the formation of the solar system, and a sample of the mantle is also required in order to find out what heat is being generated inside the earth by small amounts of radioactive uranium, thorium and potassium. The calculations based on probable abundances of these elements, together with measurements of the heat flowing out from the earth, suggest that at a depth of 100 miles or so below the surface the melting-point of rock must be nearly reached. The evidence from earthquake waves supports this, in that a low-velocity channel for the waves appears to exist in the mantle. The most obvious cause for this abnormality in the seismic velocity (since normally the velocity increases with depth) is that local softening of the rock is occurring. It is possible that the blanketing effect that is being produced in the mantle by the poorly conducting rocks of the crust may cause the low-velocity layer to creep upwards, until it is close enough to the surface to break through and lose a large amount of heat by convection and by enormous volcanic activity. There is geological evidence that periods of mountain-building and volcanic outpouring have occurred with comparatively quiet times in between.

It has been suggested that the movement apart of the continents to form the Atlantic Ocean, which took place about a hundred million years ago, was made possible by a softening of the upper mantle and the lower crustal rocks. The reason why the movement took place so recently in the earth's 4500 million years of existence could also be explained as an effect of the heat production inside the earth. The liquid core of the earth could be growing at the expense of the surrounding mantle rock. If the cause of movement at the earth's surface is, as has been suggested, the slow circulation in the mantle itself, then a change in size of the mantle will be accompanied by a change in the circulation pattern. Professor Runcorn has argued that such a change took place about a hundred million years ago, and changed the pattern of land and sea at the surface of the earth from a single land mass to the distribution that we see today. Whatever may turn out to be the true history of the earth, it is certain that the heat effects have played an important part.

A core of liquid iron

The vital statistics of the inside of the earth have been discovered by a series of different experiments starting with Eratosthenes' determination of the circumference of the earth in 200 BC. The method used is to compare the angular distance between two points on the earth's surface with their distance apart as measured with a tape on the ground. The mass of the earth is found by applying Newton's law of gravitational attraction to the force with which the earth attracts a body at its surface. A body of mass m is pulled towards the centre of the earth by a force equal to GmM/r^2 where G is the constant of gravitational attraction, M the mass of the earth and r the radius of the earth. The force with which the earth attracts the body of mass m is, of course, the weight of the body, mg, where g is the acceleration due to gravity. The value of g may be found by direct observation on a falling body (although its determination has been more frequently made by the use of pendulums). G was first measured in Cavendish's famous experiment in which he measured the force of attraction between small gold balls and large lead spheres.

p 172 (26)

p 59 (42·3)

p 58

p 14 (fig 5)

The average density of the earth, 5.5 gm/cm³, is considerably greater than that of the rocks which are visible at the surface, so that there must be a heavy core to the earth. The determination of the moment of inertia of the earth, by careful observation of the small perturbations of the earth's orbit caused by the attractions of the sun and moon, allows the mass distribution to be calculated; the density of the core is found to be about the same as that of iron under the pressure and temperature conditions expected inside the earth. Quite a different line of evidence did suggest a dense iron core in the past. Meteorites which fall from the skies could be fragments from a planet that has broken up for some reason during the history of the solar system. If this is so the composition of meteorites should yield some clues as to the way the earth is made. It is found that there are two kinds of meteorites: those which are almost pure iron, and those made of stony material.

The detailed examination of the interior is provided by earthquake waves. Earthquake shocks are often strong enough to be detected right round the world and seismological observatories are positioned to record waves that have travelled through various thicknesses of the spherical earth. The observatories that are close to the centre of the disturbance detect the waves that travel through the crust, as we have seen. As the distance from the earthquake is increased, so the waves travel deeper into the earth, until a seismograph at the antipodal point will receive a wave which has travelled right through the centre. It is possible to calculate the position of the earthquake and its instant of occurrence by combining the measurements from nearby observatories, and then the arrival times of the waves at the distant stations can be used to calculate the speed of travel of the waves in the interior.

The speed of the earthquake waves becomes greater as the waves go deeper, which is expected since laboratory measurements of velocity in rocks subjected to pressure show the same effect. The earthquake wave observations confirm that the rock mantle stretches down nearly halfway to the centre of the earth. At this point there is a sudden change in velocity and density, and this causes refraction of some earthquake waves at the mantle-core boundary. Observations of the travel of such waves confirms the picture of the earth's interior.

The earthquake wave studies also show that the core is liquid. There are several types of motion that can travel through rock. The fastest of these is the compressional wave which can be propagated through solids and liquids. A slower type of wave, called transverse or shake because the rock moves sideways as the wave passes, cannot be transmitted by liquids. Transverse waves cannot then travel through the liquid core, and, therefore, while we can follow the compressional waves right round the earth from the centre of an earthquake, the transverse wave is lost as soon as the shadow of the liquid core is reached.

There may be a solid inner part to the liquid core, but the accuracy with which earthquake shocks can be located makes it a subject for future investigation. Such investigation may be possible if a large underground nuclear explosion is used as the source of earthquake waves. In addition to knowing exactly when and where the shock waves are initiated it will be possible to station temporary recording units at critical points to distinguish the fine detail of the wave behaviour that is necessary to elucidate the exact internal structure of the earth.

The radioactive substances which produce heat inside the earth also form clocks by which the age of the earth may be computed. Each radioactive element decays at a rate which is unaffected by heat or cold, chemical change or pressure. Uranium, for example, decays into particular isotopes of lead, and the ratio of uranium to lead in a piece of rock will tell the age at which the rock solidified from an original liquid. Determinations made on rocks from the crust give a minimum age of the earth as 2.7 thousand million years, but it is generally believed that the formation of the mantle by solidifying from a molten earth took place about 4,500 million years ago. If the earth was formed by cold collection of matter, then the collection and warming up to produce the molten earth necessary for the separation into crust, mantle and core may add another thousand million years.

This age of the earth is in agreement with the age calculated from the present rate of recession of the moon from the earth as a result of tidal friction. The tides are caused by the attraction of the sun and the moon on the water of the sea, and the mass of water is set in a complicated oscillatory motion. In constricted waters the tides may become very large, and energy is dissipated by turbulence and friction. This has the effect of slowing down the earth's rotation and also of driving the moon away from the earth and causing it always to turn the same face to the earth. Some people believe that the moon was formed in the early days of the earth's history by tidal action of the sun on the molten earth. If this theory is accepted it does explain why the light continental material does not form a uniform layer over the whole of the earth's surface, as might be expected if the continents are the result of solidification of a light scum on the liquid earth. The present position of the Pacific Ocean would be the scar left by the departing moon—a scar that has probably diminished owing to continental drift. On this reasoning the moon would be composed of material similar to that of the earth's crust and mantle. The known density of the moon is compatible with this composition, and confirmation will, in the not too distant future, be made by collecting samples of the moon.

p 62-5

The earth's cold companions

The moon is 2160 miles in diameter and is 239,000 miles from the earth. This means that it subtends almost exactly the same angle as the sun (864,000 miles diameter and

p 60-1
p 67
p 66 (59, 60)
p 68
p 66 (62)
p 66 (61)

93,000,000 miles from the earth), so that during eclipses the sun is almost completely blotted out by the moon. The moon has no atmosphere to protect it and, therefore, alternates scorching days with freezing nights, each of 14 earth days' duration. The conspicuous craters on the moon's surface are probably the result of impacts with large meteorites, although some form of volcanic action may have taken place. One of the early measurements that will be made by non-manned rockets will consist of recording tremors at the moon's surface to determine whether any earthquake activity is taking place.

The planets, Jupiter, Saturn, Uranus, Neptune and Pluto are so far from the sun that they do not receive enough heat to maintain their temperature above $-240°F$ to $-380°F$. Any water on these planets will be perpetually in the form of ice, and any clouds will consist of gases such as carbon dioxide rather than of water vapour. The smaller planets, in particular Mars, have surface temperatures more like our own, but the extremes from day to night are much greater than we suffer on earth. It is not certain whether life as we know it exists on any of the planets. However, recent investigation of meteorites has revealed hydrocarbons which may be the result of organized animal or vegetable life. Meteorites probably originated in the belt of asteroids, which lies between Mars and Jupiter and may have been the result of the disintegration of a planet. The larger asteroids are a few hundred miles in diameter. They may have a warm interior caused by radioactive heating and they certainly have a surface that is below the freezing point of water. It has been suggested that somewhere inside them there could be conditions where water could play the same role that it does in earth geology, and that oxygen could support some organized life similar to that on earth.

The study of meteorites will assist planning of space travel, since meteors and comets have been experiencing the effects of cosmic ray bombardment, and of entering the earth's atmosphere, for millions of years. Comets and meteorites are members of the solar system, and this is probably also the case with micrometeorites. Many thousands of tons per day of fine material are collected by the earth as it sweeps round the sun, and now that attention has been drawn to evidence of organic matter in bodies that fall from the sky, it is possible that the fine meteoritic dust will have a story to tell concerning the origin of life.

The explosion of science

in its most dramatic form lies in man's first attempts to explore the space around him. He has had resounding successes: he plans already to land on the moon and his probes have reached Venus and Mars. He is stepping warily into the solar system, the vast, largely empty space (opposite) in which nine major bodies circle at high speeds, almost all in the same flat plane. For decades, perhaps centuries, he must be content in his probing with the few central orbits, dependent for his knowledge of his cold outer neighbours on the radiation which reaches him. But, in a few short years, he has made a beginning.

At the centre of this vast system lies the sun, no more than an average star, one of the hundred thousand million which make up our own Galaxy—but a colossal power-house pouring out radiation and matter. Through every square metre of its surface, light, heat and their family flow at a rate of 84,000 horsepower (enough to power six 4-engined jet planes); within the sun, every second, 564 million tons of hydrogen fuse to form helium—the reaction of thermonuclear power. Only a two-thousand-millionth of the sun's output of energy reaches us, but it is as much, in three days, as would be produced from burning the entire oil, coal and wood the earth contains. To us, at a distance of 93 million miles, this outpouring of solar radiation is the prime source

of all energy, of all our fuel and food: without it, life could not exist. But even with it, life could not exist as we know it except within a quite narrow band, in which the earth's orbit happens to lie. From Mercury, nearest planet to the sun, a visiting astronaut, if he could survive the 350°C temperature, would see the sun from two to three times as big as we see it here. Venus, 67 million miles from the sun, is perpetually veiled by a thick cloud of gas. Earth's next neighbour, Mars, could perhaps support some form of vegetable life, with noonday temperatures around 36°C at the equator but a black, biting frost at night. Beyond Mars lies the belt of asteroids, fragments perhaps of another planet which disintegrated aeons ago. Beyond them again lie the giant Jupiter, more than eleven times the earth's diameter, and the ringed planet Saturn, its central sphere only slightly less. Since the visualization opposite is roughly in scale, only two short stretches of the orbit of Uranus, 2,800 million miles from the sun, can be shown, while Neptune and Pluto, the farthest known, would require a page a yard wide. More than 6,000 million miles across, the sun's family of planets is joined occasionally, briefly, by a comet from even vaster distances, drawn and held by the same force of gravitation that keeps the planets in the dominion of the sun. (1)

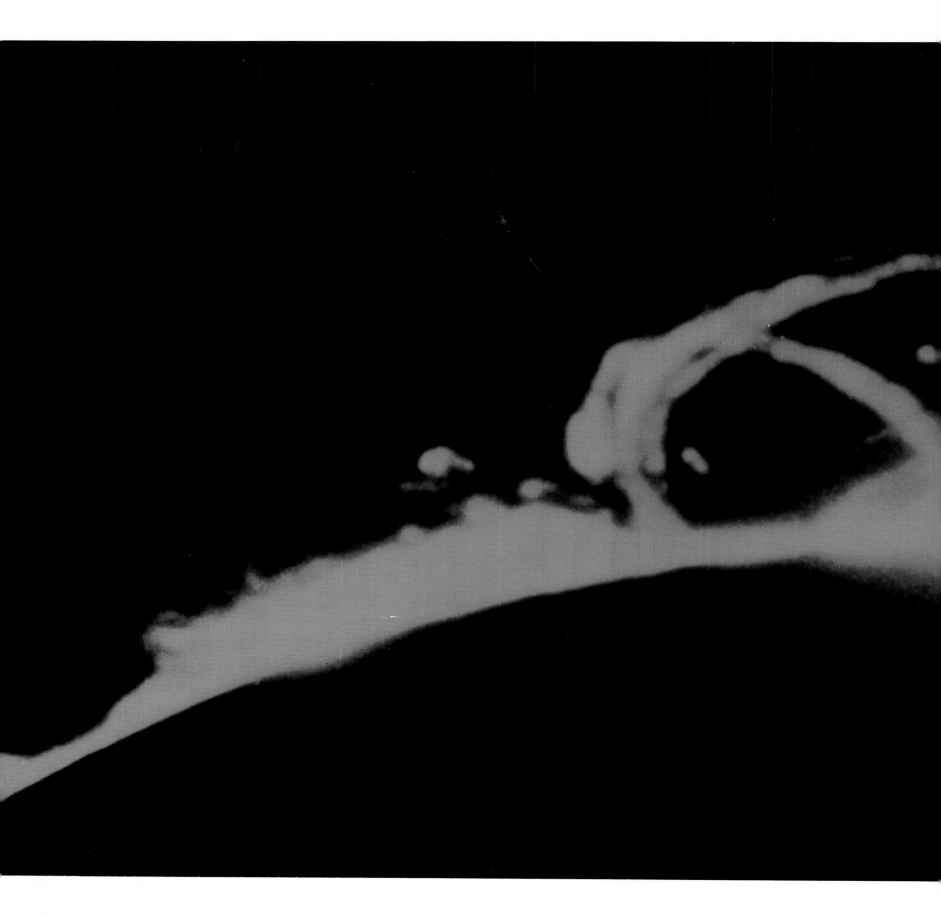

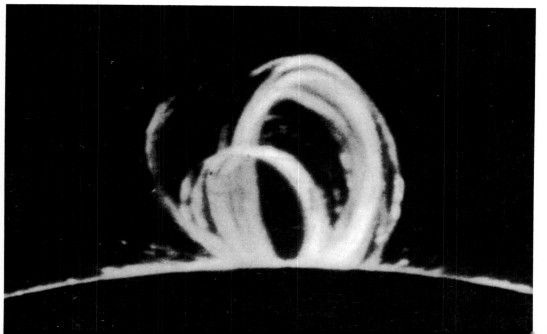

Loops and arches of flaming hydrogen shoot periodically from the sun's surface, forced up by the enormous thermonuclear explosion at the core. Hot gases, atoms stripped of their electrons, shoot out into space, drape themselves briefly round the sun's lines of magnetic force and sink back again, or break off and escape from the gravitational pull of the sun altogether. Above, glowing with the red light of hydrogen, an erupting arch on the sun's edge is silhouetted against the black sky, the sunlight masked off by an opaque disk. The looped prominence (left) is 85,000 miles high; the amazing arch of flame (far right) is the biggest ever photographed; it soared over 1,000,000 miles–more than the diameter of the sun–on 4th June 1946. The pulsing streamers of the corona, the sun's 'atmosphere', and the thin red ring of the chromosphere (right) were photographed from a high-flying aircraft during a total eclipse. The notch is an explosion on the sun which burned part of the film. (2-5)

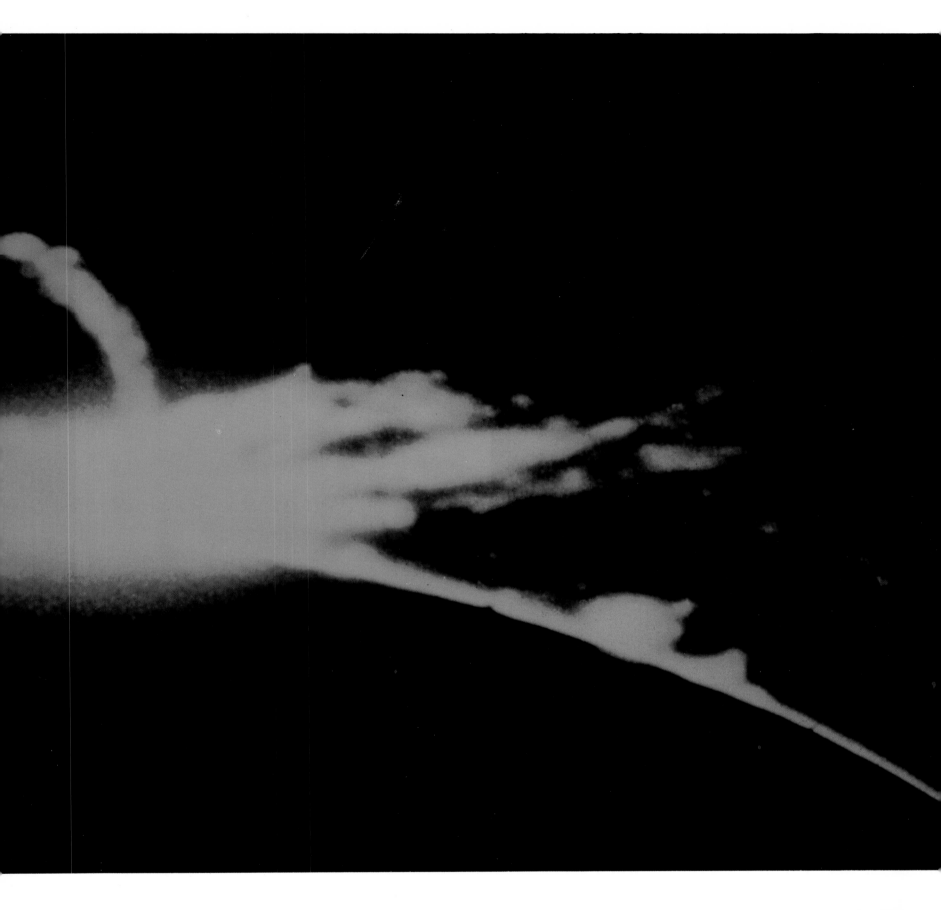

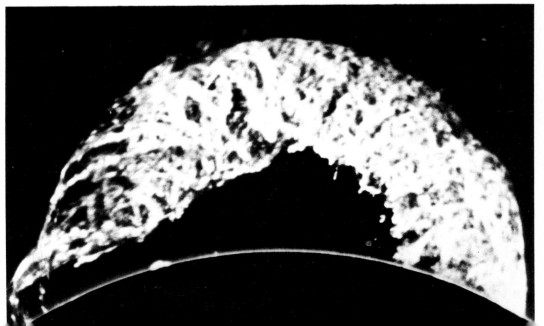

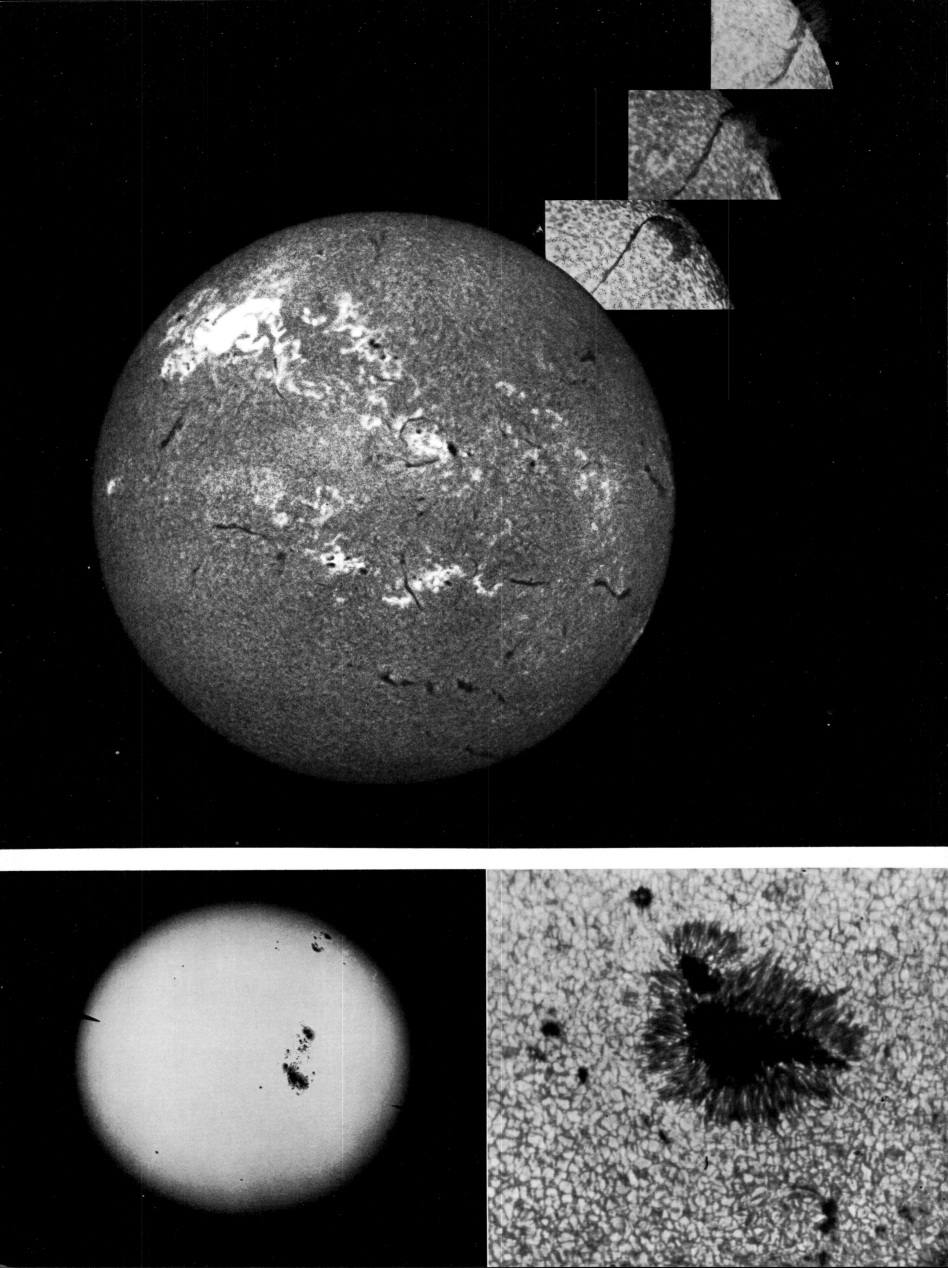

The restless sun has many faces for the astronomer. In the red light given off by the sun's hydrogen atoms it looks like the top picture opposite. The bright patch (top left) is a solar flare, a major disturbance. The scattered clouds are hot rising hydrogen, the dark round patches sunspots and the dark, ribbon-like filaments erupting loops and arches. The three inserts, in calcium light, show one such prominence at the sun's edge (top) and over the disk as the sun turned. In later photographs it was a thin, curved filament only.

Photographed in white light (opposite, below), the sun displays only the occasional dark patch of sunspots. Sunspots (and filaments) are dark only by contrast with the 6000° C of their surroundings: in fact the centre of a sunspot, though it looks like a black and bottomless hole in the solar surface, is brighter than an electric arc and has a temperature of 4000°–5000° C. A 12-inch telescope, carried to 80,000 feet by Princeton University's Stratoscope I balloon, photographed the sunspot seen opposite (below, right). In such detail, set against the granulated mosaic of the sun's skin, or photosphere, it looks even more like a hole, with jagged, cliff-like sides, but may be only a shallow depression. The size of these strange turbulences varies from 200–300 miles across to 30,000-mile monsters into which the earth itself could disappear without touching the sides. The origin of sunspots is still not clear. What is certain is that they wax and wane in numbers with the increased activity every eleven years or so, and that over the same cycle terrestrial phenomena such as the aurora, magnetic storms and radio blackouts increase and decrease correspondingly. (6,7,8)

The first space shots were satellites carrying instruments to record the charged particles which they encountered. Scientists were surprised to find, from the results signalled back, that both protons and electrons seemed to concentrate in belts round the earth. It was a discovery of intense interest to scientists and a threat of danger to future astronauts, and many satellites are now engaged in exploring both the intensity of the particles and the magnetic fields which affect them. The three-dimensional picture of the earth's magnetic field which is slowly being revealed (right) is shaped roughly like a doughnut—a fat ring with the hole descending to the north and south poles. On the night side of the earth, which is not yet fully explored, the field and particle concentrations show a slip-stream effect; on the sunward side strong bursts of particles from the sun seem to compress the earth's field at the meeting surface, normally some 36,000 miles out.

Within the earth's field are two zones (the 'Van Allen belts') in which the number of particles is particularly high, the inner one reaching from the high atmosphere to 3200 miles above the earth's surface. In it, particles may spend as much as ten years spiralling backwards and forwards at high speed along the lines of magnetic force. Both protons and electrons are involved, the protons seeming to fly upwards from the earth's atmosphere, produced by collisions between cosmic rays from space and atoms of the air. The source of the electrons is not yet fully understood, but both particles eventually decay in energy and return to become part of the normal atmosphere. In spite of the constant movement, the density of particles in the zone remains comparatively stable, the gain balancing the loss.

The outer zone is an immense area stretching from a comparatively dense region at 10,000 miles to an undefined boundary beginning about 28,000 miles and reaching to 36,000 miles above the earth's surface. The zone is crescent-shaped, its points reaching down towards the poles. Here the stream of particles from the sun (the 'solar wind') meets the earth's magnetic field, and great differences in the energy of the particles and their distribution occur. Periods when the area seems oversaturated correspond well in a general way with the onset of flares on the sun and magnetic storms and aurorae on the earth. It was thought that at these times particles spilled out or spiralled down the edge of the magnetic fields towards the poles, but the energy stored in them would not be large enough to account fully for the aurorae and the mechanism must be more complex, the chief source of particles being the 'tail' side of the magnetic field. (9)

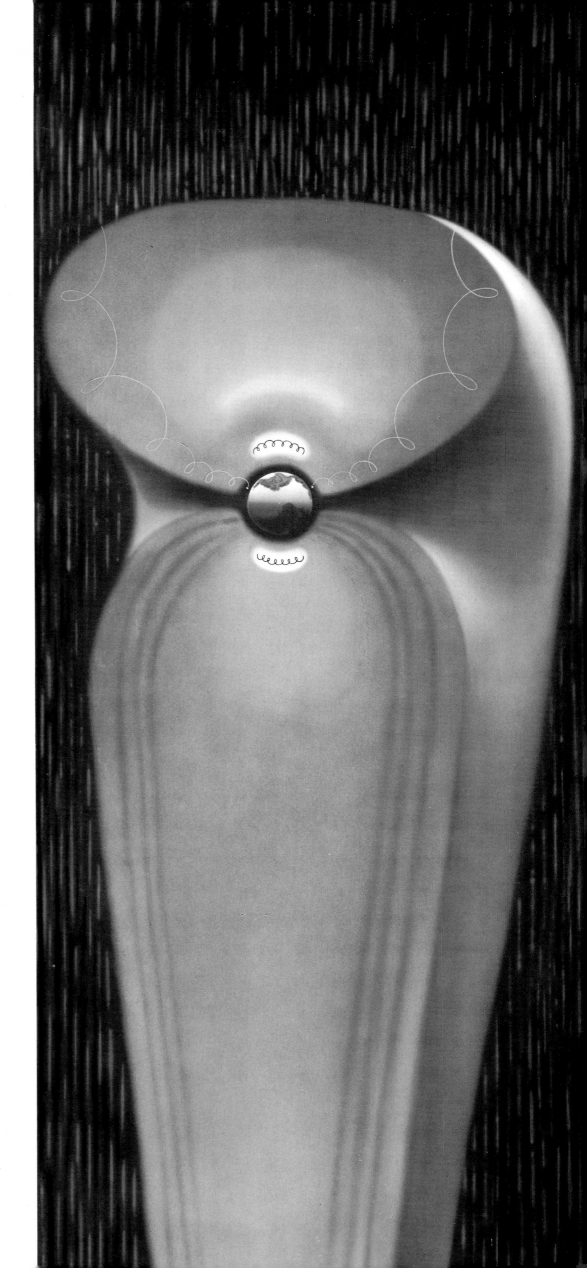

45

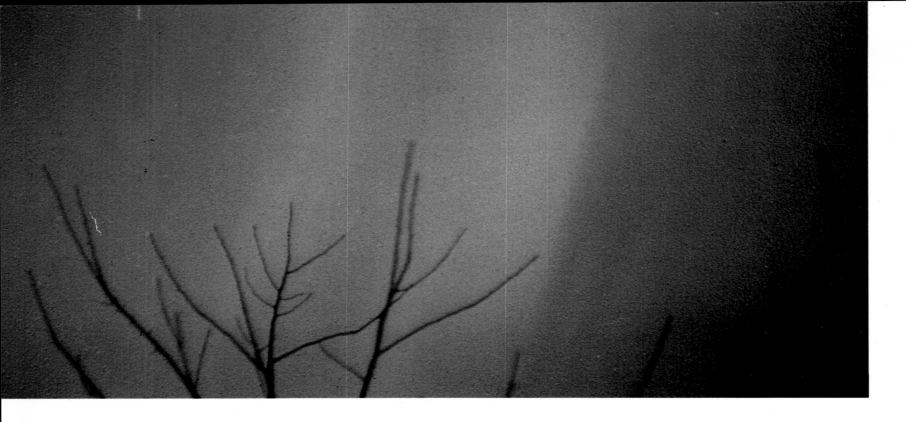

The unearthly shimmering beauty of the aurorae is a familiar sight anywhere within 1500 miles of the geomagnetic north pole, in the NW tip of Greenland, and within a corresponding zone in Antarctica. Ribbons and bands and formless patches of coloured light play across the night sky, blue and violet, green, orange and deep red, as the atoms of rarefied gas high up in the atmosphere, struck by incoming particles, become 'excited', and, as in neon street signs, glow briefly as they return to their normal state. Different elements give off light of different wavelengths and therefore different colours. The red of the aurora above (from Ithaca, New York) is a rare high-level glow from excited oxygen atoms; the orange rays and green fringe are nearer and lower, also from oxygen atoms. Nitrogen molecules that have lost electrons altogether, and acquire them again, give off blue and violet light at high levels (right, from Halley Bay, Antarctica). At low levels, excited oxygen atoms account for the green aurora (below) with a scarlet fringe from ionized nitrogen. Auroral displays take place 60 to 600 miles up and can stretch one or two thousand miles from east to west. These beautiful displays signal outbursts of particles from the sun, which stream in ribbon-like beams into the upper atmosphere. (10, 11, 12)

An anatomy of the sun's bounty (right) shows the astonishing range of the solar radiation. From this star of ours come not only heat and light but many other wavelengths of radiation. From the corona, the restless white halo which is the sun's upper atmosphere, come radio waves (right band) that can be picked up by radio telescopes. The photosphere—which is, to our eyes, the visible sphere of the sun—radiates infra-red waves, which we feel as heat, and the whole spectrum of visible light. Also from the photosphere we receive the ultra-violet rays (fourth band), shorter than visible light, that cause sunburn. They would be deadly if we received them at full strength; fortunately, most of them are absorbed in the ozone layer about 20 miles up, where they split up oxygen molecules in the upper atmosphere to form the three-atom molecule of ozone.

Shorter ultra-violet rays, and the even shorter X-rays, are absorbed by the atoms and molecules in the thinnest upper regions of the atmosphere. They strip off electrons from the atoms, leaving large numbers of charged particles or ions—the ionosphere. This belt of charged particles, 60 to 250 miles above us, forms layers right round the earth: the D layer (pale blue), where nitrous oxide is stripped of its electrons by medium-length ultra-violet rays, the F layers (dark blue) where the shortest ultra-violet rays (sixth band) ionize nitrogen, and the E layer (mid blue) where the longest X-rays ionize nitrogen and oxygen. Sometimes solar flares and sunspots pour out X-rays in unusual quantity, ionizing the D and E layers strongly (eighth band) and lowering their altitude. This causes radio blackouts, as the ionosphere, normally a reflecting 'mirror' for long-distance radio waves, becomes disturbed. The shortest and most energetic gamma-rays (left band) penetrate almost down to earth. Shifting, fluctuating, always self-renewing, the ionosphere acts as a filter without which human life would be impossible. (13)

The rare green flash from the top of the setting sun (below) was long thought to be an optical illusion, but the camera can detect it too. The flash usually only lasts for a second or less, and is best seen from a height, in clear air (the picture below was taken from the Vatican Observatory at Castel Gandolfo). As the sun sinks to the horizon its light reaches the eye through an increasing thickness of atmosphere, and the rays are bent downwards, seeming therefore to come from higher up. The red rays, bent the least, are lowest, then orange, yellow, green, blue and violet. But the blue and violet are scattered by the atmosphere; the green, less affected, reaches the eye. For a brief flash, green shows atop the squashed, orange-red ball of the sinking sun. (14)

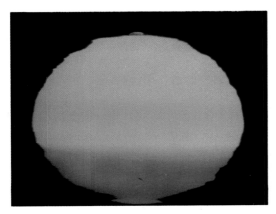

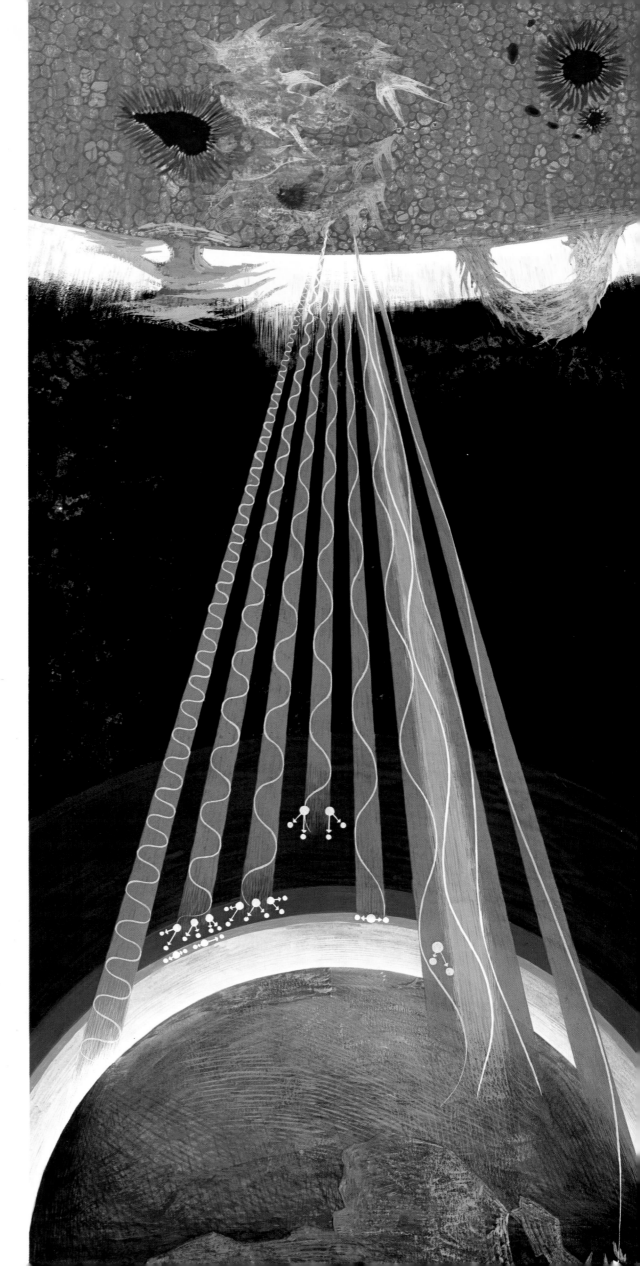

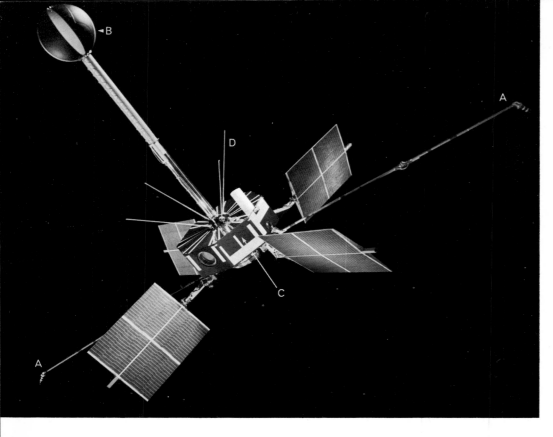

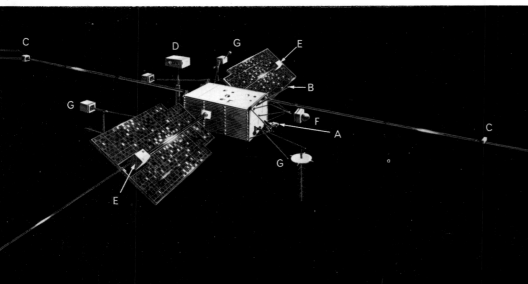

Mapping the earth's surroundings, including the Van Allen zones, is the work of several series of unmanned satellites. When those of the series IMP (Interplanetary Monitoring Probe) reach their planned orbits after launch (left, top) two 7 ft. booms and a 6 ft. boom unfold, carrying on their ends instruments (A) and (B) to measure the strength and direction of the magnetic fields as far as the moon. Mounted in this way, the instruments will not be affected by the weak magnetic fields created by the satellite itself. The octagonal body (C) is only 8 ins. thick but is a whole physics laboratory in miniature, measuring cosmic rays from solar flares and the Milky Way, the low energy solar wind and micrometeorites, and mapping the 'tail' on the night side of the earth. The instruments send information back to earth from four aerials (D). IMPs will travel right out to the moon, where a small rocket motor will kick them into a lunar orbit; here, for six months they will measure conditions in the moon's vicinity, in preparation for manned moon flights. The electrical power comes mainly from the sun, by means of four 'paddles' containing 11,520 solar cells. (15)

Nearly half a ton in weight, 54 ft. long with its booms unfolded, OGO, like the much smaller IMP, is a close-packed miniaturized laboratory. A sensitive photo-cell (A) controls a small gas jet (B) to make attitude corrections, because the solar panels and the instruments E, E need to face the sun. The booms C, C measure magnetic fields, and other instruments in D and F make studies similar to those of IMP.

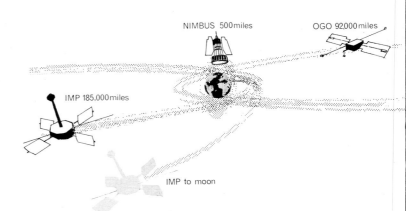

Within the 6 by 3 ft. main body are more instruments, and the equipment for transmitting information back to earth through the aerials (G). OGO is used in two types of orbit: a highly eccentric 63 ½ hour orbit going out as far as 92,000 miles, and a much nearer, almost circular orbit over the poles, in which it studies the atmosphere and ionosphere. The drawing above shows the first of these orbits, as well as those of IMP and Nimbus. (16, 17)

Keeping watch on the weather, Nimbus (left, below) has a nearly circular orbit some 500 miles up. Passing close to the poles, it orbits in 98 minutes, providing as the earth turns a complete coverage at least once every 24 hours. A photosensitive cell (A), trained on the horizon, keeps the satellite stabilized by means of gas jets (B) so that it always points vertically downwards. Two banks of three high-resolution television cameras (C) photograph the cloud cover beneath; infra-red scanners (D) photograph the clouds when they are in darkness. All these records are stored in the satellite's 'memory' (E), and given up to two receiving stations in Alaska and Canada once in each orbit on command received by the antenna (G). Two 8 ft. panels of solar cells provide the power. From the world-wide pattern thus obtained, meteorologists can picture the broad features of the world's weather, as well as keeping track of hurricanes and typhoons.

Cloud pictures of a 1000-mile square immediately under the satellite are continuously transmitted by an automatic television camera (F), to be received by over 70 small stations round the world. Two of these, received in France (opposite) show with remarkable clarity the British Isles, France (both almost free of cloud), and Spain as far as Madrid. Even low tide on the Channel coast (lighter strip) is visible. (18, 19)

The winds of the earth, infinitely variable in the whirls and eddies of local weather, nevertheless show a general underlying pattern. As we have seen, the first cause of this pattern lies in the rise of the heated air round the Equator, reducing the pressure at surface level and attracting air from north and south. As it nears the equatorial regions, this air is rotating more slowly, west to east, than the earth beneath. It is left behind and seems to be moving east to west. The emergent pattern and the consequent effects at higher latitudes are clearly seen in the upper map below, showing the general wind movements at ground level in the northern July. The N.E. and S.E. Trades flow towards the Doldrums at the equator; farther north and south lie the calms of the Horse Latitudes. Between 30° and 60° latitude, prevailing winds blow from the south-west and north-west.

The land masses, quick to heat and quick to cool, disturb the rough general picture. Over the hot lands of Asia, for instance, in the northern summer, air rises and pressure falls, attracting moisture-laden winds from the Indian Ocean, building up the massive rain-storms of the S.W. Monsoon and disrupting the girdle of equatorial low pressure (dotted line). To north-eastern India, after three months of unbearable dry heat, the punctual arrival in June of several inches of water a day is the salvation of the crops. Worshippers at Ranchi (left), assembled to give thanks, rejoice in the pouring rain. In winter the air over Central Asia is cold and dense, and the girdle of low pressure is re-united south of India. (20, 22)

The currents of the oceans (lower map, below) are clearly influenced by the winds. The Trades, above and below the equator, blow steady streams of surface water east to west across both the Atlantic and the Pacific. The Roaring Forties sweep a drift from the west around the world in the southern oceans. In the Gulf of Mexico, as the warm water cannot pile up, it issues as the Gulf Stream, up the eastern American seaboard and, assisted by the prevailing westerlies, across the Atlantic to bring a mild enough climate on the north-west Scottish coast to grow palm trees (in sharp contrast to the Gulf of St Lawrence, ten degrees farther south, which is closed by ice in winter because it is brushed by the cold Labrador current from the north). A similar flow to the north, not so strongly funnelled, occurs in the Pacific and in both oceans the circulation is completed by south-flowing currents on the east. In the south, cold streams are attracted up the west coasts of Africa and South America.

The latter, the Humboldt current, brings plankton-rich water to the coast of Peru, beginning an important ecological series. For the protein in the cold water supports a vast supply of fish, attracting birds which colonize the off-shore islands. Their droppings are rich in phosphates and are harvested to supply agriculture with a natural fertilizer. These 'guano' birds (left, below), mainly cormorants, gannets and pelicans, can cluster five million to a square mile, although intensive fishing of anchovy by the Peruvians may be the cause of their diminished numbers in recent years. (21, 23)

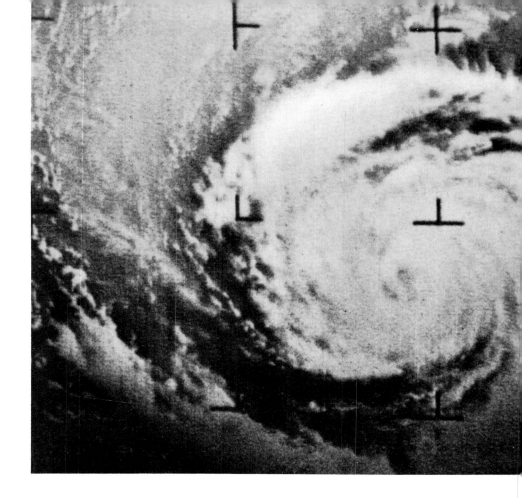

The sheer solid power of moving air is shown by this dramatic picture from Florida (above), taken in the teeth of Hurricane Cleo on 29 August 1964. Minutes later, the kiosk was smashed, the fragments airborne. The same season's Hurricane Ethel (right), photographed from 490 miles up by the Nimbus weather satellite, shows the typical whirlpool shape. About ten hurricanes a year form over the Caribbean, where north-east Trades are turned north by low-pressure pockets. A hot, moisture-laden eddy forms, the warm air rises and the moisture condenses. Heated more by the condensation, the air spirals under the earth's rotation faster and higher, a whirling cylinder with a core of still air. The hurricanes travel at speeds of a few miles an hour for hundreds of miles before they die out. (24, 25)

Most vicious of all, tornadoes (above) are thought to be spawned as fast, cold air over-runs hot, moist air. The warm air twists upwards at 200 m.p.h. or more—a roaring funnel flashing with lightning. So low is the air pressure within that houses are exploded by the expanding air inside them. A 'twister' that ripped through Hickman Mills, Missouri (right) in May 1957 left this swathe of destruction. (26, 27)

One hundred and forty million unexplored square miles of the earth's surface lie under the oceans. Man is now busy exploring them, diving down the few hundred feet of the shallower waters of the continental shelf. On the right, two of Jacques Cousteau's divers, seeking evidence of oil on the sea-bed, off Abu Dhabi in the Persian Gulf, collect rock specimens for examination by geologists.

At the depth of the greater part of the oceans, some three miles, the bed of pebbles (centre) represents a rich possible harvest from the sea—manganese. These stones, averaging a few inches in diameter, contain mostly manganese and iron, with small amounts of copper, nickel, cobalt and other elements. Submarine photography shows that in the Pacific alone, with about 24 lb. of these stones per square yard of bottom, there must be over a million million tons waiting to be mined. The origin of these 'nodules' is not clear, but it is probable that they grow at the rate of a millimetre every ten thousand years. One day the economics of recovery may make it worthwhile mining this mineral wealth.

To explore this same depth of three miles, the three-man Aluminaut has been designed (below), a Jules Verne monster of light and strong aluminium, the first submarine to operate at such depths, with floodlights, television cameras and robot arms. It was one of the craft used in the attempts to recover H-bomb material from the Mediterranean. Further down, observers have reached the sea-floor in bathyscaphes (the greatest ocean depth is the Challenger Deep in the Marianas Trench in the West Pacific, which descends 6¾ miles). (28, 29, 30)

A spectacular scene of ero
in the Aran islands off the Irish
coast is wrought by the sea, dri
by westerly winds. Salt spray
carried over the cliffs by high w
joins the rain water in a cycle
of disintegration that starts by
dissolving great fissures in the
bedding planes of the rock.
The continuous pounding of the
sea below undermines the cliff,
and pressures with the force of
explosive charge are built up
when air is trapped and forced i
cracks in the rock. As boulders
fall, they become weapons for t
sea to hurl at the cliff. So the
land is cut back, and the contine
shelf of sediments is extended
out into the ocean. (31)

It is rain, not drought, whi
carves the land forms in desert
regions. One heavy downpour c
turn a dried-up river bed into a
raging torrent of mud, rocks an
water, its abrasive effect cutting
river bed down by many feet.
The Grand Canyon of the Colo
River (below) is a gash over a
mile deep and 200 miles long, a
dramatic example of the erosive
power of rainwater on hard roc
Wind, and wind-blown sand, p
their part in sculpturing this
bizarre landscape, removing all
the hardest layers of the rock ar
leaving the familiar gaunt pinnac
of 'badlands' topography. (32)

The most powerful too
in the grinding, eroding effe
of the atmosphere upon the ear
are ice and water. Mountai
such as the Himalayas (right) a
attacked by ice, which spl
the rocks because it expands wh
it freezes; by glaciers and I
the racing streams which issue fro
them, furrowing the valle
into troughs. This section, on t
borders of India, Nepal ar
Tibet, was photographed fro
100 miles up by Gordo
Cooper in his orbiting Mercu
capsule, and measures abo
40 by 60 miles. The moon
surface from the same heig
(pl. 45, p. 60), pocked with crate
but strangely smooth, show
none of these fine-veined marks
erosion by ice or water. (3

The remorseless pressure of mountain-building forces can change sedimentary into meta-morphic rocks. The Penrhyn slate quarries in North Wales (left) show this effect clearly: in the upward thrusting and folding that formed the mountains of Snowdonia, the sedimentary clays laid down in the primordial lakes and seas were squeezed by the tremendous pressures into layers of slate and shale. (34)

The search for oil and natural gas under water is a search for likely rock formations in the sedi-mentary limestones and sandstones of the sea bed. Seismic prospecting by the reflection method (left, below, in the North Sea) consists in exploding charges, fired astern of the survey ship. Echoes from the underlying rock layers of the sea bed are picked up by detectors below the surface. The times are recorded between the explosion and the return of the sound waves, resulting in a complex picture of echoes available for analysis. Abnormally short times, for instance, might indicate under-ground humps which could contain oil. The charges are exploded just below the surface, the high plume of water indicating the escape of gas which would otherwise produce disturbing sound pulses. When likely formations are found, oil must be sought by drilling, and this, in the deeper waters of the farther continental shelf, requires the familiar, massive rig, floating at anchor or standing on the sea bed. The one below is 60 miles out in the Persian Gulf. (35, 36)

The deepest boring is 'Project Mohole' (oppo-site), a multi-million-dollar attempt to drill through the earth's crust into the underlying mantle. On land the crust is about 20 miles thick, but it thins to about 4 miles under the sea. An experimental bore-hole, to test the techniques required, brought up cores of ancient sediment, and of volcanic basalt from the second layer of the sea bed over two miles below the surface off Guadalupe Island. The oil rig used for drilling towers above the deck of the ship. To reach the mantle, the actual drilling will take two to three years. A special craft capable of working in deep water without anchoring will be used for this pioneering project. (37)

The sea boiled, and a column of ash-laden vapour rose, as a new island was born off the south coast of Iceland on 14th November 1963 (above). Draw a line joining Iceland's three volcanoes, Askja, Laki and Hekla, prolong it 20 miles out to sea, and there lies Surtsey, new-born 'Island of the fire-god'. The line marks the northern end of the Mid-Atlantic Ridge, a 10,000-mile mountain range that winds its way down the Atlantic, midway between the continents, from Iceland to Antarctic Bouvet Island. Two of its peaks which stand out of the water, the Azores and Tristan da Cunha, have also seen eruptions during the past six years. The ridge is split down the middle by a deep valley—a line of weakness in the earth's crust. Lava poured out of the new crater at 500,000 tons an hour. By the end of November (below, right) the new island, horseshoe-shaped, was 300 ft. high to the north-east, to the south breached by the steaming sea. Still the build-up of ash and lava continued, until by late April 1964 (right and below) Surtsey was 570 ft. high and covered 300 acres. In January 1966 it was still erupting, an awesome witness to the forces locked up in the earth's interior. (38–41)

A slice out of the earth (below) shows the structure revealed by the study of earthquake waves. The crust, 4–20 miles thick, is here exaggerated to twice its scale thickness. The mantle, towards which the Mohole bore is directed, is about 2000 miles thick. Under that, to the centre, lie 2000 miles of core, probably of liquid nickel and iron; there may be a solid inner core but this is still uncertain. Earthquake shocks send out trains of waves in all directions, and instruments in widely separated places, detecting these waves, make it possible to discover their path through the earth. First to arrive are fast compressional waves (white lines); they move at 5 to 13 kms. a second but slow down in liquid, so that their path is bent by the core. Behind them, at half the speed, are the transverse or shake waves (broken lines), which cannot pass through liquid. Thus the core throws a 'shadow' opposite the point of origin (red arrowed line), where only the compressional waves are detected. Surface waves travelling along the crust make up the rest of the earthquake waves. (42)

A zigzag gash a mile and a quarter long, 9 feet wide and 7 feet deep (right) shows vividly the power of earthquake waves just above the centre of a shock. This was at Orléansville, Algeria, in 1954. Most earthquakes, and certainly the most disastrous ones, originate from a slipping, buckling movement of the crust. Others start from within the mantle—some as deep as 400 miles. Earthquakes are the outward signs of adjustments in the interior of the earth, and may be the result of local expansion or contraction or of slowly circulating convection currents in the mantle. What is certain is that both earthquakes and volcanoes occur together in regular zones of the earth's surface, along the cracks and wrinkles in the skin. (43)

The dead and silent moon was expected to reveal a surface radically different from that of the earth. It shows no atmosphere, no winds, no water, no ice, to break and wash away its crust. Instead it has suffered, for perhaps millions of years, bombardment by meteorites and by particles from the sun and space. It endures extremes of temperature, from 250°F by day to −240°F during the two-week-long night. Compare the soft contours, pocked surface and half-mile-wide rills (right, in Ranger IX's photograph, from 115 miles, of the east edge of the crater Alphonsus) with the ice and water-etched Himalayas from a similar height on page 55. And is the moon, or has it ever been, hot inside? Does its surface move and split? In the 75-mile-wide Alphonsus crater, seen (above) by Ranger IX from 258 miles, the central peak, 3500 feet high, *might* be volcanic, although it reveals no gas vent. The roughness which runs through it across the crater *could* be a main line of 'faulting'; the oblique lines from it recall the moving San Andreas fault in California.

But the moon is vulnerable to meteors and many surface features must be explained by bombardment. The small, smooth crater below, photographed from six feet up by Surveyor I, suggests an impact on a cohesive surface 'like a soil, not very hard'. But the bubbly rock (12 inches long, 6 high) could be volcanic. (44, 45, 46)

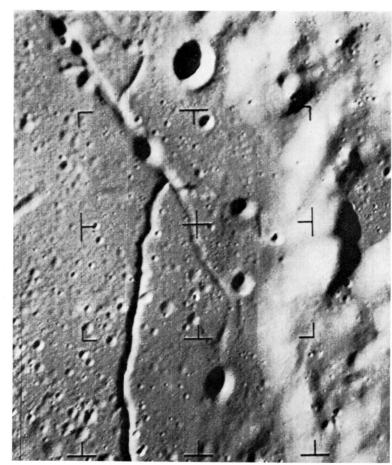

The historic first picture from Jodrell Bank (above) shows most clearly, in spite of the compression of the width of the scene, the abrasive, sponge-like surface on which Luna-9 landed. Your eyes are 2 feet from the ground; the boulder in the right foreground is no more than 6 inches across. There is no thick layer of dust. Small craters with jagged rims appear and the whole strongly recalls a field of volcanic lava. But it still could be caused by meteorites. (48)

Surveyor's 11,000 pictures were taken during the long lunar day until, at sundown, its shadow stretches (left) across a spherical mosaic of narrow-angle pictures. The fine-textured surface (right) is in soft and subtle greys, its colour discovered by photographing through the red, blue and green filters, checked by the three-inch colour wheel (far right). The padded foot has sunk an inch or so. Man can land and walk upon the moon. (47, 49)

The most fantastic vehicle built by man will put two men on the moon and leave another in orbit, waiting to bring them back. To lift it the first 40 miles, five giant engines are required (A below). On the full-scale model of Saturn V's first stage (above), lying on Boeing's spotless, dust-free floor, one dummy engine is in place, its exhaust twice the height of a man. (50)

The mighty Saturn V, and its payload, the Apollo space-craft, will stand on its launching pad 364 feet high, twice the height of the Tower of Pisa (from which only three centuries ago Galileo is said to have performed some of the first experiments of the scientific revolution). The vehicle, made of the lightest materials possible, will weigh 2724 tons. At the blast-off, liquid oxygen (tank C), under pressure from helium gas released by bottles nesting in the ribbed aluminium wall, will combine with kerosene (tank B). In 2 ½ minutes, 537,000 gallons of liquid will vanish in one colossal surge of power—a thrust of 7,500,000 lb.

At 40 miles up, the first stage, burnt out, will drop away. If the launch should fail, the escape system (P), a torpedo-shaped booster on a latticed titanium tower, would lift the astronauts away. At a sufficient height the escape system would be jettisoned and their craft would parachute to earth. If all goes well, when the second stage fires the escape system will fall away. (51, 52)

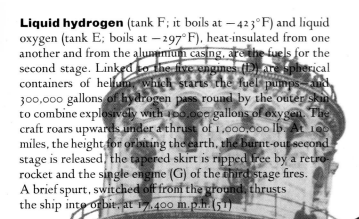

Liquid hydrogen (tank F; it boils at −423°F) and liquid oxygen (tank E; boils at −297°F), heat-insulated from one another and from the aluminium casing, are the fuels for the second stage. Linked to the five engines (D) are spherical containers of helium, which starts the fuel pumps—and 300,000 gallons of hydrogen pass round by the outer skin to combine explosively with 100,000 gallons of oxygen. The craft roars upwards under a thrust of 1,000,000 lb. At 100 miles, the height for orbiting the earth, the burnt-out second stage is released, the tapered skirt is ripped free by a retro-rocket and the single engine (G) of the third stage fires. A brief spurt, switched off from the ground, thrusts the ship into orbit, at 17,400 m.p.h. (51)

To hit the moon, where it will be in three days' time, requires a trajectory calculated by the ground computers. To escape the pull of the earth requires a speed of 24,300 m.p.h. As the computers work, the craft coasts round the earth. At the precise moment and position, after one to three orbits, the third stage engine roars out again, the liquid hydrogen (tank J) and liquid oxygen (tank H) burning for its remaining 6½ minutes. The spacecraft is off to the moon, but on a trajectory which, if failures occurred, would take it round the moon and safely back to earth.

The astronauts ride in the command ship (O); behind them is a service section (M) and an engine (L), followed by the Lunar Excursion Module (the LEM, familiarly known as the 'bug'), and the burnt-out third rocket. To free the service engine, a tricky manoeuvre now begins. The housing of the LEM is jettisoned and, under the astronaut's control, the command ship with its service section is detached and floats free. Using four tiny outboard rocket motors (N) it is turned completely round and its nose attached to the top of the LEM. At the same time the dead third stage is released. The astronauts can now crawl into the LEM to check its systems and can use the service engine, with its thrust of 22,000 lb., for midcourse flight correction.

After three days, Apollo skirts the moon. To enter its 'parking' orbit, 92 miles up, a braking thrust from the service engine is required, reducing the ship's speed, now 5200 m.p.h., to 3400 m.p.h. Time and position are calculated by the command ship's computer and, when the ship is behind the moon, the thrust is fired. At the beginning, perhaps, of the second orbit, when the computer's information has been brought up to date, the commander and co-pilot enter the 'bug' and cast off, leaving the systems engineer in orbit. With a 30-second burst from its own engine, the LEM coasts in orbit down to 50,000 feet. The landing site decided, the ship descends, with downward-jetting engine, to hover at 200 feet. Slowly, the commander at the controls, it eases down. Man stands on the moon. (51)

The stay on the moon may last two days. When the ungainly feet of LEM (a full-scale model is shown below) are firmly down, one astronaut will climb out, clad in his protective space suit and breathing pure oxygen at one-third of our atmospheric pressure. He will explore with a television camera, make scientific tests and collect samples of the surface. Then he will climb back, and at the moment computed with the orbiting ship (there must be no mistake) the ascent engine will fire. Leaving legs, landing engine and tanks, the LEM will rise to an orbit just behind the ship and lock on to it. With the astronauts back in the ship, the LEM will be cast off, and, computers updated, the service engine will thrust them at 5400 m.p.h. to meet the earth. Under the earth's pull, they approach the atmosphere at 24,400 m.p.h. With service section jettisoned, and the ship turned round, they rush in like a meteor, the heat shield flaming at 5000°C. Slowed down by the air and held from 15,000 feet by parachutes, they drop gently to a landing. Another mission is accomplished. (53)

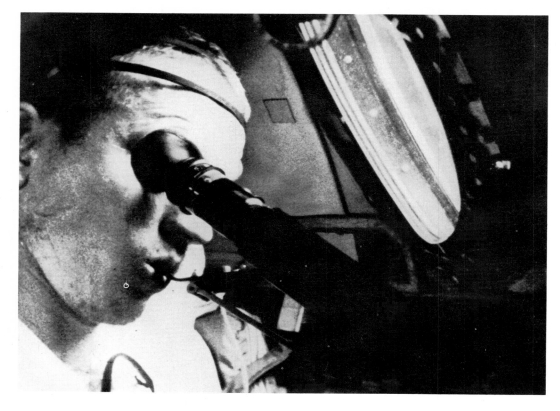

Before men can be shot to the moon,
the complex, untried theory must be tested,
the skills and techniques practised. And what
effect on man himself—the last hazard—will the
long journey have? The only stresses which cannot be duplicated on earth are those from the
prolonged weightlessness dramatically demonstrated by the first 'walks' in space of Leonov
and White. In the photograph above, taken
by Lovell during Gemini-7's 14-day flight, co-
astronaut Borman tests the effect on his vision.
With binocular pieces over his eyes, he makes a
fine adjustment of white lines, his performance
recorded by Lovell—a test of inner ear control
of balance and orientation. Also tested were
methods of maintaining the circulation, using
inflatable cuffs; a stretch-cord exerciser to show
capacity for work; loss of minerals from the
bones such as occur in bed-ridden patients and
the secretion of hormones under stress. Gemini-
7's astronauts also removed their space-suits.

Manoeuvring a spacecraft to close up with
another is a delicate operation. Gemini-6 was
fired into a lower orbit than Gemini-7, flying
faster and therefore catching it up. It then fired
a series of booster thrusts, each raising it
against the earth's gravitational pull until it
settled in a higher orbit at a slower speed. After
four such thrusts, and a further manoeuvre to
bring them in the same plane of flight, Gemini-
7's blinking lights were sighted through the
darkness at 50 miles. A further thrust and
three minor course corrections put them 120
feet apart. Two hours later, the photograph
(below) shows them within fourteen feet, later
closed to one foot. Lovell's face is visible to
them in Gemini-7's right window. Both ships,
each weighing four tons, are travelling at
17,000 m.p.h., circling in stately measure and
then flying nose to nose for hundreds of miles.
The 100,000-mile chase had taken six hours.
(54,55)

The first join-up in space was made by Gemini-8. At Cape Kennedy (left), the ascent of the Agena target rocket is seen in the background; a second exposure, 101 minutes later, catches the majestic rise of Gemini-8. In the fourth orbit, the target is approached (below) as it coasts above the curving earth, its radio antenna vertical. Then the spacecraft closes in (bottom). A brief burst from two of its thrusters and the index bar on the craft's nose approaches the notch into which it must slide. A click of mooring latches and Gemini-8 is drawn in. A green light flashes 'rigid'. But a fast spin set up by a rogue thruster exhausts the control fuel and the ship must return to earth. (56, 57, 58)

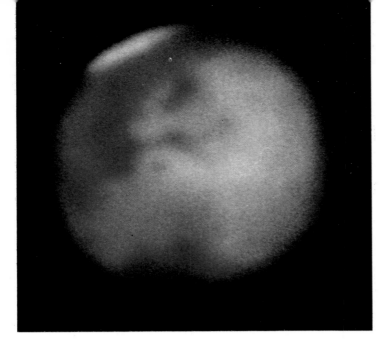

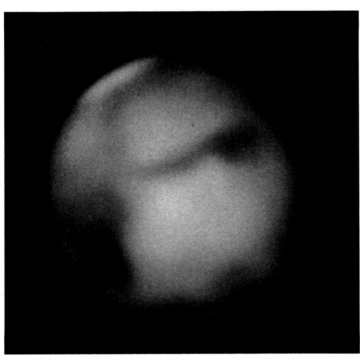

After the moon, the planets. Most promising is Mars, the red planet, shown (left) in two photographs from Johannesburg, each a composite from 25 exposures at the telescope. Between them, Mars has rotated for half its 24 ½-hour day plus night. The markings are permanent features which have been mapped and named and much has been deduced from them. Most striking are the polar caps (the *south* pole is visible top left), which, waxing and waning with the seasons, suggest ice or hoar frost; the huge orange areas were thought to be deserts, the darker patches, which change colour as the ice-caps recede, were perhaps some lowly form of vegetation. No craters were visible, but they could have been smoothed over by the huge clouds of red dust which astronomers reported. Evolving similarly to the earth, but prematurely aged, most of its water and atmosphere lost, Mars could still have mountains and hollowed ocean basins, and perhaps an iron core with a magnetic field. And although Schiaparelli's celebrated *canali* (suggesting artificial irrigation by intelligent beings) were much discredited, the range of temperature from 85°F to −140°F could still support life. Mariner IV (p. 68) was to bring sharp and surprising changes to these views. (59, 60)

The giants of the solar system, Jupiter and Saturn, are much more hostile. Photographs in colour (right) show great turbulent bands of poisonous gases, hydrogen, ammonia and methane, hundreds of miles deep, spinning rapidly with a day and night of roughly 10 hours. Far from the sun, their temperatures do not rise above −240°F or lower. Jupiter's great bulk, its diameter 10 times that of the earth, has a density only a third greater than that of water. Saturn, 9 times the earth's diameter, is lighter than water. Both have large retinues of encircling moons: Jupiter 12, Saturn 9. Jupiter's red spot may be an island of helium; Saturn's rings, only 10 miles thick, may be ice or frosted gravel. (63, 64)

Brief visitors from the far reaches of the solar system, comets can be, after the sun and moon, the most brilliant object in the sky. Ikeya-Seki, photographed (below, left) at dawn over Canberra, had survived a close brush with the sun on 21 Oct. 1965 and was now ten days on its outward journey. Its parabolic path means that if it should live to return, it will not do so for a thousand years. Its long tail, streaming behind under the pressure of solar radiation, points always away from the sun. (61)

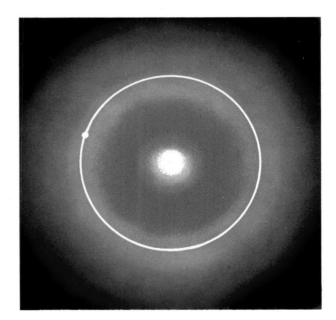

Life of our kind needs a sun of the right size (such as ours) to maintain it and could exist only at distances where its temperatures could range between the freezing and boiling points of water—within the yellow 'life-zone' shown above. And the planet must be large enough to retain an atmosphere. So vast is the number of stars, however, that many millions of planets could offer just such conditions. (62)

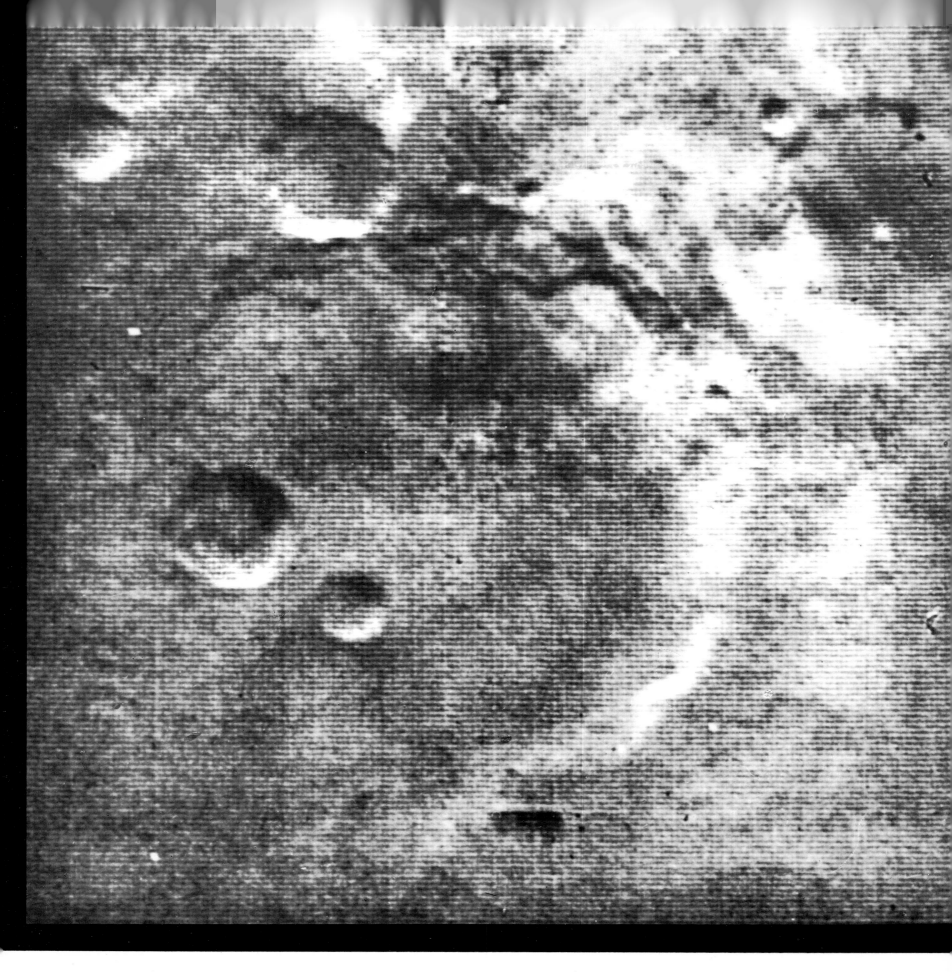

The first close-up portrait of another planet was made by Mariner IV on 14 July, 1965. It was a shock to the waiting scientists. The 21 historic photographs (the famous eleventh is shown above) revealed a landscape pocked with huge, sharply defined craters, with no mountain chains, continental land masses, great valleys or ocean basins. Although Mariner IV passed directly over areas in which 'canals' had been seen, there was no sign of them. No contrasts appeared to suggest the 'dark' areas. There was no evidence of erosion by wind or water, and Mariner's measurements recorded a much thinner atmosphere than expected (less than one-hundredth of that of the earth) and only enough water-vapour for a thin coating

of frost on the poles and the highlands in winter. There was no sign of a magnetic field and no 'Van Allen' belt of trapped particles.

Mars is more moon-like than earth-like. The pictures showed 70 craters, ranging in diameter from 3 miles to the 70 miles of the old crater, peppered with later ones, which covers most of the picture above. This means, in proportion, 10,000 such craters on the whole of the planet, compared with 200 still visible on the earth. Has Mars always been like this, for the 2–5 thousand million years which the study of the moon suggests? If so, and in the absence of an iron core to create a magnetic field, then Mars' history is quite different from that of the earth and scientists must change their views

on the evolution of the solar system. Or had Mars a long life with an atmosphere, liquid water and erosion before these disappeared and craters began to retain their sharpness (for the number of craters could suggest this)? The argument continues.

In the picture above, taken from a slant range of 7,800 miles, the white patches are due to high contrast, though evidence of hoar frost on high ground does appear in later pictures. The mark bottom centre is a lens calibration. In all, Mariner IV's discoveries on atmosphere and water were more nearly as expected, but they must mean that life as we know it can only be considered a remote possibility on Mars though no one yet would rule it out entirely. (65)

3   The range of radiant energy

Tom Margerison

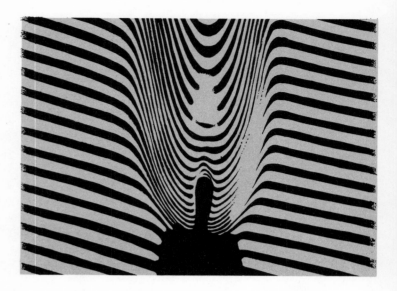

The range of radiant energy

Life on earth depends on the continuing flow of energy from p 114-15 the sun, mainly as heat and light, across 93 million miles of space. In fifteen minutes more energy arrives in this way at the earth than all the power used by mankind in a year: the coal he uses to heat his houses and drive his machines, the oil, the nuclear energy from splitting uranium atoms, and the electricity generated by hydro-electric schemes. Put another way, every square metre of the sun's surface is continuously losing into space something like 84,000 horse-power, equivalent to more than 50 thousand domestic electric fires.

How is this immense flow of energy carried through the nothingness of space? The problem is one which has concerned philosophers and scientists since earliest times. Three hundred years ago two brilliant scientists, Sir Isaac Newton in England and Christiaan Huygens in Holland, put forward opposing theories about the nature of light.

Light: a particle or a wave?

Newton believed that light, like matter, was atomic, and that the sun was shedding particles of light in all directions. The particles travelled in straight lines, as beams of light are observed to do, and could explain more or less readily all the experiments that had at that time been conducted on the behaviour of light. Huygens's approach was different. He compared light with sound and suggested that both were due to the motion of waves. Huygens's theory would also explain most of the experiments that had been carried out at the time. But there were two main stumbling blocks.

If I walk round the corner and blow a whistle, you will hear it quite distinctly: the sound waves spread round the corner. But if I shine a torch from round the corner, the beam goes straight on and no part of it is bent round the corner into your eyes. Here then was problem one: if light is a wave motion, how does it move precisely in straight lines?

The second difficulty concerned the waves themselves. Suppose we put the torch and an electric buzzer in a glass jar out of which all the air can be pumped. As the vacuum pump sucks away the buzz of the buzzer fades out. The sound waves carrying the buzz to our ears are waves in the air. And if there is no air, there can be no waves, just as there are no waves on a pond that has been drained dry. So far everything seems perfectly reasonable. But look a moment at the torch. The light is there as bright as ever it was, travelling through the vacuum in the same straight line. Here was problem number two for the wave theory: as light can travel through a vacuum, through nothingness in fact, what are the waves formed in?

Since nobody cared to imagine waves formed in nothing, the wave theory supporters had to invent a substance for them to exist in. They called it the 'ether' and assumed it existed everywhere, interpenetrating everything, but was, of course, undetectable. The 'ether' was hardly an easy pill to swallow, but as we shall see, particle theory supporters found themselves in even greater difficulty.

Today the great controversy over the nature of light which lasted more than two hundred years can be seen in its true perspective as just another instance where man's own physical size and limitations prevented him from appreciating a phenomenon on a different scale. What the 17th-century philosophers were trying to do was to apply the experience they had gained in mechanics and the study of waves in air and on the surface of water to the uncharted territory of light. But the rules which apply satisfactorily to cannon balls and buck-shot give little insight into the behaviour of light. And extrapolation from the behaviour of sound waves in air was hardly more satisfactory.

Sound travels at sea level in air at around 750 miles an hour, and the wavelength of 'middle C' under these conditions is just over four feet. So sound waves are the sort of size that compares easily with a human being. On the other hand, light is of extremely short wavelength. The wavelength of the yellow sodium light used in many places for street-lighting is 5890 Ångström units, or 24 millionths of an inch. One of the results of the small wavelength of light is that light waves are bent to a much smaller degree around corners than are sound waves, and are, in general, very much easier to confine into a beam. So one of the major problems the wave supporters faced was swept away. In fact, when the effects of this slight bending round corners of light rays were discovered they formed strong ammunition against the particle supporters.

p. 86-7
(20, 26)

In step and out of step

The bending of light round corners is known as diffraction. It becomes obvious only when we are dealing with pinholes and narrow slits which are not much larger than the wavelength of light. Look at a sodium street light through an ordinary pinhole in a piece of card and it looks sharp: the pinhole is large compared with the wavelength of light. But if the hole is made very small, not only does less light come through, but the street lamp appears to develop a halo: the light coming through the small hole is being spread out by diffraction.

If you could examine the light coming through this small hole closely, there would be the central patch, due to the main beam, surrounded by a series of rings of light, growing rapidly less bright as their diameter increased. The cause of this is another very important effect, called 'interference'.

Suppose we have two sources of waves side by side, producing waves in step with one another. You can think of two loudspeakers connected to the same radio set so that they produce sound waves exactly in step with one another. Or the two sources can be two narrow slits or pinholes through which light from a single point source passes. If the slits are small enough, the light waves will be diffracted, so that they spread over a wide angle. We shall also assume the waves are of a single wavelength.

Now what happens when these two sets of waves overlap? Where the peak of one wave coincides with a peak of the other wave, the two join together and reinforce one another. But where the peak of one joins the trough of the other, the two waves cancel one another out.

fig 1

If we put a screen at some distance from the two slits, a series of bright and dark bands appears on it. They are known as Young's fringes. The bright bands are where the two sets of waves have landed on the screen in step and reinforced each other. The dark bands are where they have cancelled one another out. At the point on the screen equidistant from both slits, the two waves are bound to be in step, so that this means the central band is bright. Now look at the first bright band to one side of the central one: because the band is bright, the waves must be in step. One wave has travelled farther than the other, and the difference between the two paths is exactly one wavelength, so that they are in step once more.

fig 2

p 82
(2·5)

Tom Margerison

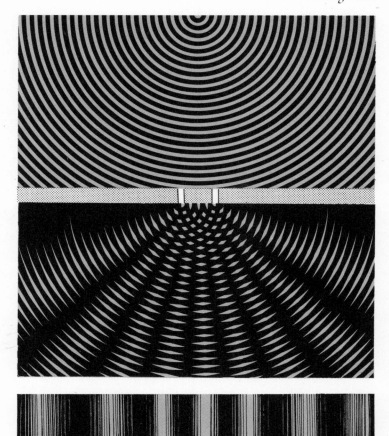

If a train of waves from a point source of light falls on a screen in which are two narrow slits, a new train will emerge from each slit. The two augment or cancel one another in a kind of moiré pattern, which falls on a screen as successive light and dark fringes. The central point, equidistant from the slits, is bright; on each side, where the distance from the slits differs by half a wavelength, are dark fringes, followed, as the distance differs by a whole wavelength, by bright fringes. (2)

Interference effects cause the pattern of rings in the diffracted light surrounding the central spot of light coming through a very small hole. Light waves are bent round the edges; this bent light from one part of the edge interferes with light from other parts to form the ring pattern.

Diffraction and interference are extremely important phenomena with many applications in science and industry. The spacing of interference bands is the most direct method of measuring the wavelength of light. Equally, when the wavelength is known, it is a very accurate method of measuring length. In fact the wavelength of a particular type of light is now used as the standard of length. The comparison between lengths is made with an instrument called an interferometer, in which the two sources of light are obtained by dividing a single beam in a semi-silvered mirror. Part of the beam goes through the mirror, and part is reflected. The direct and reflected beams travel over separate paths (the distances to be compared) and are reflected back into the semi-silvered mirror, where they recombine to form interference bands or fringes.

If one of the two paths is changed in length, for example by warming the arm supporting the mirror a little, the fringes appear to move. A change in length of the arm of half a wavelength of light causes the pattern to move so that one bright fringe is replaced by its next door neighbour. The method is an extremely sensitive one, widely used for precise measurement.

We have dealt so far only with diffraction and interference of monochromatic light, that is light made up of a single wavelength. What happens if we use white light? Returning to the experiment with the two slits, we can see that so far as the central bright band is concerned, the

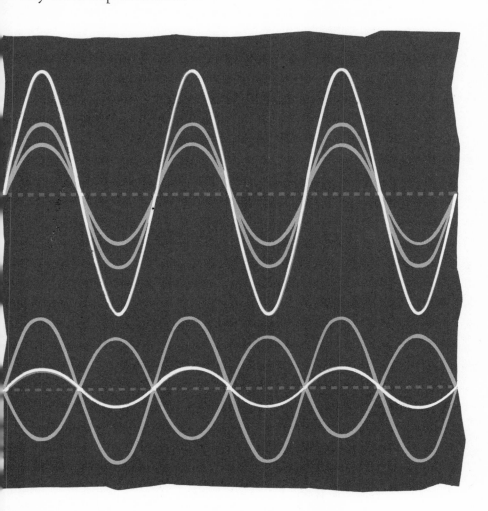

Two trains of light waves are represented above, of different amplitudes (in colour)—i.e. different heights of their crests and depths of their troughs. If they are 'in step' (top) they will augment one another (white) and when they fall on a screen will produce a bright fringe; if they are 'out of step' (bottom) they will tend to cancel one another and produce a dark fringe. (1)

p 82
(2, 3)

mixture of waves will still be in step. The distance travelled by the waves to this central fringe is identical, so that if (as we have assumed) the waves emerging from the slits are exactly the same, there is simple reinforcement of all wavelengths. In other words, the central fringe will be white.

But if we move away from the central fringe these conditions no longer hold good. There is now a difference in path length between the two beams, and when that difference is an exact number of wavelengths reinforcement will occur. So on either side of the white fringe we have a whole series of coloured fringes. First, because the wavelength is shortest, come blue fringes, then green, then red. After the red fringes, the blue waves come into step again and so on.

p 82 (4)

This effect can be seen by looking at an ordinary (clear) electric light bulb through terylene net curtains. The lamp needs to be some distance away so that it is effectively a point source. Then, on either side of the central image a spectrum of colour appears.

This effect is used to sort out the wavelengths of light, in order to examine the constituent parts which, as we shall see later in this chapter, are characteristic of the atoms which are producing it. Instead of using a pair of slits, a very large number are ruled onto a single piece of glass to form what is called a diffraction grating. The grating has many advantages over a prism in forming a spectrum.

This same principle of interference produces the bright colours of butterflies' wings and has been copied recently by scientists to make light filters which allow a restricted selection of wavelengths to pass. The principle of interference applies to all waves, including the other members of the family to which light belongs (see below). Interference of radio waves is used in navigational aids like Decca, and interference of X-rays diffracted from the regularly arranged atoms in crystals has proved one of the most useful methods of extending our knowledge of the structure of matter.

p 83 (6·10)

p 172 (21·4)

Changing forces in 'empty' space

The evidence of interference and diffraction was overwhelming support for the wave theory. But the problem of waves in nothingness remained, and a way to tackle it only became clear during the 19th century through the study of electricity and magnetism. If you rub a fountain pen briskly on your sleeve, it will attract little pieces of paper. The process of rubbing is said to charge the pen with electricity and any charged body will attract other small uncharged bodies in this way.

Now we may ask what this attraction really is. It clearly operates over a distance. Most important, the attraction occurs just as easily in a vacuum as in air. Whatever the nature of the force, it can operate without the intervention of a physical substance. Simple experiments show that this electric force can operate in more than one sense. Two similarly charged bodies repel one another instead of attracting.

One of the most important concepts which arose during the second half of the 19th century was the idea of a 'field'. The region all around the electrically charged body in which the attractive force operates is called an electric 'field'. At any point the field has a certain strength, proportional to the force which would act on a minute electrified object we put there, and a direction, the direction in which this force is pulling. So for many purposes we do not need to worry about the details of the electrified bodies which produce the attraction, but need think only in terms of the 'field'.

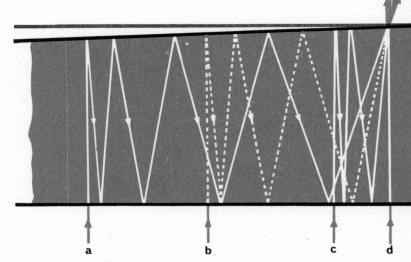

*The colours of a soap bubble or an oil film on water are caused by many reflections of the light to and fro between the two surfaces of the film. The diagram above represents two semi-transparent surfaces, extremely close together, one at a slight angle (as in a film of varying thickness). Ray **a** passes straight through; part of ray **c** reaches the same exit point after four reflections, ray **b** after six reflections and ray **d** after eight. The rays have travelled slightly different distances and their waves will be 'in step' of 'out of step' accordingly, producing bright and dark interference fringes on emergence. If white light is used, the fringes will be rainbow coloured. This phenomenon, applied with greatly refined techniques, has many uses: if for instance the first sheet is optically 'flat' glass and the second a polished diamond, irregularities in height on the diamond surface will slightly change the distances travelled and be revealed as 'contour'-shaped fringes, magnifying the changes in height by as much as a million times. (3)*

fig 4

This same idea of 'field' can be used to describe other kinds of force which act at a distance. We live in the gravitational field of the earth, which at each point has a certain strength and direction, usually pointing directly downwards towards the centre of the earth.

The same idea can be applied to the region round a wire through which an electric current is flowing from a battery. In this region a force acts on small particles of iron, like iron filings, and on small magnets. In this case we call the region a magnetic field and again the force exerted by the field will vary in strength and direction from place to place.

In the last few paragraphs I have referred to two different kinds of electricity. First, there was the case of the fountain

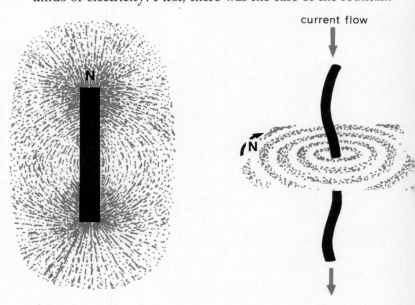

The conception of electric and magnetic fields in space has led to great advances in science. The familiar positions taken up by iron filings round a bar magnet (left) show clearly the direction of the forces in the magnetic field which surrounds it, operating as well in a vacuum as in air. Electrons moving in a wire (an electric current) produce a magnetic field, its forces directed round the wire. If the bar magnet moves, it produces an electric field; if either field changes, it produces the other. (4)

pen which became electrified when it was rubbed and attracted morsels of paper. It produced an electric field. Then there was the wire carrying an electric current from a battery, which attracted iron filings. But, in spite of the differences, these two kinds of electricity can be shown to be closely related. Suppose we give the fountain pen a good brisk rub and then attach it to the edge of a fast rotating wheel, so that it is whirled round and round in a circle at very high speed. If with a compass or some iron filings we test the region around the whirling pen we shall find evidence of a *magnetic* field.

This link between the two kinds of electricity means that there is a link between the two kinds of field: electric and magnetic. Think again of the whirling pen experiment. As long as the pen spins round at constant speed the magnetic field it produces remains the same. But the electric field which is centred on the pen itself is changing all the time as the pen moves. Imagine the force due to the electric field acting on a morsel of paper just above the top of the wheel (and protected from the wind, of course). When the pen is near the top the pull is directly downwards and quite strong. But as the pen moves on the pull weakens and the direction changes to follow the pen.

The great advantage of the 'field' concept is that we can forget about the way in which the fields were produced. We can simply say that a changing electric field is always accompanied by a magnetic field. The converse is also true, as Michael Faraday demonstrated more than a hundred years ago: a changing magnetic field is always accompanied by an electric field.

We may seem to have strayed a long way from the discussion of how light travels through a vacuum. But in fact we are very near to an answer. Electric and magnetic fields can exist in space without matter being present. Of course, we have not explained what they are: we shall just assume that they are a property of space. We have also seen that the electric and magnetic fields are closely inter-related so that a change in one causes a change in the other. So at last we have a possible theory of light: ripples or waves in the electric and magnetic fields in space. As the electric field changes in one direction, the magnetic field should change in a complementary way, rather like the negative and positive of a photograph.

But if electromagnetic waves existed, it should be possible to make them artificially by making an electrified body like the hard-worked fountain pen oscillate to and fro very rapidly. A German physicist, Heinrich Hertz, demonstrated the existence of electromagnetic waves in 1887 using a rather different method. Instead of actually moving an electric charge he used a spark to generate a high-frequency electric current.

As it happens, Hertz was fortunate. The apparatus he built produced electromagnetic waves of 24 centimetres wavelength, what we would now call ultra-short radio waves. Because the wavelength was so short he was able to demonstrate that the electromagnetic waves could be reflected and refracted and had many other properties identical with those of light. Had the wavelength been much longer, it would have been much more difficult to show the similarities between light and Hertzian waves. Still more telling was the discovery that the Hertzian waves moved with the same velocity as light, a fantastic speed of 186,000 miles a second.

The difference between Hertzian waves and light is simply a difference in wavelength. In fact, a whole family of electromagnetic waves exists which all move at the same velocity

p 84–9 and are identical apart from their wavelength. One or two gaps still remain to be filled, but recently one of the major ones was bridged: the gap between the shortest radio waves and the longest infra-red or heat waves.

The man-made waves of radio

We have seen that electromagnetic waves are produced when an electric charge accelerates or decelerates, or, what amounts to the same thing, when an electric current oscillates. Hertz's original method of making electromagnetic waves was to make use of the natural oscillations which occur in an electric spark and to use a circuit which was tuned to the frequency he required. This method was used for many years in wireless telegraph transmitters.

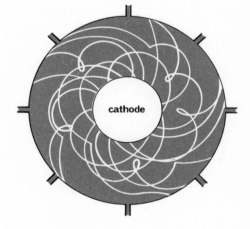

The short waves of radar, and microwaves, are produced by methods such as the cavity magnetron (above). Electrons given off by a central cathode are attracted towards a copper anode, a circular block in which are cylindrical holes entered by slit-shaped openings. But the whole is contained between the poles of an electromagnet producing a strong field perpendicular to the plane of the diagram (left). The two forces whirl the electrons in circular paths past the slits, producing radio wave oscillations in the holes.

The waves react on the electrons, bunching them, and with proper tuning the bunches pass the slits just at the time to increase the strength of the waves. The whole effect is similar to the resonance of sound waves in an organ pipe. The wavelength produced is controlled by the diameter of the cylindrical holes. (5)

fig 5 Later the thermionic valve was invented, which gave a much improved method of producing an oscillating current. For broadcast wavelengths ordinary valve transmitters are still used. At shorter wavelengths, below about 1 metre, the valve oscillator begins to become inefficient and different methods are used. One of the most important, which was developed during the war, was the cavity magnetron. The idea of this oscillator is similar to a policeman's whistle. A stream of electrons is whirled into a circular path by a strong magnetic field. The electrons move past slit-shaped openings in a copper block. Each slit leads into a cylindrical hole which is tuned to the frequency required. The electrons sweeping past the slits set up an oscillation in the holes, just as the blast of air striking the sharp lip of a whistle causes the air in the barrel to vibrate.

But the magnetron is more complicated than the whistle because the oscillations set up in the cylindrical holes affect the stream of electrons passing the slits. At one moment the electric field in the slit tends to slow down the electrons. A moment later it has changed and is speeding them up. So each oscillation in the cylinder tends to bunch the electrons, slowing some down and speeding others up. If this bunch of electrons reaches the next slit at just the right time it gives the oscillation in that cylinder a 'push' at the right moment, like timing the push on a swing to make it go higher. So the whole magnetron can be made to resonate by changing the speed of the electrons until the 'pushes' in the various cylindrical holes all come at just the right time. In other words, a bunch of electrons moving from one slit to another takes the same time as one, two, three or any whole number of complete oscillations in the cylindrical holes.

The cavity magnetron is typical of the methods used for generating electromagnetic waves in the microwave region at wavelengths down to a few millimetres. In nearly all these devices the waves are produced by accelerating electrons, although of course any charged particle would do. The frequency of the wave, that is the number of complete cycles which occur in one second, is fixed by the geometry of the system. In the case of the magnetron, the frequency is controlled by the diameter of the cylindrical holes. p 88 (34, 35)

In nature this 'tuning' which forces the electrons into orderly bunches does not usually occur. When electrons and other charged particles are accelerated violently, as in a flash of lightning, the electromagnetic waves produced are not of a single wavelength or frequency, but are jumbled up and spread over a great range.

Hot, red-hot, white-hot

This is true of the most common kind of electromagnetic radiation: the heat and light produced by a hot body. The way in which all matter is made up of charged particles will be discussed in a later chapter. Each atom is made up of an positively charged core surrounded by negatively charged electrons, so that the whole atom is electrically neutral. These atoms are not stationary. In a solid, for instance, they vibrate about fixed positions. In a gas they are completely free to move and wander from place to place colliding from time to time with other atoms. In liquids the atoms are not completely captive as they are in a solid, nor completely free as they are in a gas, but move in some intermediate way. p 130

The fact that the atoms move and change their direction means that electric charges are being accelerated and decelerated and that in turn means that all matter produces electromagnetic waves. As in the case of the lightning flash we would not expect the waves to be of one single frequency, but a jumble of different frequencies.

Now the amount of jostling that goes on among atoms is a measure of their temperature. As we approach absolute zero, a temperature of −273.2 degrees on the centigrade scale, the motion of the atoms gradually disappears. Equally, as the temperature rises, the jostling increases, and the accelerations become more and more violent, as atoms clash or spring back to their allotted positions.

Let us think of a simple experiment. Suppose we heat a lump of iron in a furnace. At first the iron looks just as it did, but bring your hand close to it, without touching it, and you feel heat. You could carry out a whole series of experiments with this hot piece of iron to show that the heat behaves in just the same way as light, and that like light it can pass through a vacuum.

So, we conclude, the iron after moderate heating emits infra-red or heat waves. As the temperature rises the appearance of the lump of iron changes. Soon it is glowing dull red: a proportion of the electromagnetic waves are now being produced as light. Raise the temperature still further and the light becomes whiter until eventually it matches the white light of the sun or a modern electric light bulb.

The energy packets of Max Planck

It is quite easy to analyse the electromagnetic radiation produced from a hot body and to show how much there is of different wavelengths in the form of a curve for each temperature. All the curves have a similar shape with a hump in the middle, and as the temperature increases this hump moves to shorter and shorter wavelengths. fig 6

Now here was a great problem. What caused the hump? Why did a hot body not produce a small but equal quantity of electromagnetic waves of all wavelengths? To understand this we have to think again about the cavity magnetron. It produces waves of a single wavelength because the cavities are tuned, like an organ pipe, to this frequency. But the cavity, or the organ pipe, will also vibrate at twice this frequency, or three or four, or any whole number of times the frequency. The resonance occurs whenever an exact number of wavelengths happens to fit the length of the pipe or the geometry of the cylindrical hole.

Now in the case of our hot body the size of the 'pipe' is very large compared with the wavelength of the electromagnetic waves, so a large number of resonances is possible. All sorts of different numbers of waves will fit exactly into an object of this size, ranging from a single wave in the radio region to a few hundreds of infra-red waves, thousands of light waves, and millions of ultra-violet waves. Now there seems no particular reason why one of these frequencies should be favoured more than another, so, if we use the laws of physics which have stood us in good stead for hundreds of years, we must assume that the energy is divided equally between them all. So far from having a hot body that emitted all wavelengths in equal quantities, we see that there should be much more ultra-violet than visible light or infra-red, even when the body was quite cold.

This is obviously nonsense. It does not accord with experience. The sun shows no signs of suddenly burning up in an ultra-violet catastrophe. The kettle on the stove remains warm. It does not suddenly emit a burst of intense ultra-violet light. But where has our reasoning gone wrong? Once again the fault has been to try to think of light in terms appropriate to billiard balls or sea waves. The error was discovered by a German, Max Planck, who had spent many years studying radiation and realized that something was needed to discriminate against the ultra-violet rays so that it was less likely that they would be produced. Planck's solution was to discriminate against the shorter wavelengths by assuming that they occurred only in rather large and indivisible packages.

You can imagine this situation by thinking of a woodyard well stocked with pieces of wood of every conceivable size.

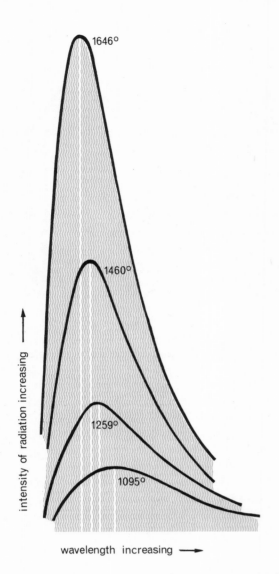

1646°
1460°
1259°
1095°

intensity of radiation increasing →

wavelength increasing ⟶

All matter gives out electromagnetic waves. The radiation from a hot body is produced by the jostling of its atoms and is therefore a jumble of different wavelengths. If, for any given temperature, the intensity of the radiation for each of these wavelengths is measured, it is found that it rises to a maximum at one wavelength and then falls away again. At higher temperatures, the maximum occurs at a shorter wavelength—a heated body becomes first hot, then red-hot, then white-hot. If the energy were distributed equally among all waves, the curves would rise steadily as the wavelength became shorter. Why do they reach a maximum and then fall off? The answer to this question was the beginning of the revolutionary quantum theory. (6)

The manager of the yard chose to make up his stock in an unusual way. Every piece of wood in the yard weighs an exact number of pounds, and there is only one piece of each weight. One piece, the smallest in the whole place, weighs 1 lb., one weighs 2 lb., one 3 lb. and so on. In the bigger sizes many of the pieces weigh nearly the same: there is one weighing 1000 lb., another weighing 1001 lb., another weighing 1002 lb. and so on. These big pieces of wood correspond to the ultra-violet rays, the smaller ones to light, and the smallest of all to infra-red rays.

Looking at the woodyard as a whole, there are many more large lumps of wood than small ones. The pattern is as we predicted with the emphasis on the big lumps, the ultra-violet. But now suppose that someone goes to the yard to carry away the wood. The small pieces are quite easy to carry away but contain very little wood. The very big ones are too heavy and have to be left behind. The medium-sized pieces are the best way of removing wood from the yard.

The mere fact that the big pieces are big and need the expenditure of a great deal of energy to move them discriminates against them. If we now plot a curve showing the weight of wood carried away in pieces of different size, its shape would be similar to the radiation curve with a hump in the middle corresponding to the medium-sized pieces.

Now suppose that instead of sending a man to the woodyard, we sent a young boy to collect the wood. He would

have no difficulty with the small pieces but, being less strong than the man, he could not lift as many heavy pieces. So when he got home with his spoils, the graph he plotted would look different, with the hump at a smaller size. In fact it would look very much like the radiation curve of a red-hot piece of iron compared with that of a white-hot one.

Planck applied the principle of this unorthodox woodyard to electromagnetic waves. He assumed that electromagnetic waves came in packets, and that these packets were indivisible. The size of the packet varied according to the frequency of the electromagnetic wave. In fact the energy in the packet was always a certain constant number of times the frequency. This constant is called after Max Planck and is equal to 6.6×10^{-34} joule-seconds. Mathematically, $E = h\nu$, where E is the energy, h Planck's constant, and ν the frequency.

p 84-9 Planck's theory changes our whole attitude to electromagnetic waves. Instead of dealing with a steady flow of waves we must now talk in terms of a number of packets of waves. We have introduced a kind of graininess and changed what was a smooth flow into something much more nearly like a sand blast. How big are the individual grains? If Planck's constant were equal to nothing, there would be no grains and we would be back with the old difficulty of too much ultra-violet light. If it were larger than it is, then ultra-violet light, and even visible light would disappear altogether except at extremely high temperatures. As it is, the value of Planck's constant happens to be sufficiently small for the packets to be too small to detect easily in the radio region. They are just about large enough to have sufficient energy to flip over spinning parts of atoms and molecules. In the infra-red the packets are just a little bigger, with enough energy to spin or vibrate a molecule.

When we come to visible light the packets are bigger still. Red light comes in packets of energy equal to the energy of an electron accelerated by an electric potential of 1.8 volts. Blue light is in still bigger packets, or *quanta*, of energy equal to an electron that has passed through about 3 volts. For convenience we say the quantum of blue light is 3 electron volts.

Ultra-violet light has still larger quanta, energetic enough to remove electrons from atoms and leave them electrically charged or ionized, while x-ray quanta are packets of energy equal to many thousands, or even millions of electron volts. The size of the quantum or packet underlies the different behaviour of the different electromagnetic waves. A high-energy X-ray fired into a human body will damage some of the cells, a phenomenon used in treating diseases like cancer, since the quantity of energy released when one X-ray quantum is absorbed is considerable. Radio waves do not have the same effect because the quanta are so very much smaller. Though the total energy absorbed by the body may be as great or greater, the chance that many quanta will be absorbed in the same cell is small, so the concentration of energy within a cell is much too low to cause damage.

Wave and particle: the photon

Max Planck originally put forward his quantum theory to explain the discrepancy between theory and experiment in the simple case of a glowing hot body. A few years later, in 1905, Albert Einstein took the idea a stage further. Planck had assumed that the graininess of light was due to some property of the atoms producing it, just as tea comes in packages because of a 'property', the packaging machine, of the company that produces it. But Einstein went further. He argued that the packages were an integral part of electro-magnetic radiation: that they could not be subdivided, and although from many points of view light behaved as waves, we must now return to a particle theory. These particles or indivisible packages of electromagnetic energy he called 'photons'.

At first sight it looks very much as though we are back with the old controversy between Newton and Huygens. But this is not so, for we have learned not to try to express the behaviour of events on this atomic scale in terms of everyday things. If they appear to behave strangely com-pared with the familiar objects about the house, this is hard-ly surprising when one is dealing with events so very far removed from our own experience.

Now if light is really made up of these photons or particles moving at an immense speed, we would expect them to exert a pressure when they bumped into a solid body. The pressure of the sun's radiation is becoming important in some branches of astronomy and space science. For in-stance, it pushes on comets' tails and explains why they always point away from the sun. Sunlight also exerts a modest push on satellites, especially small ones, like the American 'needles' in space. The pressure is sufficient to bring the needles gradually back to earth again, otherwise they would remain indefinitely in orbit a few thousand miles above the earth's surface. Sun pressure probably also causes the earth to have a long tail stretching thousands of miles into space from its dark side. The tail, consisting of hydro-gen atoms and dust, allows matter to escape constantly from the earth.

fig 7

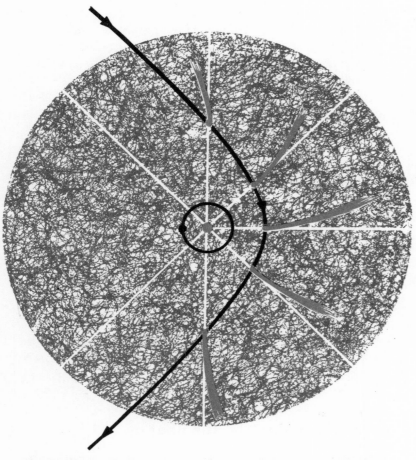

The quantum theory led to the conception of light as particle-like packets of waves or photons, moving at immense speed. These, when the wavelength is right, impart an impetus to molecules in their path. As a comet approaches the sun, the rarefied gas molecules of which its head is composed are struck more and more by photons of the sun's light. They stream away behind the comet's lengthening tail, curved by the various motions involved, as a jet of water curves if the hosepipe is swung in a wide arc. (7)

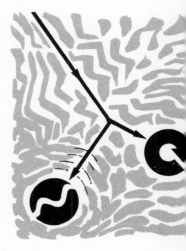

What happens when an X-ray photon strikes an electron? Some of its energy passes to the electron, which moves away with an extra velocity; but the photon bounces off at the same speed as that with which it approached (the speed of light). It can do this only by changing to a longer wavelength, needing a smaller quantum of energy. (8)

A. H. Compton, an American famous for his work on X-rays, has even been able to show how an electron will recoil if struck by an X-ray photon. The photon, of course, bounces off the electron. And here there is one very big difference between the kind of collision which occurs between a pair of billiard balls or motor cars and an en-counter with a photon. As in other collisions, the energy before the impact is shared between the two bodies. But the recoiling photon bounces off the electron at precisely the same speed, the speed of light, as when it hit it. But part of its energy has gone into moving the electron. How has the photon lost energy?

fig 8

The answer is that the wavelength of the recoiling photon has been lengthened. It is as though in a collision between a car and a bus, the car bounced off the bus without reduction in speed but subsequently was found to weigh only a fraction of its original weight.

All this supports Einstein's idea of the photon. But how does this fit in with the highly successful wave picture? First, we must realize that in the normal way we do not deal with individual photons, just as we do not normally handle individual atoms. So most of the experiments on electro-magnetic radiation are carried out with million million millions of photons. But suppose we use a source of light so weak that photons are emitted quite rarely. Will it still show the characteristic behaviour, like a degree of bending round corners, which gave strength to the old wave theory? The answer is yes.

We must accept the fact that photons also behave like waves: that the photon is a particle 'guided' by a wave. As p 130–1 we shall see later, other particles, in particular electrons, have this dual character and show marked wave properties.

The violent collisions that produce X-rays

We have seen how electromagnetic waves are produced by the jostling of atoms in a hot body. The characteristic of this radiation is that it spreads over a wide range of wave-lengths. Measurements made from rockets and satellites show that sunlight is rich in the longer-wavelength X-rays as well as ultra-violet, visible light and infra-red. But X-rays only appear when the body is extremely hot because the change in energy which produces an X-ray photon must be greater than the X-ray quantum. Even in the sun, where the temperature is 6000 degrees centigrade or more, only an occasional collision occurs that is violent enough to produce an X-ray photon.

If we want to produce X-rays, a much better method is to ensure that all or nearly all the collisions are violent enough by flinging electrons (other charged particles would do, but electrons are the most convenient) at a metal target. The sudden stopping of the electrons is accompanied by the production of X-ray photons.

This is the principle of the X-ray tube. The electrons produced in a cloud from a heated filament are accelerated by an electric field towards the target. Usually the electric field is produced by connecting the target to a source of high voltage. The voltage used is chosen according to the wavelength of X-ray required. The shorter the wavelength, the larger the X-ray quantum, so the higher the voltage that has to be used. For some purposes, such as the radiography of very large metal castings, and for the extra-penetrating X-rays needed for cancer treatment, very high voltages are needed. In these cases the electrons are often given the energy required in an accelerating machine which speeds them up by 'surf-riding' on an electromagnetic wave. In this way electrons with energies equivalent to being accelerated through 10 million volts or more can be obtained very easily.

If we measure the quantity of X-rays of different wavelengths produced in this way the shape of the graph we obtain, called the spectrum, is very similar to that from a white-hot body. Starting at the longer wavelength end it rises smoothly to a maximum, and then falls sharply. A curve of this shape, where all wavelengths over a wide range

fig 9

p 84–5
(13)

fig 6

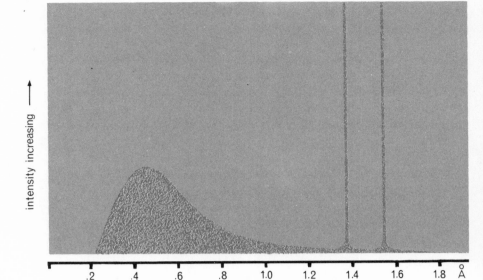

intensity increasing →

.2 .4 .6 .8 1.0 1.2 1.4 1.6 1.8 Å

The spectrum of a beam of X-rays shows the intensities of the various wavelengths contained in the beam. If a copper target is struck by very high energy electrons, the spectrum shows tall narrow peaks at fixed wavelengths—the spectrum 'lines', points at which the energy has been sufficient to dislodge electrons from the innermost shells of the copper atoms. The curve of continuous radiation rises to a maximum and then falls off abruptly—we have reached the highest energy electrons (and shortest length photons) that particular voltage (50,000) can produce. If the voltage is raised further, the maximum will move to the left. (10)

are present, is called a continuous spectrum. The shape of the continuous spectrum from an X-ray tube is different from that from a hot body because all the electrons striking the target are travelling at around the same speed. This means, too, that there is a clearly defined shortest wavelength, for obviously X-rays cannot be produced with photons carrying more energy than the original electrons.

The shape of the continuous X-ray spectrum is quite independent of the metal we choose to make the target which stops the electrons. As the voltage increases, the peak of the spectrum and the shortest wavelength simply move to the left. If we were to carry out this experiment with a target made of tungsten or molybdenum we would get precisely these results. But if we used a copper target, the results would be different. When the voltage was low the spectrum would look precisely like that using the tungsten target. But with increasing voltage first one and then more irregular 'pips' appear on the smooth outline of the spectrum. At still higher voltages the pips grow into tall narrow peaks, but do not shift their wavelength. These peaks are called 'lines'.

Exactly the same effect can be seen if we analyse the red light from a neon sign. In this case the spectrum consists almost entirely of these tall sharp peaks or 'lines'. What is their origin? Planck and Einstein developed the idea of the graininess of light. It came about because the existing theories could not explain the shape of the continuous spectrum of a hot body. Only ten years later in 1911 Niels Bohr, a young Danish physicist, was faced with a similar problem. Ernest Rutherford, a New Zealander, then Professor of Physics in Manchester University, showed that the atom consisted of two parts: a very small central nucleus surrounded by a number of electrons. At first the electrons were thought of rather like planets revolving round the sun. The nucleus was charged positively and the electrons carried a negative charge, so the first problem was this: why did the electrons not simply fall into the nucleus? What kept them in their orbits?

Bohr found the clue in the mysterious lines found in the spectrum of hydrogen gas. The presence of these lines means

fig 10

p 86–7
(28)

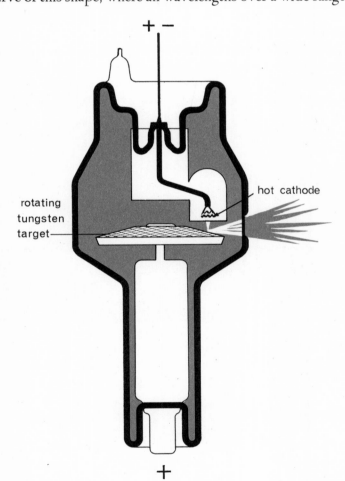

+ −

+

rotating tungsten target

hot cathode

+

X-rays are produced when electrons, moving at high speed, are suddenly stopped by a metal target. In the modern X-ray tube, the electrons are given off from a cathode consisting of electrically heated wires. They are attracted by a tungsten anode which is at a high voltage, striking it violently. The target, which rotates, is so shaped that the X-rays are beamed through a window at the side. The whole is sealed in a hard glass envelope at a high vacuum and enclosed in a shield (not shown) of aluminium alloy. (9)

that for some reason the atoms of the substance emitting them are producing photons of only one or two sizes. To refer back to the photon woodyard, the management has changed. Instead of stocking lumps of wood of every size provided the weight was a multiple of one pound, the new management has decided to specialize and offers only three 'lines' of 10, 100 and 1000 lb.

Bohr concluded that this reflected the structure of the electrons in the atom. And he decided that some rule similar to Planck's quantum rule for electromagnetic radiation must be at work in the atom controlling the energy changes of the electrons. For if an electron always changed its energy by the same amount, it would always produce a photon of the same wavelength. Bohr's theory of the atom is discussed later at length. Here we shall simply say that electrons can only exist in atoms at certain energy levels and that the number of 'spaces' they can occupy in the atom is limited. When a space is filled, no other electron can get into it.

p 130

You can imagine the situation as rather like a flight of steps, wider at the top than the bottom. These are the energy steps or levels in the atom. Imagine we have a number of beachballs just a little larger than the height of the step. Now suppose that we start with a single ball and trickle it over the top step. It rolls down to the bottom with a series of bumps. This corresponds to the simplest atom, the atom of hydrogen with just one electron. Normally the electron, like the beachball, sits quietly on the bottom step or energy level. But now think what happens when a youngster gives the ball a kick. It rises up the steps, according to how hard it has been kicked, and then a moment later falls back to the bottom again. It may have fallen only one step, or two steps, or any number of steps. But however far it falls, it will always be some exact number of steps. By the time the ball reached the bottom step it had an amount of energy equal to falling *n* steps where *n* is some whole number.

Now had that ball been an electron its energy on returning to the bottom step would be converted into a photon and the photon would have a wavelength corresponding to the number of steps fallen. In other words photons would be produced of certain wavelengths corresponding to the number of steps fallen.

In more complicated atoms the number of beachballs on the stairs is much greater. By the time one reaches a heavy atom like uranium, the stairs are thronged with 92 balls all competing to fall back to as low a level as they can. These big atoms not only have more electrons, but have a bigger electric charge on the nucleus, so that the pull inwards on the electrons is much greater. That means, of course, using our flight of steps analogy again, that the downward pull on the balls is increased greatly. To represent uranium on the steps we not only need 92 balls, but must increase the pull of gravity 92 times. That, as you will understand, means much harder work for the kicking boy, for instead of weighing a few ounces the beachball at the bottom of the steps now weighs half a hundredweight.

Of course, our step analogy is rather crude because the pull of gravity is almost the same at the top of the steps as at the bottom, while the pull of the nucleus falls off very rapidly. An electron which is twice as far from the nucleus as the nearest one will feel only one quarter the pull. So electrons which are near to the nucleus, especially if the nucleus is a big one, are much more difficult to dislodge than electrons which are, as it were, at the top of the steps, and a long way from the nucleus. Also, the electrons which are difficult to dislodge release more energy when falling back into place and so produce photons of higher energy, that is

shorter wavelength. Now we have the full picture of line spectra. They are produced by knocking electrons off their perch in the atom and allowing them to snap back into place again. The energy to knock the electron out can be obtained in various ways.

In the case of the X-ray tube the electrons striking the target may have sufficient energy to knock out electrons from the lowest energy levels of the target atoms. Here is the explanation of the sudden appearance of the lines on the continuous spectrum. They appeared only when the voltage was high enough to give the electrons sufficient energy to kick the firmly bound inner electrons out of their safe positions alongside the nucleus. And, as we would expect, a higher voltage is needed to knock inner electrons out of a large atom with a big electric charge on its nucleus, like tungsten or uranium, than a smaller one like copper.

These characteristic lines are used in a new method of analysing metals. A very thin beam of fast electrons, only a thousandth of a millimetre across, is scanned over the piece of metal to be analysed. The electrons are stopped suddenly and produce X-ray photons characteristic of the atoms which stopped them. The number of photons of wavelength characteristic of iron or cobalt, or whatever metal we may be interested in, is measured and used to build up a television picture of the metal surface whose brightness or darkness is a measure of the amount of that metal present.

Jumping electrons, glowing light

Knocking electrons out of position by bombarding them with other electrons or other charged particles will also produce light. In this case, because the photons of light are less energetic, the speed of the electrons can be much lower. Some quite complicated substances, like mixtures of minerals, happen to have energy levels separated by just the

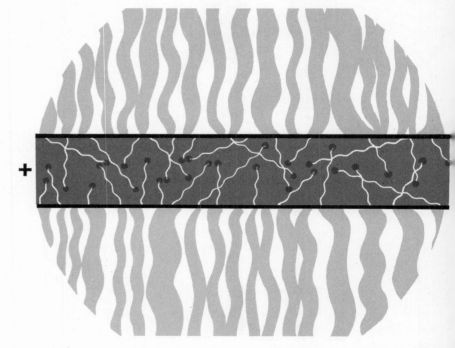

The mercury lamp of street lighting, to those who have experienced it, is clearly deficient in some of the colours of daylight. Its light is produced by passing an electric discharge through rarefied mercury vapour. Its excited atoms give off some wavelengths in the visible spectrum—but also a high proportion of invisible ultra-violet rays. If the inside of the tube is coated with suitable phosphors, the ultra-violet light lifts their outer electrons to higher-energy levels; as the electrons snap back they emit photons in all the wavelengths of visible light. With a skilful blend of the phosphors, this, the fluorescent tube, gives a much nearer match to daylight; its spectrum is continuous, with the original mercury lines superimposed. (11)

right amount to produce a photon of light. Often there are a very large number of these energy levels clustered together, so that instead of getting a single line, the spectrum is broadened out into a band. The light of a television screen p 174–5 is produced in this way. And certain areas of the moon's surface which have a strange greenish glow are thought to be producing light after bombardment with particles from the sun.

The neon tube, the sodium light and the mercury light work in rather a different way. In this case the atoms are in the form of a gas. When an electric field is applied to the gas the positively charged nuclei tend to move in one direction, and the electrons in the other. And as a result of collisions electrons get knocked off and the gas becomes ionized. In the course of the general mix-up some electrons snap back into place again and produce photons.

The ordinary fluorescent lamp is a gas discharge tube of this kind. But a line spectrum is not very satisfactory for general illumination. The peculiar colours seen under sodium or mercury street lamps would hardly be acceptable in the home. So the fluorescent lamp is filled with a gas chosen to produce some of its lines in the ultra-violet, and the inside of the tube is coated with a fluorescent material, similar to those used on television tube screens. Now the photons of ultra-violet light absorbed by the fluorescent paint have sufficient energy to lift electrons to a higher energy level, provided the step up to the new level is not too great. Later the electrons snap back, sometimes in several stages, to their old positions. If one of these steps down corresponds in energy to a light photon, a flash of visible light is emitted. Notice that the light emitted must be of a longer wavelength than the light absorbed to kick the electrons out. The fluorescent tube manufacturers blend the paint they use to give a mixture of photons that is a tolerable match to white light. *fig 11* p 86–7 (19–29)

Exactly the same principle is used by some detergent manufacturers for washing clothes 'whiter than white'. The detergent contains a fluorescent dye which converts ultra-violet light in daylight into blue visible light so that the clothes dyed in this way reflect more blue light than they otherwise would. As the blue light is most easily lost, the clothes look whiter. The secret is quickly discovered by looking at a shirt washed in this way under ultra-violet light. p 85 (16–17)

The same idea has been used by the fluorescent poster ink manufacturers, who incorporate substances in their inks which glow red or yellow or green in the ultra-violet light contained in daylight. Luminous paints work in much the same way. In one type the fluorescent substance is chosen because the electrons get temporarily stuck in their higher energy level and fall back only gradually, so the glow continues long after exposure to light. In the second type a little radioactive material is incorporated with the paint and the charged particles it throws off lift the electrons to the higher level.

The disciplined waves of the maser and laser

These quantum methods for producing electromagnetic radiation apply not only to X-rays, ultra-violet and visible light, but to infra-red rays and radio waves, although the size of the 'step' in energy is very much smaller. Often the sort of energy difference needed to produce infra-red or radio waves corresponds to a slight rearrangement of the geometry or mode of vibration of an assembly of atoms.

White light contains waves of many lengths, 'out of step' with one another.

Light of one colour singles out one wavelength but is still 'out of step'.

Coherent light is more narrowly one wavelength with all the waves 'in step'. (12)

This makes the investigation of infra-red and radio spectra of great importance to chemists who are concerned with the way atoms are assembled into molecules.

One of the most important applications of this principle is the 'maser' or microwave amplification by stimulated emission of radiation. The energy difference between the steps which produce radio waves is so small that the excited state can exist for quite a long time. Suppose that we have a number of molecules all in this excited state and we shine onto them a beam of radio waves with photons of the same energy as the step. The result is that the excited molecules are tipped off their pedestal, fall back to the lower energy level and emit more radiation of the same frequency as we supplied. In other words the excited molecules act as a kind of amplifier. Amplifiers like this are very useful for detecting extremely weak signals and are used in radio-astronomy.

One interesting point about the maser is that the radio waves that trigger the excited molecules and persuade them to fall back to the low energy level exert a kind of discipline over the whole proceedings. The photons are not emitted haphazardly, as they are if there is no trigger, but produce their photons strictly in step with the triggering photon.

Radiation produced haphazardly by a lot of independent events is called incoherent. The effect is like a choir who although they are all singing the same note of the same wavelength and frequency produce waves starting at different moments, so that they are not synchronized. On the other hand an organ pipe exerts discipline over the vibrating air column it contains so that it produces a single synchronized wave. It is coherent.

Another example is the electricity supply system. In the old days every town had its own generator and although they might all be working at the same frequency of 50 or 60 cycles a second, because they were independent the system as a whole was not synchronized. It was incoherent. But nowadays all the stations over wide areas are interconnected and so all the generating stations, although they have not changed their frequency, have got in step with one another. They are coherent.

Radio waves generated in the ordinary way with an oscillating current are coherent. The current exerts discipline on the electrons moving through the aerial wire and ensures they all act together. But light, X-rays and the like, which are produced by atomic processes, are incoherent. Each photon *fig 12* is produced at a moment in time unrelated to the others.

The idea of the maser seemed to offer a way of producing coherent light for the first time. A substance had to be found with an energy step suitable for producing visible light and which would remain in the excited state for a sufficient length of time to enable one photon to trigger off the rest. The first of these optical masers, or lasers as some people call them, used a kind of ruby as the working substance. An intense flash of light raised some of the electrons up the energy step. And when the first fell back again and produced a photon, it triggered the remainder. To ensure this would happen the two ends of the ruby crystal were silvered to make them into mirrors, one of them less than perfect so that some of the light could eventually escape.

fig 13

Of course, the flash from the electronic tube had to be of shorter wavelength than the coherent flash expected from the ruby, so that there was enough energy to lift the electrons up the step to the higher energy level.

The laser was first demonstrated in 1959. Since then improved lasers have been developed, including one that is energized in a different way and will work continuously instead of in flashes. It uses a mixture of gases instead of a ruby and produces a strong beam of infra-red radiation.

p 90–1 (38–41)

This coherent form of light shows much more clearly the similarities between light waves and radio waves. The coherent light beam will probably have many applications. One that is being much discussed is its use for long-distance communication in space, since the light waves can be used to carry an immense number of television pictures or telephone messages. In fact, this latest development, apart from its possible future applications, shows finally the correctness of the original slightly suspect theory that light and radio waves are identical apart from their wavelength.

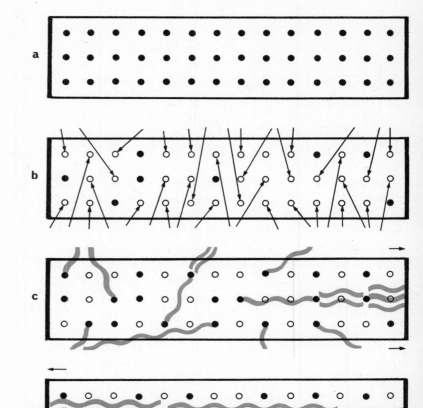

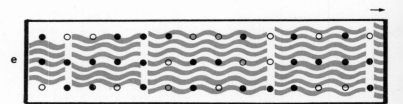

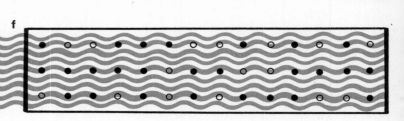

The ruby crystal contains, as an impurity, atoms of chromium. If green light is shone through it, the outer chromium electrons are lifted to higher energy levels, fall back to an intermediate level and then, more slowly, to their lowest level. At this last stage they emit a photon of red light: the ruby fluoresces. To produce a laser, the crystal is drawn into a cylinder, fully silvered at one end, semi-silvered at the other. In the diagram above, (a) the chromium atoms are shown quiescent, their electrons at 'ground' level. (b) Green light is flashed through, raising most of the atoms to the excited state (circles). (c) Electrons begin the last stage of their

fall, emitting photons. Those in irregular directions pass out of the crystal, but those parallel to the axis of the tube strike other atoms and stimulate their electrons to fall, producing more photons of the same wavelength, 'in step' and in the same direction (d, e). As the photons flash to and fro between the silvered ends the electrons cascade and the red light builds up. When the intensity is great enough, a burst issues from the semi-silvered end in an almost parallel beam (f). The whole has taken less than a millionth of a second and is repeated every few millionths of a second. (13)

The immense flow of energy

which streams from the sun and stars reaches the earth only in part, and of that part our natural senses can detect only the very narrow band of visible light and some of the rays which bring us warmth. Before man can understand the rest of the great range of incoming radiations, or turn it to his advantage, or set it in motion for his own purposes, he must convert it into the band which his eyes can detect, or into the sound waves which are meaningful to his ears. In responding to this challenge he has shown great skill, and many of the recent advances of science and technology stem from his mastery of the problems involved.

The air traffic control officer opposite, who sits in the darkened Control Tower of London Airport, is making sophisticated use of these advances. His finger is on the switch which enables him to speak, by the use of short radio waves, to the crew of approaching aircraft. His eyes are fixed on the screens which, used when poor visibility clouds the

sight of the aircrews, show him by moving blips of light the positions of the aircraft closely approaching the landing strips and enable him to 'talk them down'. The pictures are brought to him by radar pulses which flash almost instantaneously to the aircraft and bounce back to his instruments. Around him are other screens which show him, by means of similar radar pulses, the positions of all aircraft within twenty miles or more.

How is this energy carried through space? As a stream of particles which respond to the mathematics of wave-motion, or as waves which sometimes act like a stream of particles? We have seen that scientists use both concepts with advantage; in the following pages it will suffice to think of waves, all travelling through space with the unimaginable speed of 186,000 miles per second and differing one from another only in wavelength. (1)

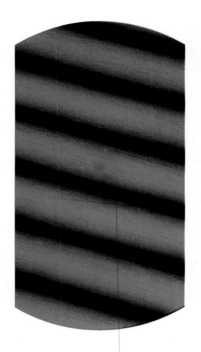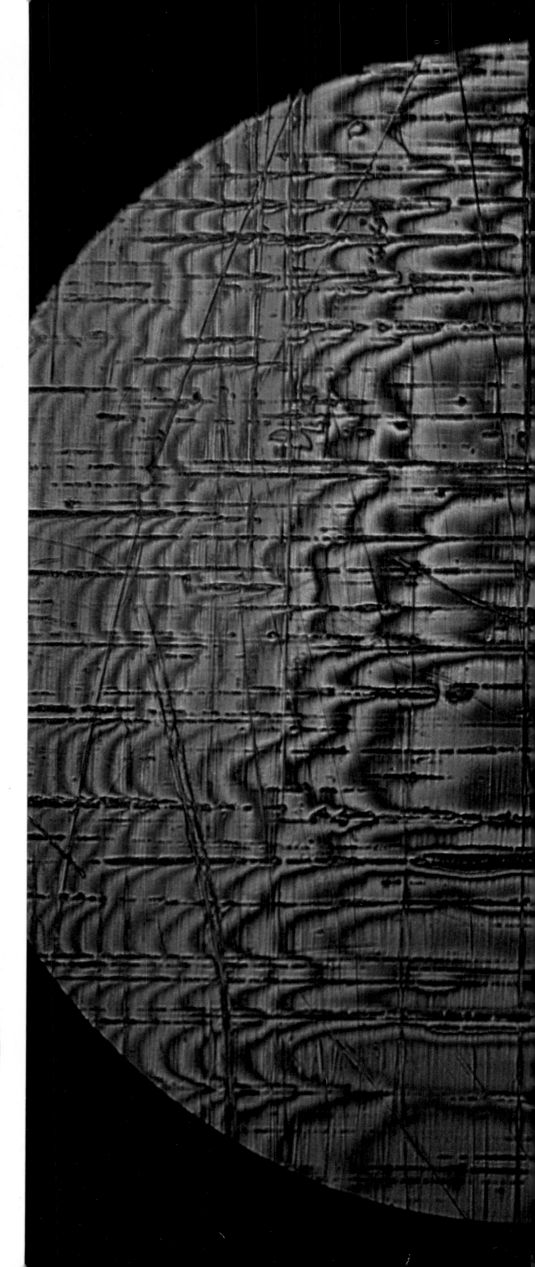

The battle between waves and particles has raged for three hundred years. One class of phenomena which gave impetus to the wave concept occurs when two beams of light alternately augment and annul one another. To produce the photographs above, a beam of green light of a single wavelength, coming through a narrow slit, was split into two and then reunited at a small angle. To reach any one spot on the film, the two beams have travelled slightly different distances; when the difference is a whole number of wavelengths, the beams are in step and augment one another—a light fringe results. When the difference leaves half a wavelength over, they are out of step and produce a dark fringe. If the angle between the beams is increased, the differences change more rapidly and the fringes are narrower.

If on the other hand the beam is of white light, composed of many different wavelengths, the photograph below results. Where the blue wavelengths are in step, a blue fringe appears. Since the red part of the light has a slightly longer wavelength, two red beams are in step, and produce a red fringe, after travelling slightly further. The effect is to edge the light fringes with rainbow colours. (2, 3, 4)

The vivid contours in the photograph on the right are produced by reflecting the split beam of white light from a plate of polished metal. Coloured fringes are formed as above, but how do the contours arise? The metal surface, smooth and plane to the eye, is in fact covered with micro-size plateaus and valleys, their differences in height enough to change the points at which the light waves get in and out of step. The 'contours' therefore accurately reveal, to millionths of an inch, the irregularities in the polished surface. (5)

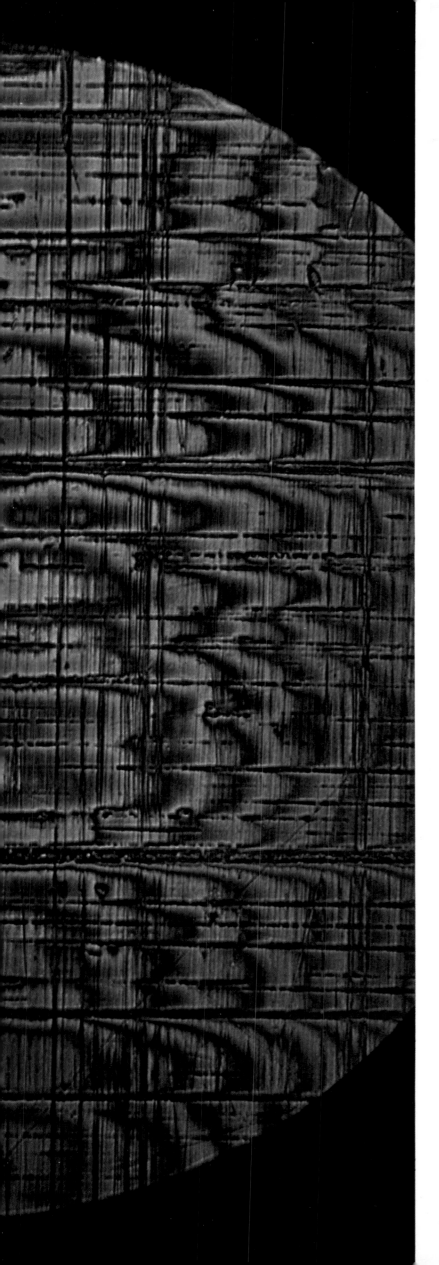

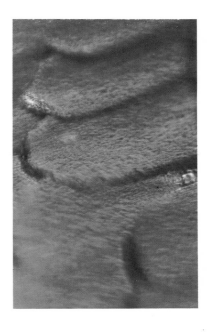

The iridescent, shot silk hues of the South American Morpho butterfly are well known. From above, the butterfly is a brilliant turquoise blue (top); from an angle, a glowing purple (second picture). The colours are not pigments, but optical effects similar to those on the opposite page. Magnified 90 times, the wings are seen to be composed of overlapping scales; at 224 times, each scale is covered with darker stria. Under the electron-microscope, × 24,000, the stria become the tops of upstanding fir-tree-like structures (right), some 10,000 to a centimetre. With surfaces such small distances apart, the light waves are thrown in and out of step—by reflection from the 'branches' or by multiple reflection at several layers. Blue or purple wavelengths are 'in step' depending on the angle of view of the 'branches'. (6–10)

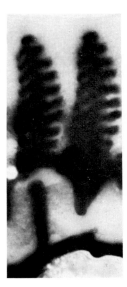

Gamma rays

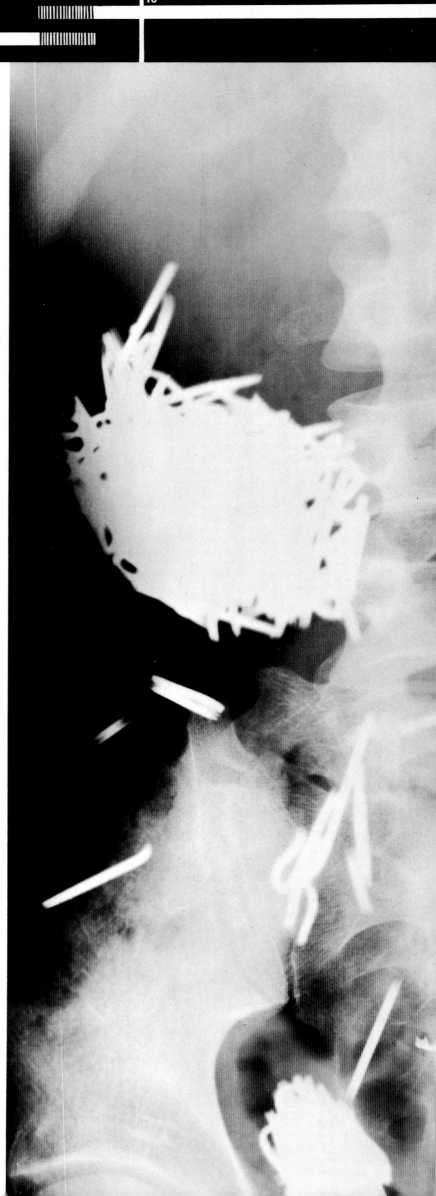

The range of radiant energy, from short wavelengths to long, is scaled in metres across the top of these two pages and the succeeding four. Shortest of all are the gamma rays. A few thousand millionths of a millimetre in length, more penetrating than X-rays, they are used to detect flaws in metal welding and casting. The body of the instrument in the boiler above contains a radioactive isotope of iridium, shielded so that the gamma rays emerge only from the nozzle. As the nozzle is directed along the seam weld in the boiler's side, the rays pass through to register on a photographic film placed outside. Flaws disturb the even penetration and are revealed as changes in the negative. In the stopcock for an oil pipeline below, the rays penetrate the thinner metal parts (dark areas) and make quick internal inspection possible. (11, 12)

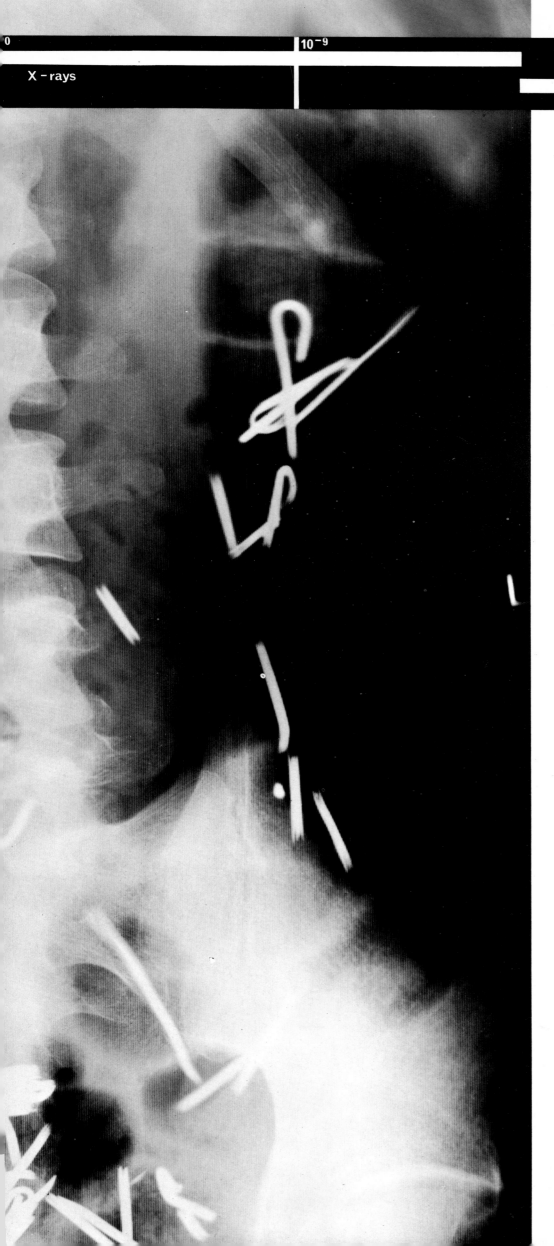

X-rays penetrate flesh but are absorbed to some extent by the denser bones and still more by metals. The familiar negative films of medical practice therefore show the flesh dark, more solid objects white. The patient whose stomach and intestines are examined in the negative (left) had a weakness for swallowing his bed springs. They are collected as an impacted mass at the exit from his stomach. A few are on their way through his intestines. X-rays, waves of very short length and high energy, are common in space, where they are produced by collisions between fast-moving electrons in the sun and stars. We are protected from them by their interaction with the atoms of the ionosphere. (13)

Ultra-violet rays are put to skilful use. Above, gherkins, left in daylight, develop a thick surface of bacterial scum; if they are irradiated with ultra-violet, no scum forms. Clothes *can* be washed 'whiter than white'. If the detergent contains a fluorescent dye it will convert the ultra-violet component of daylight into blue visible light. The blue of the daylight spectrum is easily weakened on reflection from the cloth; the extra blue replaces the loss and the cloth looks whiter. Below, left, photographed in daylight, are standard and treated cloths. The same two (right) under ultra-violet light show the effect enhanced. (14-17)

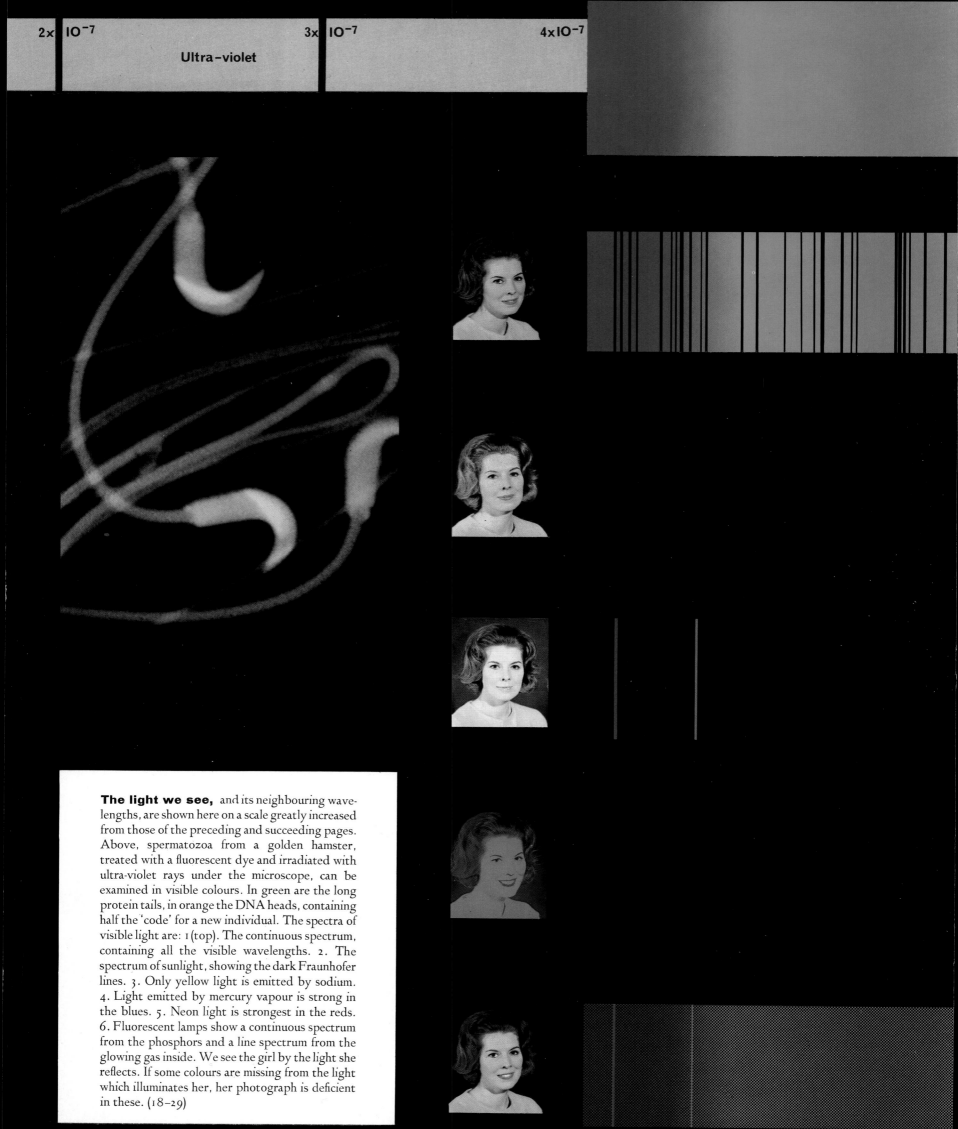

The light we see, and its neighbouring wavelengths, are shown here on a scale greatly increased from those of the preceding and succeeding pages. Above, spermatozoa from a golden hamster, treated with a fluorescent dye and irradiated with ultra-violet rays under the microscope, can be examined in visible colours. In green are the long protein tails, in orange the DNA heads, containing half the 'code' for a new individual. The spectra of visible light are: 1 (top). The continuous spectrum, containing all the visible wavelengths. 2. The spectrum of sunlight, showing the dark Fraunhofer lines. 3. Only yellow light is emitted by sodium. 4. Light emitted by mercury vapour is strong in the blues. 5. Neon light is strongest in the reds. 6. Fluorescent lamps show a continuous spectrum from the phosphors and a line spectrum from the glowing gas inside. We see the girl by the light she reflects. If some colours are missing from the light which illuminates her, her photograph is deficient in these. (18–29)

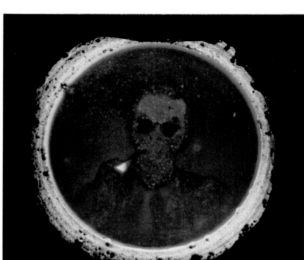

The energy which brings warmth is carried by waves beyond the red end of the spectrum. The man above, who wears a white shirt, necktie and jacket and smokes a pipe, emits such invisible waves. They cast a heat 'image' on a diaphragm, on which a thin film of oil condenses, its thickness varying with the image. Light reflected from the film forms a visible image in interference colours, as in an oil film on water. Infra-red radiation also has therapeutic value. The chimpanzee with muscular trouble basks in the rays, which keep him comfortably warm and penetrate through skin and flesh. (30, 31)

Microwaves

The shortest waves in the radio band are a thousand million times longer than gamma rays, but are still only of the order of a few millimetres. These microwaves are the latest region of the electromagnetic spectrum to be explored; the uses to which they can be put are developing rapidly. Their ability to carry a very large number of telephone conversations simultaneously, their comparative freedom from extraneous 'noise' and the ease with which they can be concentrated into narrow beams by specially shaped reflectors make them the medium for new networks of land and space communication and carriers for the short wavelengths of colour television. They must, however, be transmitted above terrestrial obstacles for, like infra-red rays, they are absorbed by solids.

Experiments have recently been made to use this absorption, for it generates heat in the absorbing body. Thus microwave energy has been injected into holes drilled in rock and concrete and the heat generated has split small rocks (below) and made others more readily breakable, especially if the rock has a liberal water content.

In fact the degree of absorption is a measure of the amount of moisture present and comparison of power input with power output on the other side of the material being tested will show, on a calibrated meter, whether the moisture is within the proper limits. It is important, for instance, to control the drying out of brickwork; bulk grains, shredded tobacco, animal feeding stuffs and other products can be tested in bulk and without damage. In the picture below a horn aperture transmits microwaves through a brick wall, to be received and measured through a similar horn. (34, 35)

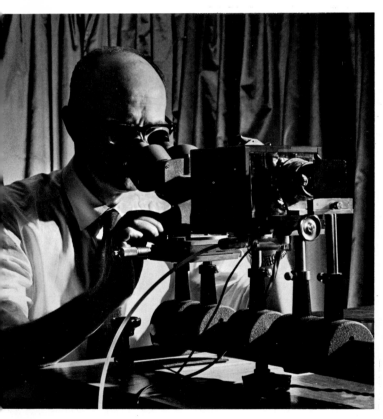

Seen in complete darkness, the buildings above were made visible by infra-red rays. In this image converter, the instrument that helps a sniper to see in the dark (and could possibly help a motorist to drive by night), a beam of heat rays from a filtered incandescent lamp is reflected back from the buildings. The rays are focused on a cathode coated with silver oxide, silver and caesium, which emit electrons when they are struck by infra-red rays. These electrons hit a fluorescent screen and excite it to glow, like a television screen, in proportion to the intensity of the electrons—and the invisible picture becomes a visible one. The tubes are made in sterile 'clean rooms' and are rigorously tested (above), because one speck of dust or fluff can ruin the cathode or the screen. (32, 33)

A hundred miles out in the Atlantic stands one of three man-made islands (above) which screen the American coast-line from Cape Cod to New Jersey—part of the Early Warning system. 'Texas Tower Three' is a three-sided, three-storey raft, stabilized on long steel legs, and manned by a crew of sixty. It carries three radar antennae, shielded from the Atlantic gales under bulbous plastic domes, ceaselessly scanning the sky for hostile aircraft or missiles. Twenty-four hours a day, each antenna sweeps its allotted area, sending out short bursts of waves in the range from 3 metres to a few centimetres; between bursts it becomes a

receiver, 'listening' for the returning impulse, feeding it into the receiver circuit, transforming it into a 'blip' on the screen of the cathode-ray tube, and transmitting again. This alternation of transmission and reception takes place many times in a second, so that a picture is built up which looks to the eye like a continuous representation of what is 'out there', although in fact it is composed of spots that briefly shine and quickly fade. The tall masts which rise above the domes are for telephonic communication with the mainland. The crew is served (and taken for shore leave every 45 days) by helicopter and ship. (36)

Modern communication uses all the wavelengths of the radio range, from microwaves to the 100–2000 metre sound broadcasting. The shorter wavelengths can carry more channels, but are stopped, as light is, by buildings and hills. The new Post Office tower in Central London is therefore built higher (at 620 feet) than any obstacle between it and the next relay stations, and transmits in microwaves, providing for 150,000 simultaneous telephone calls and up to 40 television channels. At the top is a mast for radar, to help in weather forecasting; below it are public galleries and a restaurant; below these are the aerial galleries and the floors of transmitting apparatus. (37)

The most exciting short-wave discovery of recent years is perhaps that of masers and lasers. They are incredibly intense, thin pencils of microwaves (masers) infra-red rays or visible light (lasers) in which the waves are coherent ('in step'), and spread very little even over thousands of miles. They can be produced, we have seen, from a ruby crystal, in which the electrons of the chromium atoms (there are about twelve million million million such atoms in a 5-inch crystal) are raised to higher energy levels and then triggered to cascade in short bursts, emitting the photons of coherent waves.

The narrow beam can be used to concentrate great heat very quickly on small areas. The engineer (left) is welding the terminals on miniature electronic equipment with a laser focused on the spot by a lens. The cascade of white hot sparks below (left) is caused by directing a laser on a sheet of extremely hard tantalum which boils only at 10,000°F. The beam, a million times brighter than the sun, requires less than a 1000th of a second to pierce the metal. Laser methods can also be used to amplify microwave and light signals and may well be ideal for communication in space, where there is no obstacle to their straight lines. (38, 39)

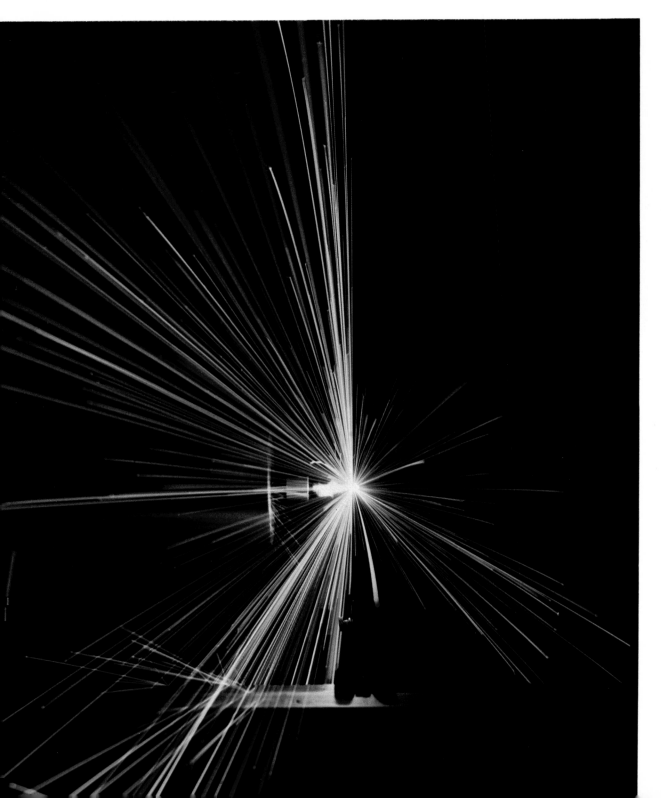

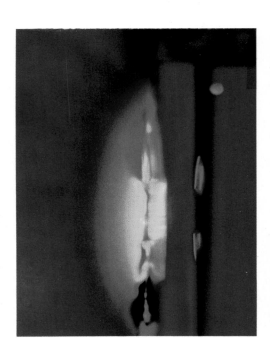

To destroy malignant growths without the knife, lasers may be used to burn them out. In the photograph above, a laser from the right directs a pulse for a 1000th of a second on a surface tumour on the side of the chest, the surrounding skin protected by aluminium foil and black felt. The colours are on infra-red film, not those seen by the eye. (40)

The brilliant red laser in the picture opposite is continuous, not a series of short bursts. It is produced from a mixture of helium and neon gases through which an electric discharge is passed. The discharge raises electrons of the helium atoms to high-energy levels close to upper levels of the neon electrons. Energy is transferred to the neon electrons by collision and these are then triggered to cascade to a lower level, emitting coherent photons of red light. Such visible lasers, and others in the infra-red obtainable from all the 'noble' gases, require little power, are on extremely narrow wavebands and promise to be one of the most efficient information carriers ever conceived. (41)

World-wide, live television

can be achieved only with the help of satellites, since the short television waves are useful only over line-of-sight distances and are not reflected by the ionosphere. Early Bird is the first of these on a commercial basis, owned jointly by forty-five or more countries. It was launched from Cape Kennedy by a Thrust-Augmented Delta rocket, the main rocket, liquid propelled, firing first, followed by three solid propellant rockets strapped round its base. It was first directed into a transit orbit and then, at the highest point of the fourth orbit, 'kicked' by a small motor in the satellite itself into an orbit 22,300 miles above the earth. Here it circles at the same speed as the earth turns, seeming stationary over a point in mid-Atlantic, neither rising nor setting.

The satellite (under test, right) derives its power from 6000 solar cells which form the outer surface of the drum and two batteries which operate during the short periods when it is in the earth's shadow. Below it projects the dipole transmitting and receiving aerial, above it the cone of the motor and whip antennae to receive commands from the ground while in the transit orbit. In orbit, it spins like a gyroscope to keep stabilized and is held on station by firing delicate puffs of steam from its hydrogen peroxide thrusters. Early Bird provides 240 two-way channels for telephone or television and is capable also of carrying teletype, facsimile and high-speed data. A new satellite under construction will have 1200 voice channels and a third can have as many as 50,000.

Messages via the satellite are transmitted from ground stations at Andover, Maine; Mill Village, Nova Scotia; Goonhilly Downs, Cornwall; Raisting, South Germany; Pleumeur-Bodou, Brittany; Fucino, Italy and Grinon, Spain. At the Andover station, a giant horn antenna (below) is housed inside an inflated radome as high as an 18-storey building, made of fabric impregnated with rubber seven hundredths of an inch thick but designed to withstand 100-mile per hour gales and fully transparent to radio energy. The horn, 68 feet in diameter, follows the satellite automatically, receiving and transmitting communications, the faint received signals being concentrated and then amplified 10,000 times by a ruby maser, refrigerated by liquid helium to 4 degrees above absolute zero to keep down noise. On the side of the cone is a 14-foot dish antenna which transmits instructions to the satellite by microwaves. (42, 43)

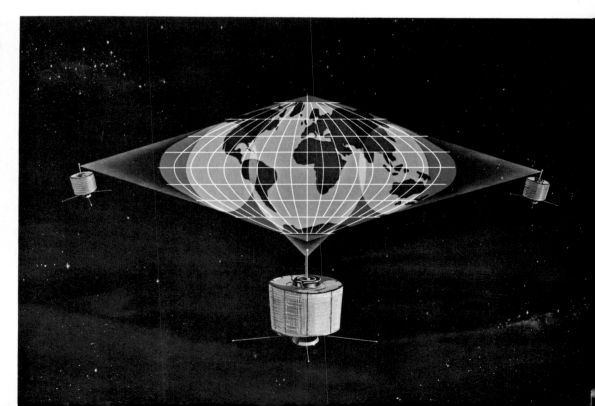

To cover the world, three such 'stationary' satellites are required (right). Early Bird links the Americas, Western Europe and Africa. (44)

4 Into the depths of space

Sir Bernard Lovell

Into the depths of space

In this age when Sputniks, space probes, radio and optical telescopes constantly bring us new information about our environment in space and about the depths of the universe, it is salutary to recall the slow progress of mankind to this stage. For the greater part of his history man has only been able to study the heavens with his unaided eye. With little knowledge of the earth other than his local environment it is not hard to understand that ancient man assumed that he and his abode were fixed in space at the centre of the unchanging system of stars, and that the sun rotated around the earth.

These ideas were first decisively challenged by Copernicus, and the integration of his basic scheme with the accurate measurements of Tycho Brahe led Kepler to formulate his laws of planetary motion in the early 17th century. Thereby man became aware that the earth was not fixed in space, but, together with the planets, moved in an elliptical orbit with the sun at one of the foci of the ellipse. At the same time Galileo introduced the telescope to assist man in his study of the stars. Soon it became obvious that man's ability to obtain detail about the stars and planets depended on the construction of telescopes of greater size. For nearly three and a half centuries the progress of astronomy was then dominated by the construction of optical telescopes of ever increasing size culminating in the great 200-inch telescope on Mount Palomar in California which began its work in 1947.

fig. 1
p 111

Much of our present knowledge of the universe which will be described in this chapter has been achieved through the use of these telescopes with their ancillary photographic and spectrographic equipments. In recent years the development of radio telescopes had led to another revolution in astronomical research and the integration of the results of the radio and optical astronomers has deepened our understanding of the nature of the universe.

p 124·5

Peering through a dusty window

When one reflects on the knowledge of the universe which man has achieved through the use of his eyes, assisted in the last few centuries by the optical telescope, one is impressed by the evolutionary sequence which has led to this possibility. The earth is enveloped by an atmosphere which is either opaque to, or transforms in some way, much of the electromagnetic radiation incident from the stars and galaxies in space. There is a gap or window in this atmosphere which allows a small band of radiation to pass through comparatively without hindrance. The range of wavelengths in this band represents the part of the spectrum occupied

p 114·5

by the colours of the rainbow from the violet to the red—just the region to which the human eye has adapted itself and is sensitive. Radiation of shorter wavelengths in the ultra-violet, and of longer wavelengths in the infra-red, is scattered or absorbed by the dust, water vapour, or gaseous constituents of the atmosphere. Thus, an evolutionary sequence involving a relatively small shift in the wavelength sensitivity of the eye would have resulted in beings who could have had no direct visual awareness of the heavens.

Although this gap in the visual wavelength range exists there are many obstacles to its full deployment for astronomical observations. Cloudy skies and smoky towns are the obvious additions to the opacity of the natural atmosphere which have driven astronomers with their big telescopes to seek the high mountains. As telescopes became larger it became increasingly difficult to realize their full potential. The light-gathering power of the telescopes became so great that small amounts of scattered moonlight and distant city lights limited the number of occasions on which full use could be made of their ability to record faint and distant objects. Further, as the size of the telescope increased so did its definition, and small irregularities in the atmosphere which gave rise to scintillation or twinkling of the image began to set limits to the image quality, rather than the size of the telescope itself.

p 112
(2)

Many expensive and lengthy expeditions have been made to find the best sites for the modern large optical telescopes. The operation of the 100-inch telescope on Mount Wilson which came into use at the end of the first world war became increasingly difficult as the city of Los Angeles expanded, and the search for a suitable position for the 200-inch telescope culminated on Mount Palomar, nearly two hundred miles south of the city, at a height of 5000 feet. The Russian telescope on a mountain near Simeiz on the south coast of the Crimea was destroyed by the Germans during the war and they moved inland to build their 100-inch in order to obtain adequate 'seeing' conditions. Now, a protracted search throughout the entire Soviet Union for a suitable situation for the projected 236-inch telescope has resulted in the choice of a site at a height of 6000 feet in the North Caucasus. Even with the best possible situations on earth there is a growing belief that telescopes of this size are at the limit of usefulness because of the relatively few occasions when the atmosphere is stable enough to enable their full resolving power and light-gathering capacity to be realized.

The prospects of improvement in conventional optical telescopes are therefore limited not only by the practical difficulties of constructing the large mirrors with sufficient accuracy but also by the earth's atmosphere. The overall performance of optical telescopes has been improved steadily over the past half-century by the development of ancillary photographic and spectrographic equipment. The latest development in such ancillary equipment has been the use of image intensifiers or image convertors. In this equipment the image of the star or nebula formed by the telescope is focused not directly on a photographic plate, but on a photocathode which emits electrons proportional to the intensity of light. After amplification the image can be viewed on a cathode ray tube, or photographed. Under suitable conditions this can result in a large gain in sensitivity.

In 1956 at the Haute-Provence Observatory, Lallemand demonstrated the potential of these image convertors when he succeeded in using this new technique on the Observatory's 47-inch telescope to obtain stellar spectra, which if they had been observed by conventional methods would have required a telescope with an aperture of 275 inches. Hence, in certain kinds of work, these new electronic devices attached to optical telescopes can increase significantly the effective aperture as far as the light-gathering power is concerned. Alternatively, for stars and nebulae of an intensity within the range of the telescope the exposure can be shortened by many times. Although such equipment can be used with a small telescope to simulate a larger one in terms of light intensity, it does not, of course, effect a similar improvement in definition, or in any way overcome the fundamental hindrances introduced by the earth's atmosphere even on the best available sites, although the reduced exposure required (because of increased sensitivity) may increase greatly the number of occasions in which the maximum definition of the telescope may be used.

A clearer view from balloon and rocket

Optical astronomy has been based, until now, primarily on the radiation emitted by stars within the visible region. But recently it has become clear that further information could be obtained from the ultra-violet and infra-red spectra

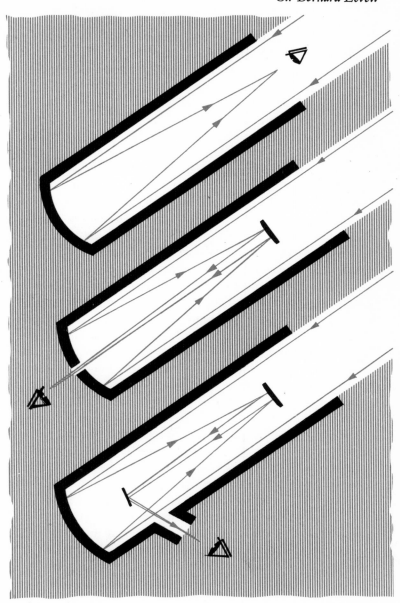

p 111
p 112
(3)
(4)

Three ways of viewing the image formed by the Mount Palomar telescope. (Top), the observer is at the focus of the mirror (the prime focus). (Centre), a convex mirror in front of the prime focus reflects the light back through a hole in the centre of the mirror to the Cassegrain focus. (Bottom), the light is reflected again by a plane mirror, sideways to the Coudé focus. Both foci outside the telescope allow bulky viewing apparatus which does not obstruct the light from the stars, that at the Coudé focus being fixed and permanent, although the telescope moves; both give a longer path for the reflected light, increasing the size of the image in proportion. (2)

which cannot be observed in the normal way because of absorption of the earth's atmosphere. The advent of artificial earth satellites and space probes has now opened the possibility of making astronomical measurements with optical telescopes outside the atmosphere, so that the restrictions, both as regards definition and spectral coverage, would be imposed by the telescope and its recording equipment only, and not by the atmosphere.

p 115

Indeed a most significant advantage can be obtained by using balloons to lift optical telescopes to altitudes of 15 to 20 miles. Infra-red rays are predominantly absorbed by water vapour and carbon dioxide. Nearly all the water-vapour absorption occurs below altitudes which can be reached by balloon-borne telescopes and a great improvement in performance is obtained. Carbon-dioxide absorption, however, continues to higher altitudes. This dramatic improvement is not observed for ultra-violet rays since they are mainly absorbed at much greater heights.

Significant progress with balloon-borne telescopes has already been made because of the enthusiasm of a group at Princeton under Dr Martin Schwarzschild. In 1957 this

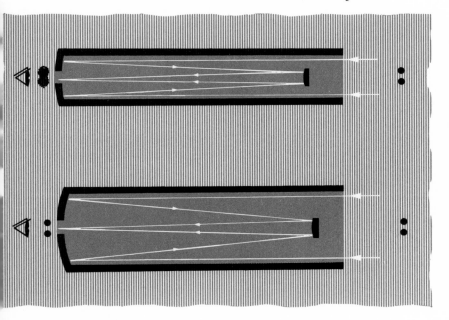

Larger and larger telescopes, culminating in the massive 200-inch reflector on Mount Palomar, have been built because the wider aperture and mirror gather more light and increase the brightness of the image. They also improve its definition. Although a star is a point source of light, the image is always a finite disk. If two very close stars, for instance, are viewed through a small telescope, the two image-disks overlap. Through a larger telescope the images are, paradoxically, smaller, but distinct – the resolving power is greater. (1)

group launched a 12-inch telescope in a balloon and succeeded in this and subsequent flights in taking excellent photographs of the 'granulation' (or speckled appearance) of the solar disk from a height of about 15 miles. Apart from the spectral extension, the results showed that the atmospheric hindrances to good seeing conditions were absent at this altitude. Encouraged by this success, a 36-inch telescope was constructed and successfully launched in March 1963. This instrument, which weighed 3 tons, made a number of scans of the planet Mars from an altitude of 15 miles before descending to earth.

p 44 (8)

The restrictions introduced by the residual absorption at the balloon heights of 15 to 20 miles are largely overcome at the altitude of 60 miles or so reached by sounding rockets and over the last ten years many successful launchings have been made of rockets containing small telescopes which have been used to study the parts of the ultra-violet spectrum obscured at lower altitudes. Naturally, the duration of such experiments is limited to minutes and significant pointing accuracies have not yet been attained. Even so, these experiments have revealed the rich harvest of results which awaits the successful use of a telescope on an earth satellite where observations can be carried out for an almost unlimited time.

p 114

The United States and the Soviet Union are working hard towards the realization of such projects. In the initial stages it seems that both countries propose to place in orbit a 36-inch aperture telescope. The U.S. space telescopes will be carried in the series of Orbiting Astronomical Observatories which are remotely controlled on command from earth; while the USSR intends to build a space platform of such size that the telescope it carries can be manned by cosmonauts working in space for periods of 5 to 7 days.

p 114

There has been much discussion about establishing optical telescopes on the moon where, since there is no atmosphere, their full value could be realized in spectral coverage, penetration and resolution. It seems certain, however, that this project lies much further into the future than that of the orbiting telescope, and its realization may have to await success in the manned lunar enterprise. There are, indeed, sound arguments for the establishment of telescopes at a much greater distance from earth than the satellite altitudes. Even outside the earth's atmosphere there seems to be a general glare of radiation from the sky in a part of the infra-red spectrum. This may originate by scattering from particles in a local region of the earth's environment out to distances of 15 times the radius of the earth. This residual interference with the optical observations would therefore be overcome by telescopes on the moon or in space probes.

Mapping and counting the stars

A photograph of the sky taken with a modern telescope under good conditions reveals an apparently bewildering array of stars. To the systematic study of the heavens over the centuries we owe our present insight into the nature of the stars and their arrangement in the universe. This knowledge has slowly accumulated because astronomers have concentrated on a number of well-defined types of astronomical measurement according to the ability of their equipment.

Measurements of the positions of the heavenly bodies were made long before the introduction of the telescope, the essential requirements being a knowledge of time and a fixed reference on the earth. Primitive man distinguished the

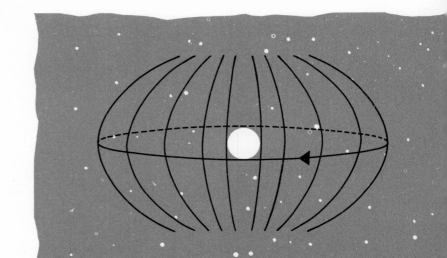

To define the position of a star in the sky, we imagine the sky as the inside surface of a vast sphere, which we then divide into 24 segments, each 15° wide, starting from a fixed 'prime' meridian (in the constellation Aries) and counting eastwards. We also imagine an 'equator', in the plane of the earth's equator. As the earth spins, the sphere will seem to revolve past the observer in the opposite direction (arrowed), at the rate of one segment each hour. If the prime meridian passes the observer at 0100 hours, a star that passes 63 minutes later is said to be at 02ʰ 03ᵐ. If it is 30° above the 'equator', its full position is described as 02ʰ 03ᵐ, +30° (or −30° if below the 'equator').

This time lag behind the prime meridian can be measured by a meridian transit circle, a small telescope firmly fixed in the north-south line. In the centre of the eyepiece is a fine wire. The exact moment when a star crosses this wire is electrically noted, and this time is compared with the time when the prime meridian passed across the wire. If the difference is already known exactly, the moment of crossing can be used as an accurate time check. The angle the telescope is pointing at – north or south of the equator – can be read off on a dial at the side of the instrument. (3)

wandering stars (the planets) from those fixed in the firmament, but no systematic measurements of sufficient accuracy were made until Tycho Brahe constructed large quadrants in the 16th century. Indeed his observations were so precise that he was able to produce convincing evidence that the new star of 1572 (the supernova of that date) had appeared amongst the fixed stars—hitherto regarded as unchanging. In the case of the planets he found that the predicted times of certain conjunctions were grossly in error, and it was his determinations of planetary positions which provided Kepler with the basic material for his laws of planetary motion.

The need for accurate catalogues of the stars increased in urgency with the advance of astronomy. For example on a perfectly clear night only about 6500 stars are visible to the naked eye over the entire hemisphere, but even Herschel, with the telescope he made in the 18th century, was able to count many thousands in a square degree of sky in certain directions. The great star catalogues of the late 19th century such as the *Bonner Durchmusterung* (B.D.) and the *Cordoba Durchmusterung* (C.D.) give the positions and details of over half a million stars. In this century the photographic plate has enabled comprehensive photographic charts of the stars to be compiled down to the limiting magnitude of the modern telescopes. In the great international enterprise which has produced the *Carte du Ciel* the position of many millions of stars has been accurately determined from the photographic plates. These catalogues and the photographic atlases of the heavens—such as the *Palomar Sky Atlas* compiled by the 48-inch Schmidt telescope—are the basic references for the day-to-day work of the modern astronomer.

p 112
(3)

The precise definition of the system of co-ordinates to which the positions of the stars in these catalogues are related—their 'latitude and longitude'—depends on the positional measurements of the brighter stars made by the meridian transit circle. The instrument usually consists of a small refracting telescope (aperture of the order of 10 inches). The horizontal axis of the telescope is fixed rigidly to the earth, usually by two deep pillars, so that the telescope itself can swing only in a precise north-south plane. The eyepiece is associated with a precisely calibrated micrometric scale, and this together with a sidereal clock enables a determination to be made of the exact time of transit of the various stars across the local meridian. A similar telescope with a different type of eyepiece is used for the measurement of the separation of double stars and the accumulation of these data has facilitated the compilation of the orbits and masses of the components of the binary stars.

fig 3

These positional measurements provide the material on which the science of celestial mechanics is based. Early measurements of this type led Halley to conclude in 1718 that certain stars had been displaced relative to others over the centuries—in other words he had detected the first 'proper motions'. Today with modern instruments the proper motions of over 40,000 stars are known. We know that our own sun is moving towards a point on the star sphere near Vega at 12 miles per second, and that certain stars, although widely separated in space, seem to be physically connected because they form a star stream moving through space together. The interpretation of this star streaming led, in 1927, to the concept of the rotation of the Galaxy as a whole, and of differential rotations within it.

A measure for brightness

Perhaps the most obvious feature of the stars is their wide variation of brightness. Today we still use the system of classification of the stars in terms of their brightness introduced by Ptolemy, who divided the stars into six groups. The brightest stars seen by the eye belong to the first magnitude and the faintest to the sixth, the difference in brightness being 2.5 times between each magnitude group. Thus a star of the sixth magnitude, just visible to the naked eye under good conditions, is 100 times fainter than a star of the first magnitude.

p 86-7
(25)

Although the ancient magnitude system has been retained, the method of estimation of brightness by eye has been replaced by more exact measurements, and, of course, the range of magnitudes has been greatly extended as faint stars below the naked-eye visibility limit have been revealed by the telescopes. Even a small telescope with an aperture of two inches enables the eye to extend the visibility limit under good sky conditions down to the eleventh magnitude, whereas a 100-inch reveals stars of the nineteenth magni-

tude. By the use of photographic plates this limit can be extended down to the twenty-first magnitude to reveal stars which are a hundred million times fainter than the bright stars of magnitude one.

At the brightest end of the scale, the intense stars were originally all placed together in the first magnitude but when measurements, as distinct from estimates, were made, it was found that the stars in this first magnitude differed in brightness by more than 2.5 times. Then the original scale was extended to include these brighter objects by the introduction of zero and negative magnitudes. Thus the bright star Capella is nearly of 'zero' magnitude and Sirius, the brightest star in the sky, has a magnitude of −1.4, that is a thousand times brighter than a star of the sixth magnitude.

The first accurate measurements of stellar magnitudes, as distinct from the estimates by eye, were made in the middle of the 19th century by a photometer. In this device an artificial star derived from a small electric light bulb provided a standard image alongside that of the real star in the eyepiece of the telescope, and arrangements were made by a system of prisms so that the intensity of the artificial star could be varied until it coincided with that of the real star. This basic system of visual photometry has been increasingly replaced by photographic methods, which have the advantages of permanency of the record, the ability to record many stars simultaneously and the extension to fainter objects. By modern methods it is possible to achieve accuracies of a few hundredths of a magnitude in the measurements.

Of course the response of the photographic plate is different from that of the eye and there is an important distinction between the visual and photographic magnitudes. Stars differ widely in their colour and those whose light is rich at the blue end of the spectrum will create a more intense photographic image than those whose light is strong at the red end. The difference between the visual and photographic magnitudes is the colour index of the star and this provides an important indication of its temperature.

p 117

The spectral lines: a powerful probe

Three hundred years ago Newton made his famous observation that when sunlight passed through a prism it deviated to form the brightly coloured bands of the familiar rainbow colours. For a long time after that experiment it was assumed that the spectrum of the sun was undifferentiated, or continuous. Early in the 19th century Wollaston noticed that the solar spectrum formed by a prism from the light coming through a narrow slit illuminated by the sun was crossed by a number of dark lines. Some years later, Fraunhofer, with an improved arrangement of slit and prism, discovered 574 dark lines crossing the continuous spectrum. The interpretation of these phenomena was given a hundred years ago by Kirchhoff. It is that every substance has a specific and unique spectrum, and under suitable conditions any substance can absorb the lines which it emits. As applied to the dark lines in the solar spectrum the interpretation is that the gaseous atmosphere of the sun absorbs some of the wavelengths in the radiations emitted by the photosphere.

From that point it was a straightforward matter to identify the lines of many common elements in the solar spectrum, and, with the introduction of the photographic plate for recording the spectra, the study of the actual chemical constituents of the remote matter in the sun and stars made rapid progress. The integration of spectrographic equipment with large telescopes is now a primary matter in their design. The spectroscopic classification of the stars is fundamental to any investigation of their nature, and the interpretation of the processes occurring in objects such as novae is largely based on the characteristics of their spectral 'lines', the particular and characteristic wavelengths at which light is emitted. In the presence of a magnetic field the spectral lines may split into two or more components. By measuring the difference in wavelength between the components the magnetic fields of the sun and of many hundreds of stars have now been determined.

p 112
(4)

Spectral lines from the same element identified in the spectra from different stars frequently show quite different widths—even when all instrumental effects have been eliminated. Spectral lines have a natural width of about 0.002 Ångströms (that is 2×10^{-11} cms.); but the lines of elements observed from the sun and stars are broader than this natural width. The broadening may arise from several causes.

First the random motion of the atoms increases with temperature and the wavelength of light emitted by each individual atom varies according to its speed. At the temperatures involved in the stars, the line width may be broadened in this way to 0.01 Ångströms or more. Second, if the stellar atmospheres are dense there will be many collisions between the atoms and this will also broaden the lines. Third, in high electrical fields, the spectral lines are split (as in a magnetic field). Electrical fields of the necessary intensity arise in stellar atmospheres when the temperature is high enough to ionize the atoms so that they are no longer electrically neutral. This effect also results in a broadening of the line, especially in dense atmospheres. Finally the rotation of a star on its own axis may result in the broadening of the line through the Doppler effect, if light from the whole disk is entering the telescope.

The famous 'red shift'

The broadening of a spectral line emitted by a rotating star is a somewhat minor consequence of the Doppler effect in astronomical measurements. The familiar manifestation of the Doppler effect occurs in sound. To an observer standing on a railway platform the whistle of a moving train seems to change in pitch as it passes by. (The same effect occurs when an aircraft passes low overhead.) It is not a result of a variation in the pitch of the whistle, but arises because the sound waves coming from an approaching source reach the ear at shorter intervals (and therefore at a higher pitch) than those from a stationary one. Similarly, sound waves from a receding source arrive at longer intervals, and therefore at a lower pitch. With light waves, frequency corresponds to the pitch of sound waves. Red is the low-frequency end of the visible spectrum, blue to violet the high-frequency end. If the source emitting light is moving towards the observer then the frequency will be higher and the light will have moved towards the blue end of the spectrum. If the source is receding the frequency will be lower and the light will be reddened.

p 122
(26)

If a spectral line is observable in the light from a star then the change in frequency of the lines as a result of the relative movement of the star and the observer on the earth can be measured precisely with modern spectrographic apparatus.

In stellar astronomy the information available from a study of the shift in the spectral lines of the stars covers a wide field; for example the measurement of the radial

fig 4

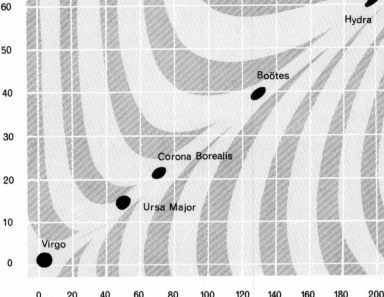

The shift towards the red in the spectra from distant galaxies reveals that they are rushing away at enormous speeds, which increase rapidly as the distance increases. Hubble showed that the relation between the distance of the galaxy and its velocity is the simple straight line above, where velocities (vertical) are in thousands of kilometres per second and distances in units of ten million light years. (4)

velocity of a star with respect to the solar system, the study of the motion of the components in a binary star and the investigation of the expansion and contraction of the gaseous stellar atmospheres in novae. It is in the study of the light from the nebulae, however, that the spectrographic investigations of the shift in wavelength of spectral lines have had the greatest repercussions.

In 1912 V. M. Slipher of the Lowell Observatory in the United States found that the spectral lines of the nebulae were shifted towards the red. In the succeeding ten years he determined the shifts of the lines in over 40 of these nebulae. If this red shift was to be explained as due to the motion of the source, the Doppler effect, the nebulae must be receding at speeds, in some cases, of about 1000 miles a second, an order of magnitude greater than the radial velocities measured in the case of the stars. The significance of Slipher's measurements was not realized until Hubble obtained conclusive evidence in 1926 that these nebulae were extragalactic; that they were great star systems external to the Milky Way. Three years later Hubble was able to show that a simple linear relationship existed between the distance of a nebula and its red shift: the greater the distance of a nebula, the greater the velocity with which it is receding. Today, although there have been modifications in the value of the Hubble constant relating the velocity of recession with the distance, no exception has been found to the linearity of the relationships out to the greatest distances of penetration of the large optical telescopes. As we shall see the consequences of these measurements to our understanding of the nature of the universe have been profound.

How far are the stars?

The linear relationship which Hubble established between the red shift of a nebula and its distance is now a standard relationship which is used to estimate the distance of the extragalactic nebulae. However, Hubble's establishment of the relation implies that other methods were used to determine the distance of the nearer nebulae on which the relationship is based. This work was based on an observation made by Miss Leavitt of Harvard in 1912. The light of certain stars in the Galaxy is variable and many categories of variable stars are recognized today. One prominent class, known as the Cepheid variables, has a special characteristic, first delineated by Miss Leavitt. It is that the light of the brighter Cepheids fluctuates more slowly than that of the fainter ones. The fundamental cause of this relationship is not yet clearly understood, although it seems that the brightness variation is associated with the expansion and contraction of the stellar envelope. Although the fundamental process giving rise to the variability is not clear, the establishment of the empirical relationship between the period and brightness enabled the Cepheid variables to be used as distance indicators. Given one Cepheid whose distance is known, one can measure the distance of any other Cepheid that fluctuates at the same rate, simply by comparing its apparent brightness with that of the 'yardstick'. If it looks brighter it is nearer, if fainter, farther away, in proportion to the two apparent brightnesses. In fact, although there have been subsequent modifications in the relationship originally established by Miss Leavitt, this development led to two great revolutions in our knowledge of the universe. First, Shapley, by studying the Cepheids in the globular clusters, revised the entire scale of the Milky Way, and showed that the sun was far removed from the

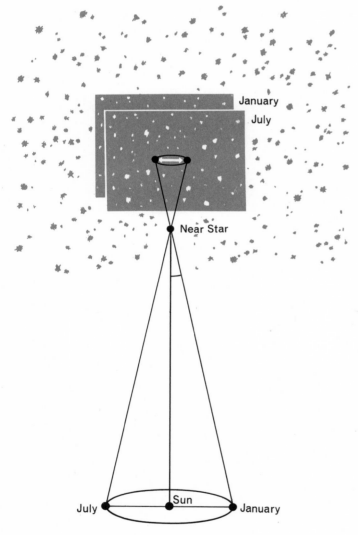

Viewed from the earth as it swings in its orbit round the sun, a near star seems to move to and fro against the fixed background of stars much further away. Photographs taken at six-monthly intervals show this shift at its maximum. The displacement, microscopically measured, can be translated into terms of the angle made by the two directions at the near star. Half this tiny angle (called the 'parallax') and the 93-million-mile radius of the earth's orbit, can be used to calculate the star's distance. (5)

centre of the system, and secondly Hubble was able to establish the red shift–distance relationship for extragalactic nebulae.

The establishment of the absolute scale of distance on which the period-luminosity relationship of the Cepheids is based must depend of course on a fundamental measurement of the distance of some samples in this class of star. Man had little idea of the actual distances involved in the stellar system until 1838 when Bessel measured the parallax of a star in Cygnus. The method used by Bessel and subsequently extended to many other stars is the familiar trigonometric method used by terrestrial surveyors, but using as a baseline the diameter of the earth's orbit around the sun. Attention was concentrated on the stars with large proper motions, since those were likely to be the nearest. The star in question is photographed, say in January and July when the earth is at opposite points in its orbit around the sun. The displacement of the star on the photographic plate, as determined against the fixed background of the remote stars, then enables the distance to be calculated.

The baseline used in this technique is 186 million miles—twice the distance of the earth from the sun. Even with this vast baseline it is possible only to measure the parallax of a few stars. In astronomical work the parallax is defined as the angle subtended by half this baseline, that is by the radius of the earth's orbit around the sun. Of course, the parallaxes involved in these measurements are exceedingly small. No known star has a parallax greater than 1 second of arc (equivalent to a distance of 206,265 times the radius of the earth's orbit). Stellar distances are expressed in parsecs; one parsec being the distance at which the parallax is 1 second of arc (19 million million miles or 3.26 light years). The parallax of the nearest star, Proxima Centauri, is 0.76"—corresponding to a distance of 1.31 parsecs or 4.3 light years.

This direct trigonometrical method of distance determination is difficult even in the case of the nearer stars and with present instruments it cannot be applied at all for distances greater than about 100 parsecs (326 light years). Fortunately the stars included within this limit provide the distances of a sufficiently representative collection of stars for it to be ascertained that the absolute magnitudes of the stars (that is their intrinsic luminosities) are related to certain fundamental features in their spectra. Hence once a star has been classified by its spectral lines, its intrinsic luminosity can be inferred and hence its distance estimated from its apparent brightness in the sky.

A hundred thousand million stars: the Milky Way

The application of modern instruments pursuing these different types of measurement has vastly increased our knowledge of the local Galaxy or Milky Way system of stars. Historically the work of Shapley and Hubble with the 100-inch Mount Wilson telescope between 1920 and 1930 revolutionized our concept of the universe. Within this short period Hubble provided the convincing evidence for the extragalactic nature of the nebulae, and Shapley's work fundamentally changed our understanding of the size and arrangement of the stars in our own Galaxy. The contemporary consequences of Hubble's work will be discussed later. This section will be concerned only with the local Galaxy of stars.

It has already been mentioned that on a perfectly clear night the naked eye can distinguish about 6,500 stars. This

fig 5

p 102

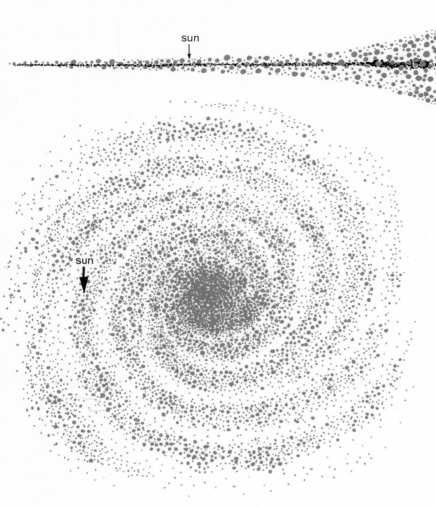

The shape of the Milky Way is now known to be a flattened disk 100,000 light years across, swelling to a hub (exaggerated in this drawing), some 4,000 light years thick. In the sun's neighbourhood, 30,000 light years from the centre, it is less than half that thickness. Seen from above, the Galaxy would appear as an open spiral with trailing arms, rather like the Andromeda nebula. (6)

number is negligible compared with the fainter stars which are revealed even in quite small telescopes. The rapid increase in numbers of the faint stars is to be expected, since the volume of space explored increases as the cube of the distance of penetration, and if the stars were of the same intrinsic brightness and uniformly distributed then their numbers would increase similarly. In fact, for extremely faint and distant stars the progression is found to be even more rapid. At the sixth magnitude (which is near the naked eye's limit) there are about 3000 stars visible, at the 10th magnitude 165,000, at the 18th magnitude 142,000,000. and at the 20th magnitude 506,000,000. By photographic techniques stars of the 21st magnitude can be recorded with the large optical telescopes. At that limit there are about one thousand million stars.

By extrapolating the trend in the change in numbers with magnitude Seares estimated that if we could see all the stars in the Galaxy the faintest magnitude would be 60 and that the total number of stars in the Galaxy was about 30,000 million. However, this is an extrapolation from a small percentage of the total and no allowance has been made for the effects of absorption of starlight by the interstellar gas and dust. Our current estimate of the number of stars in the Galaxy is based on dynamical considerations of the rotation of the Galaxy. From detailed interpretations of the proper motions and star streaming it is estimated that in the solar neighbourhood the period of rotation of the Galaxy is 200 million years. Within the sun's orbit in the Galaxy the total mass of the stars and gas is 1.6×10^{11} solar masses. When the additional material outside the sun's orbit is added the

mass of the entire Galaxy is estimated to be about 2×10^{11} suns distributed about equally between stars and the interstellar material. Hence, on this basis the Galaxy must contain about 10^{11} (one hundred thousand million) stars—more than three times the number arrived at by Seares from an extrapolation of the star counts.

A cursory glance at the sky indicates that the stars are not uniformly distributed in space and from the 18th century onwards several astronomers considered that the system of stars was like a flattened disk. However, even William Herschel, who made the most detailed telescopic investigations of the problem, believed that the sun was at the centre of the system. The true extent of the Milky Way was not recognized until Shapley studied the distribution of the globular clusters from measurements of their distances, using the Cepheid variables as indicators. These clusters are enormous aggregations of stars containing perhaps a million members. About 100 are known and most of them had already been recognized by Herschel in the 18th century. A close study of the distribution of these clusters on the star sphere indicates that they must be distributed in a manner closely connected with the structure of the Galaxy. Shapley concluded from his studies of these clusters that the flattened disk of the Galaxy extended for 250,000 light years and that the solar system was not in a central position, but 50,000 light years from the centre of the Galaxy which was in the direction of Sagittarius.

Shapley's dimensions had to be modified in the light of more detailed knowledge of the Cepheid variables and today we believe that the total extension of the Galactic disk is about 30 kiloparsecs (100,000 light years) with the sun 10 kiloparsecs (30,000 light years) from the centre. The thickness of the Galactic disk in the solar neighbourhood is one or two thousand light years, and in the central regions about 4000 light years. Within this rotating disk the stars are concentrated in spirals emerging from the central nucleus in a manner now so familiar from the photographs of many of the extragalactic spiral nebulae.

Hot and cool, giant and dwarf

The wide variation in the brightness of the stars seen in the sky is only partly due to their varying distances from us. The stars differ widely in their size and intrinsic luminosity. As far as brightness is concerned it is standard practice to convert the apparent luminosity of a star to the luminosity which it would have if it was situated at a distance of 10 parsecs (about 33 light years). Our own sun, which is so brilliant that its apparent magnitude is −27, would appear as a faint star at this standard distance. Its *absolute magnitude* would be + 5. In fact the sun occupies an intermediate position within the range of absolute magnitudes. Some stars (the supergiants) have absolute magnitudes of −5, and they radiate ten thousand times more energy than the sun. At the other extreme the red dwarfs with absolute magnitudes of + 15 radiate only a ten-thousandth of the energy of the sun.

The dimensions of the stars similarly cover an enormous

p 118
(13)

fig 6

fig 7

range, from the supergiants which may be 2000 times the diameter of the sun to the white dwarfs, some of which are probably only a few thousandths of the sun's diameter. Another obvious variation in stellar characteristics is the differing colour of the various stars. For example, some of the bright stars like Sirius are white while Aldebaran and Antares are red. These colour appearances are closely related to the measured temperatures of the stars. The surface temperatures of the red stars are 2000 to 3000°C, of the yellow stars like the sun 5000–8000°, of the white stars 8000–12,000°, and of the bluish stars 12,000–20,000° or more.

The introduction of spectroscopic methods in observational astronomy enabled progress to be made with the classification of the stars, since the identification of the line spectrum in the light from a star provides an index of the elements present in the stellar atmosphere and of the temperature. The system universally adopted was developed at the beginning of this century on the basis of the study of nearly a quarter of a million stellar spectra undertaken at Harvard and published as the Henry Draper Catalogue. The spectra are divided into 10 main classes designated O, B, A, F, G, K, M, R, N, S, in order of decreasing temperature, each class being subdivided so that throughout the series there is a smooth progression from the hottest type O stars to the cool stars. The sun is a G-type star with spectra characterized by prominent lines of ionized calcium and many metallic lines, particularly iron.

Compared with these enormous variations in luminosity, size and spectral characteristics the masses of the stars are restricted to about a factor of ten more or less than the solar mass. This implies that the densities of the stellar material must exhibit extremely wide variations. Indeed the variations are striking. Antares, nearly 500 times larger than the sun, has a density only a ten-thousandth of that of air (the density of the sun is about 1.4 times that of water). At the

p 116

p 117

other extreme, in the companion of Sirius, which has a diameter only about twice that of the earth, the density of the material must be 150,000 times greater than the density of water.

The life and death of a star

p 117

In the early years of this century much attention was given to the possible interdependence of these various stellar characteristics, and these investigations resulted in the famous Hertzsprung-Russell diagram. In this diagram the stars are plotted with absolute magnitude (that is intrinsic luminosity) as ordinate and spectroscopic type (that is equivalent to temperatures) as abscissa. On this diagram a star which is near the top will be intrinsically brilliant while one at the bottom will be faint. Stars at the left will be hot and those to the right cool. (The sun, type G, with absolute magnitude +5 and temperature 6000° is nearly at the centre of the diagram.)

When the positions of the stars are plotted in this way it is found that there is a striking concentration from the top left of the diagram running obliquely across to the bottom right. This line, along which both luminosity and temperature decrease steadily, is known as the Main Sequence. The supergiants, red giants and white dwarfs appear as subbranches of this main sequence.

It is not possible here to consider the detailed variations in the properties of various stellar types in relation to their position on the H-R diagram, but mention must be made of the significance of the diagram to the probable evolutionary sequence of stars. In its initial stages a star is a condensation of interstellar gas and dust, relatively cold and low in density. The condensation contracts under the influence of its self-gravitation, assisted by the pressure of radiation from outside. As the condensation continues the star becomes hotter and denser and moves along an evolutionary track on the H-R diagram from right to left towards the main sequence. This stage of evolution for a solar-type star may take about 50 million years. When the star reaches the main sequence stage the temperatures and pressure in its interior have risen to such an extent that the main energy-producing reactions are initiated, involving the conversion of hydrogen into helium through the carbon-nitrogen cycle. In the case of a solar-type star, this energy production continues for, perhaps, 10,000 million years, during which time the star remains in a nearly stable position on the main sequence branch of the H-R diagram.

After this order of time the hydrogen fuel begins to be exhausted, the star leaves the main sequence and moves with increasing rapidity along an evolutionary track to the right, to the condition of a red giant. In this condition the star is rich in helium and under normal circumstances energy production might be expected to cease. However, helium is more opaque to radiation than the hydrogen from which it is formed and hence more and more of the energy produced in the final phases of the hydrogen exhaustion will be retained in the interior of the star instead of being radiated into space. Thus the central temperatures will reach exceedingly high values, ultimately attaining values at which nuclear energy processes involving helium occur. The star will then move to the left, cross the main sequence, and, with the increasingly rapid exhaustion of its fuels, will collapse to the stage of a white dwarf.

The time scale for the movement away from the main sequence to the red giant stage probably takes only ten

The familiar constellation of Orion, with its stars ranging in apparent magnitude from about 1 down to 5 or more (left) would look very different if each star could be seen from the same standard distance (right). The faint stars in the sword would blaze out, dominating the constellation, with an increase of brightness greater than a drawing could show. (7)

million years or so in the case of solar-type stars and the final stage of collapse and contraction to the white dwarf probably occupies a similar time. From these estimates it is evident that a star spends most of its life in a nearly stable condition on the main sequence. Thus, these contemporary beliefs about the evolutionary processes fit in well with the fact that the majority of stars live on the main sequence in the H-R diagram. The enormous quantities of material involved may be realized from the fact that in a star like the sun on the main sequence 564 million tons of hydrogen are being transmuted into 560 million tons of helium every second. The sun, which has already been on the main sequence for at least 5000 million years, will probably continue to exist as a main sequence star for another 5000 million years.

Young stars and old stars

One important question which remains to be considered is whether the various types of star which form the H-R diagram are distributed randomly throughout the Galaxy. Indications that they were not evenly distributed were found by Shapley in his work on the globular clusters. He found that red giants predominated in the clusters and that their population seemed quite different from that of the stars in the solar neighbourhood (on which the H-R diagram is based). The significance of Shapley's observations was not appreciated until Baade's work on the nuclei of galaxies in the years 1940–1950. He found that the stars in the nucleus of the Andromeda nebula M.31, in the elliptical galaxies and in the nucleus of our own Galaxy were similar to those in the globular clusters—that is predominantly red giants. Baade called these the Population II stars. They are the old stars existing in regions where star formation has largely ceased. The Population I stars are a rather recent phenomenon, appearing in regions like the spiral arms of galaxies where stars are still being born from the gas and dust.

The Population II stars must be the result of a stellar population born 4000 million years ago under circumstances such that all the primeval gas was converted in a rather short period into stars. In some galaxies, particularly in the elliptical galaxies, all the gas was consumed in these processes. In others, such as M.31 and the Milky Way, only the gas of the central regions was consumed, and star formation continued to take place in the spiral arms and other regions which retained sufficient of the original primeval gas.

The situation is strikingly illustrated by some recent estimates made by J. H. Oort. Within 30 light years of the centre of our Galaxy the density of material is 24,000 times greater than the density near the sun—but this is entirely due to the great concentration of stars in the nuclear regions. In the neighbourhood of the sun, 30,000 light years from the centre, the interstellar gas contributes one-fifth of the total mass. Even within 1500 light years of the centre the hydrogen gas contributes only one four-hundredth of the total mass. We do not know why, but the gas was either consumed by star formation or swept away from the nuclear regions in the early evolution of the galaxies.

A hundred thousand million galaxies

As soon as astronomers were able to study the stars with telescopes of reasonable size a large number of diffuse, hazy objects, termed nebulae, were discovered. Herschel be-

p 120
(23)

p 113

p 121

p 119
(20)

p 121

lieved that they were external to the Milky Way and Lord Rosse with his 72-inch telescope sketched the face-on spiral nebula M.51 in Canes Venatici and thought that he had succeeded in resolving this and many other of these nebulae into stars. The subject remained in a state of confusion particularly when spectrographic investigations in the late 19th century showed that at least some of these nebulae were composed of rarefied gas with a spectrum of isolated bright lines, whereas others (like the nebula in Andromeda) had a continuous spectrum indicative of a stellar content. The problem was settled decisively by Hubble's work with the 100-inch Mount Wilson telescope in 1925. His photographs of the Andromeda nebula clearly showed a resolution into stars, amongst which he identified Cepheid variables, giving a distance for the nebula far beyond the limits of the Milky Way. Soon it was realized that the objects hitherto classified as nebulae were of two different types: the gaseous nebulae, like the one in Orion, which are clouds of diffuse gas within the Milky Way system of stars, and the extragalactic nebulae, which like M.31 in Andromeda are separate star systems at great distances from the Milky Way.

Only three extragalactic objects are visible to the naked eye—the two Magellanic clouds from the southern hemisphere and the great spiral nebula in Andromeda. However, many more become visible even in small telescopes. In 1784 Charles Messier published a catalogue of 103 nebulae of which we now know that 50 are extragalactic. The numbering in his systematic list is still used today—for example the Andromeda nebula is Messier 31 (M.31). In 1890 Dreyer collated the lists of the Herschels and others in the *New General Catalogue* (N.G.C.). Supplements to the N.G.C. lists were published in the *Index Catalogues* (I.C.) of 1895 and 1910. Already more than 12,000 extragalactic objects appeared in these Catalogues and their numbering in these various Catalogues is now universally employed (The Andromeda nebula is M.31 or N.G.C. 224, for example.)

When photographic techniques were used with the large telescopes so many extragalactic objects became accessible that detailed cataloguing was impossible. For example in 1932 Harvard Observatory compiled a list of half a million extragalactic nebulae to magnitude 18 within 100 million light years of the Milky Way. These comments give an idea of the vast numbers of extragalactic nebulae within reach of the modern instruments—and, furthermore, their numbers increase proportionally as the telescopic power enables fainter and fainter nebulae to be recorded. The 100-inch telescope on Mount Wilson has photographed a million galaxies brighter than 18th magnitude, and it is instructive to estimate how many galaxies might lie within the scope of the 200-inch Palomar telescope. With photoelectric devices the faintest apparent magnitude which can be recorded is + 24. The absolute magnitude of the Milky Way is −20, and if we take this as a typical galaxy it could be recorded as of apparent magnitude + 24 if it was at a distance of 19,000 million light years. In fact, taking account of the expansion of the universe, this figure would have to be reduced considerably but remains several thousand million light years—a distance of penetration which, as we shall see, has certainly been achieved. The average number of galaxies in the region of space more easily accessible to the telescope is 3 per cubic megaparsec (3 per cube of side about 3.3 million light years). A simple extrapolation then indicates that there must be a hundred thousand million galaxies within the scope of the world's largest optical telescope.

One question which arises immediately is whether such an extrapolation is justified—that is whether the average number of galaxies per cubic megaparsec remains the same as we penetrate further and further into space. As we shall see the question is fundamental to the problem of the origin and evolution of the galaxies. The interpretation of data relating to such great distances in the universe is manifestly difficult but, at least as far as the optical telescopes are concerned, there is no real evidence for any significant change in this average number out to the distances of the order of several thousand million light years which have so far been investigated.

This uniformity in the average distribution of galaxies throughout observable space is essentially a large-scale effect, since the distribution of the individual galaxies is far from uniform. There is a marked tendency for the galaxies to exist in groups or clusters. For example the Milky Way system and the Andromeda nebula M.31 are the major galaxies in the local group of about twenty. This local group occupies an ellipsoidal volume of space, with a major axis of about two million light years, a minor axis of a million light years and a thickness of about 500,000 light years. The Milky Way and M.31 are separated by two million light years near the extremes of the major axis.

This local group is a minor affair compared with some of the clusters which are visible in the large telescopes. The Coma cluster, 220 million light years distant, probably contains 10,000 galaxies. In parts of this cluster, in an area of sky equivalent to that occupied by the full moon, many hundreds of galaxies are concentrated.

The shape of the galaxies

p 118. 119

The classification of the galaxies was attempted by Hubble, who recognized three basic categories, the S-type spiral galaxies, the E-type elliptical galaxies, and the irregular galaxies (I). The spirals account for 80% of the galaxies so far catalogued and within this broad classification there are several recognizable forms. First the normal spirals, which comprise 50% of the total, are divided into classes Sa, Sb, Sc according to the size of the nucleus and the development of the spiral arms. The Sa spirals have large nuclei and un- developed arms. The Sb spirals (like M.31) have smaller nuclei and well-developed arms, and the Sc spirals (e.g. N.G.C. 5364) have nuclei which are insignificant compared with the well-developed arms. The other 30% of spirals are

p 119 (14, 16)

p 119 (17, 19)

known as barred spirals (SB). In these the spiral arms appear to originate from the extremities of a 'bar' of matter coming out from the nucleus. The sub-divisions SBa, SBb, SBc indicate the relative prominence of the bar and spirals. It has already been mentioned that the nuclei of the spiral galaxies are largely devoid of gas and dust and are made up of Population II stars, whilst the Population I stars and the dust and gas are concentrated in the arms of the spiral galaxies.

p 118 (9, 10)

The elliptical nebulae consist predominantly of Popula- tion II stars with a low content of gas and dust. The sub- classification is from E0 to E7, indicative of the degree of flattening; E0 being circular and E7 lenticular. About 17% of the catalogued nebulae are E-type. The remaining 3% of catalogued nebulae are of abnormal structure which do not fit into any of the S or E classifications. Some of these, like the Magellanic Clouds, have no nucleus or obvious sym- metry, others are structureless or defy classification.

p 119 (20, 21)

Hubble arranged the S and E galaxies in a continuous sequence E0 to E7, then dividing into two branches, Sa to Sc and SBa to SBc. The possibility that this sequence represented the evolutionary trend of galaxies has often been discussed, but the contemporary ideas about the age of the various stellar types makes this seem unlikely—for example the E-type galaxies consist predominantly of Population II stars and are probably the oldest. At present it is not pos- sible to speak with any degree of certainty on these points; in particular the evolutionary age of a galaxy may be differ- ent from its age in the chronological sense.

26,000,000,000,000,000,000,000 miles

The measurement of the distances of the nearer stars and the use of the period–luminosity relationship of the Cepheid variables has been described earlier. The identification of Cepheid variables in some of the nebulae enabled Hubble to establish their distances and prove that they were extra- galactic objects. However, this criterion of distance meas- urement can be applied only to relatively few galaxies, since even modern optical telescopes cannot identify the Cepheids in galaxies which are more than about 5 million light years distant.

The next criterion applied by Hubble was that of the brightest stars in each galaxy. In the galaxies whose distances

light years	326	5 mill	25 mill	1000 mill	4500 mill

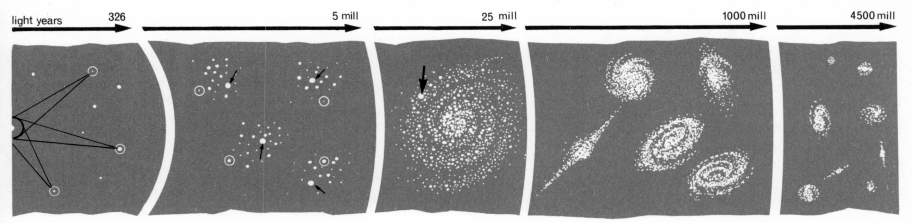

Distance can be measured by par-allax only as far as 326 light years: beyond that, accuracy becomes im-possible. But Cepheid variables within that range, pulsing brighter and fainter at regular intervals, give a measure for the next step.

Cepheid variables can be iden-tified out to 5 million light years. From the period of pulsation, in-trinsic brightness can be calculated. Comparison with apparent bright-ness gives the distance of a few galaxies, and their brightest stars.

Assuming the brightest stars in each galaxy to be supergiants of absolute magnitude −6, as in our Galaxy, and comparing their ap-parent magnitudes, we can esti-mate how far they are. This gives the next yardstick – the galaxies.

Spiral galaxies of type Sc have an average magnitude of −14. As long as they can be identified, their distance can be gauged by their apparent brightness. There may be 20% error but this is acceptable at such distances.

On measurements like these, Hubble based his velocity–distance law, by which distance can be calculated from the 'red shift' of a galaxy's spectrum. (This diagram, done to scale, would have to be 300 miles long.) (8)

are known from the Cepheid observations it is possible to
determine the absolute magnitude of the brightest stars in
the galaxy. It is found that in all these galaxies the half-dozen
or so brightest stars (the supergiants—spectral class O), have
the same absolute photographic magnitude (−6) as in the
Milky Way, our local Galaxy. Thus by making the reasonable assumption that in galaxies of similar type the brightest
stars have this intrinsic luminosity it is possible to derive
the distance of the galaxy from a measurement of the apparent magnitude of these stars. With the large telescopes
the supergiants can be identified in galaxies out to about 25
million light years and this brings into the scope of the
distance measurements over a thousand galaxies of a wide
variety of types.

fig 8

The inclusion of so many galaxies facilitates an even
further step in the distance measurements because it is
possible to use the intrinsic or absolute magnitudes of the
galaxies themselves to extend the distance scale. For
example, in the case of the galaxies for which the brightest
star criterion has been used to measure their distance it is
found that the absolute magnitudes of the Sc spirals range
from about −16 to −11.5, a mean of −14. Thus by
assuming that the intrinsic luminosity of Sc spirals is the
same everywhere in the universe the distance of any Sc
nebula can be estimated provided its apparent magnitude
can be measured. The uncertainty in the estimate of great
distances by this method may be 20%, but this is a small
margin of error as far as the major problems of cosmology are
concerned.

It is by these successive methods that Hubble established
the linearity of the relationship between the velocity of
recession of the nebula and its distance. The extension of
this relationship to greater distances must, of necessity, involve the determination of the intrinsic luminosity of the
galaxy involved as well as its red shift. Out to the distances
of a few thousand million light years to which the linearity
of the relationship is firmly established, the measurement of
the red shift may often be used as a convenient distance
indicator.

fig 4

During the last few years the greatest distance of penetration of the telescopes has steadily increased under the
stimulus of the need to identify the strong radio sources
which are discussed later. In 1960 a new limit was established when the distance of a cluster of galaxies in Boötes
was found to be 4,500 million light years with a recessional
velocity of 86,000 miles per second, that is 46% of the
velocity of light. We shall see that it is possible that many
radio sources, not yet firmly identified optically, may be at
even greater distances, and further extensions to this present
observable scale of the universe may be anticipated in the
immediate future.

p 122
(32)

Listening to the universe:
the radio telescope

The transparency in the earth's atmosphere which allows us
to see with our eyes and telescopes into outer space extends
over a wavelength range from about 40 millionths of a
centimetre at the violet end to 72 millionths of a centimetre at the extreme red end of the spectrum. With the
development of radio techniques after the first world war it
was recognized that another transparency in the earth's
atmosphere occurred at much longer wavelengths in the
radio wave region. This window extends from a wavelength
of a few millimetres to wavelenghts of about 30 metres. The

p 114-5

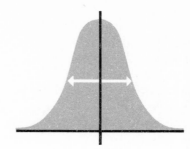

*As the parabolic reflecting dish of a radio
telescope sweeps across the source in
space, the strength of the 'noise' received
increases to a maximum and then decreases. The sharper the curve, the better
the telescope can pin-point the source.
The 'half-width' of this curve is known
as the telescope's beam width.*

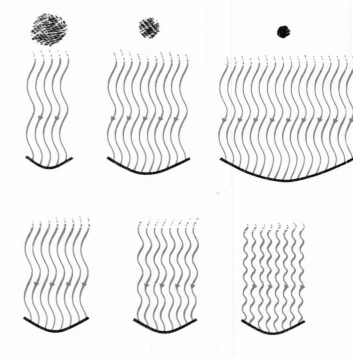

*As with the optical telescope, the larger the reflector the greater its gathering
power – the sharper the beam width curve (above) and the more distinct the
'image'. The curve is also sharper, and the resolving power of the telescope
greater, the shorter the length of the incoming radio waves. (9)*

short-wave cut-off is caused by water-vapour absorption in
the atmosphere and the long-wave cut-off by absorption and
reflection at the ionized regions which exist 100 to 400
kilometres above the surface of the earth.

Although the width of this transparency in the radio wave
part of the spectrum is so much greater than that in the
optical region it was not expected to be of any significance
to astronomy. According to the classical laws of physics hot
bodies like the sun and stars pour out most of their energy
in the visible or near-visible parts of the spectrum, and there
was no reason to anticipate that radio waves would provide
any medium for studying the universe. The basic discovery
of the existence of radio waves from extraterrestrial space
was made in December 1931 by Karl Jansky who was investigating problems in atmospherics on a wavelength of
14.6 metres at the Bell Telephone Laboratories. Jansky found
that the radio noise level varied diurnally with a period of
23 hours 56 minutes. This is the period of the earth's
rotation with respect to the stars and provided an unambiguous indication that the source of the radio noise must be
radio waves emanating from regions of space outside the
confines of the solar system.

Astronomers failed to recognize the enormous significance
of this discovery. In fact little more work was done on the
topic for 10 years until Grote Reber, an amateur investiga-
tor, built privately a device which we should now regard as
a typical radio telescope, with which he confirmed and
extended Jansky's work. Subsequently with the ending of
the second world war the investigations of these radio waves
from space were stimulated by the availability of apparatus

and new techniques developed during the war. Striking discoveries were soon made and the advances during the last 15 years can already be seen as constituting a revolution in astronomy paralleled only by the invention of the optical telescope three and a half centuries earlier.

The most elementary form of a radio telescope is the simple rod dipole aerial (similar to a television aerial), often accompanied by reflectors. The dipole receives with almost equal strength from all directions; the addition of the reflectors (as in fringe-area television aerials) narrows down the beam of reception—the resolution and gain of the aerial has been thereby increased. Such an aerial can readily be changed to receive on various wavelengths by altering the length of the dipole and reflectors. However, for scientific use in radio astronomy its value is limited because the beam can only be narrowed sufficiently for detailed investigations by making an array of such dipoles, which becomes unwieldy.

Probably the most frequently used form of radio telescope is the parabolic reflector, with a single dipole at the focus. For a given wavelength the width of the beam of reception decreases linearly as the diameter of the reflector is increased. This paraboloidal type of radio telescope can be used over a wide range of wavelengths by simply altering the dipole at the focus. For a given diameter of reflector the beam width decreases linearly as the wavelength is decreased. The paraboloid can be mounted and steered to any part of the sky with relative ease, nevertheless rather large instruments are necessary to achieve a significant degree of resolution over the range of wavelengths used in the radio astronomical investigations. For example the largest completely steerable paraboloid in the world is the 250-foot reflector at Jodrell Bank, but on a wavelength of 1 metre the beam width of reception is 2 degrees—more than the angle subtended by the major axis of the M.31 nebula. The degree of resolution attainable by small optical telescopes is therefore unapproachable even by the largest and most expensive radio telescope of this type.

p 124-5

fig 7

An 'aerial' 80 miles long

The progress in optical astronomy over the past few centuries has been possible because telescopes of ever-increasing size have been constructed. As the diameter of the mirror is increased more light is collected, thereby enabling fainter objects to be seen, and also the resolving power of the instrument is improved, thereby producing better definition in the photographs of the stars and nebulae. The analogy to these twin requirements in radio astronomy was soon realized to be vital to the progress of the subject. As far as collecting power is required the only method for a given wavelength is to increase the size of the aerial. However, in many applications, increase in resolving power is a greater necessity than increase in gain or collecting power, and ingenious methods have been developed which simulate exceedingly large telescopes as far as resolution is concerned, in which increase in gain is not a prime requirement.

The simplest illustration is the interferometer, which consists of two aerials spaced a considerable distance apart and connected to a common receiving system. The reception pattern of this device is a series of lobes or fringes, the angular width of which decreases as the distance separating the aerials is increased. For example, on a wavelength of 1 metre, if the separation between the aerials is 3.5 kms. then the lobe width is only 1 minute of arc. Difficulties arise

fig 10

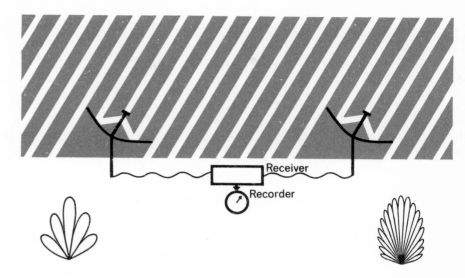

p 71

To pin-point the radio source more sharply, two reflectors are used, some miles apart. The two sets of impulses, recorded together, interfere, as we have seen two streams of light-waves will interfere. The intensity curve becomes a series of lobes, the sharp central lobe defining the position of the source. If the distance between the reflectors is increased, the lobes are narrower still. (10)

because of the multiple nature of the lobes and the technical problem of combining the signals from two widely separated aerials. Many sophisticated versions of this simple interferometer have been developed and the technique has been widely used for the precise measurement of the position of radio sources and for the measurement of their angular diameters. In some experiments at Jodrell Bank the 250-foot reflector has been used as one leg of an interferometer, the other being a smaller aerial 80 miles distant. The signals from the remote station were conveyed over a radio link and in this experiment resolving powers of one-tenth of a second of arc have been realized. Thus, in principle and for a specific purpose, the resolution of an 80-mile-diameter aerial was obtained.

In Cambridge, Martin Ryle has evolved a system known as aperture synthesis, using two or more aerials which are moved over periods of days to cover a large area of ground. The results from each position are combined in a computing machine and it is thereby possible to realize both resolving power and gain approaching that of an aerial covering the entire area of ground covered in the survey.

The arguments in favour of these various systems are highly technical but, in general, there are so many types of observation required in radio astronomy that the more complicated types of interferometer and multiple arrays are not competitive with the large steerable paraboloids but are used in complementary programmes for the study of the radio emissions from space.

The radio sources in space

p 126 (39)

It is a comparatively simple matter with a steerable radio telescope to plot the strength of the radio emission from different parts of the sky. The 'isophotes' so obtained show a striking similarity to the distribution of the common stars. That is, the radio waves are most intense from the direction of the plane of the Milky Way and reach their greatest intensity in the direction of the Galactic centre. Reber was the first person to carry out this experiment with any reasonable definition and the similarity in the distribution of the radio wave intensity and the common stars led him to believe initially that the stars themselves were responsible for the radio wave emission. But he failed to find any radio

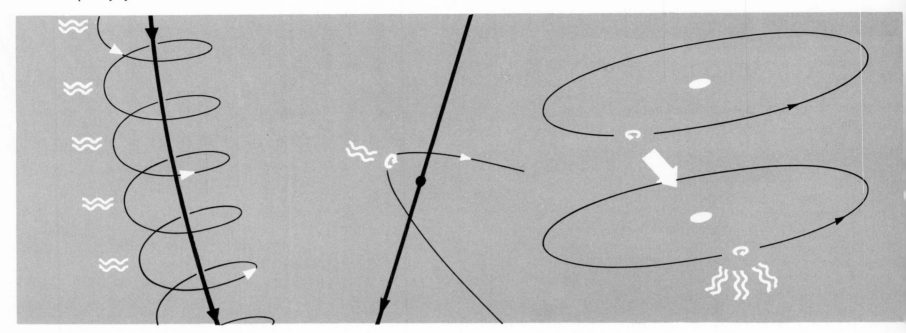

Three sources of radio 'noise'. (Left), an electron, travelling at nearly the speed of light, spirals in the magnetic field of the Galaxy. As it accelerates in the magnetic field long-wave radio waves are emitted. (Centre), an electron from ionized hydrogen is accelerated as it is almost but not quite captured by a proton. It emits radiation in a shorter wave-band, the centimetre region.

The single electron in a neutral hydrogen atom (right) suddenly reverses its spin; the change in energy is such that radiation is emitted at the precise wavelength of 21 cms. – a 'spectral line'. In any one atom this happens only once, on the average, in 11 million years, yet so vast is the number of atoms in the gas clouds that the emission can be measured by radio telescopes. (11)

emission from the individual bright stars or other prominent visible objects and his final conclusion was that the interstellar hydrogen gas was the source of the radio waves.

Now we know that the situation is far more complicated and our present beliefs may be summarized as follows.

1 The generally distributed radio emission from the Milky Way which can be received over a wide range of wavelengths is composed principally of two components. One component arises from the ionized interstellar hydrogen gas (as suggested by Reber). This emission occurs when an electron is accelerated in the field of a proton without capture. The process is known as a free-free transition and the energy is emitted in the radio wave band. The other component is emitted by electrons which are moving at speeds approaching the velocity of light in the magnetic field of the Galaxy. This is known as the synchrotron process. The radio emission arising from the synchrotron mechanism predominates at long radio wavelengths—in the metre waveband—and that from the ionized hydrogen is prominent at the short wavelengths.

2 The combination of the two processes described in (1) gives rise to the smooth contours of radio emission. In addition there are several localized sources of radio emission arising from supernova remnants. The two most notable are the radio sources in Cassiopeia and Taurus. The Cassiopeia radio source is the strongest in the sky—although the gaseous remnants of the supernova are so faint that they can be photographed only by large optical telescopes. The Taurus radio source is the third strongest in the sky and is associated with the famous Crab nebula—the gaseous remains of the supernova explosion recorded by the Chinese astronomers in AD 1054. There are several other localized sources of this nature in the Milky Way, only a few of which can be related to known supernovae.

3 In addition to these localized radio sources associated with the gaseous supernova remnants there are also a number of sources observable at short wavelengths in the centimetric band. This radio emission comes from the emission nebulae—the clouds of ionized hydrogen gas surrounding some of the hot stars.

fig 11

p 120
(24)

4 The neutral hydrogen gas in the Milky Way also emits radio waves but, as distinct from the other cases mentioned in (1), (2) and (3), this emission occurs on a definite wavelength of 21 cms. The radio waves are emitted on this wavelength as a result of the change in energy of the hydrogen atoms when the spin of the electron reverses in the magnetic field of the proton. Until recently this was the only spectral line emission known in radio astronomy, and has turned out to be of tremendous importance because by measuring the Doppler shift of the line it has been possible to determine the speeds of motion of the hydrogen clouds with respect to the solar system. These investigations have given us a new insight into the detailed structure of the Milky Way.

Towards the end of 1963 the existence of a second spectral line at a wavelength of 18 cms., associated with the hydroxyl radical (OH), was confirmed by American observers.

5 As far as the stars themselves are concerned the sun is a powerful radio wave emitter, particularly when it is disturbed by sunspots and solar flares. It was realized that because of the vast distance of the other stars compared with the sun, even if they also emitted radio waves like the sun, then the contribution to the radio emission observed on earth would be small. In fact, only in 1963 was definite proof obtained that certain of the nearer red dwarf stars did indeed emit radio waves detectable on earth, when their atmospheres were disturbed by large flares. These measurements have verified that the contribution of the stars to the radio emission is small compared with the other processes enumerated above.

Strange and powerful 'radio stars'

A survey of the radio emission from the sky with a high-definition radio telescope reveals the existence of large numbers of distinct sources, variously called point sources, discrete sources, localized sources or radio stars. A few of these are concentrated in the Milky Way and are the remnants of supernovae, but the majority are distributed almost uniformly in every direction and originate from beyond the Milky Way.

About 50 of the nearer extragalactic spiral nebulae have been individually identified as contributing to this extragalactic radio source population and it is known that, in general, the radio intensity of these nebulae is about the same as might be anticipated from the Milky Way radio emission. A significant conclusion is that even with the most sensitive radio telescopes available today the radio emission from the more distant spiral nebulae could not be detected and hence some other objects must be responsible for the majority of these evenly distributed extragalactic radio sources.

The first indication of the possible solution to this problem came in 1951 when the second strongest radio source was identified with an extremely faint photographic object in Cygnus. The photographs in the 200-inch telescope showed two spiral nebulae apparently in a state of close interaction at a distance of 550 million light years. The surprising part of this discovery was the strange disparity between the output of energy in the optical and radio parts of the spectrum. Optically the galaxies were of sixteenth apparent photographic magnitude, whereas the object was intense in the radio wave part of the spectrum. The realization that a similar object at ten times the distance would be almost beyond the limit of the 200-inch telescope but would still be easily accessible to the radio telescopes led to the suggestion that the difficulty encountered in identifying the radio sources was simply because they were at great distances, beyond the range of the optical telescopes. p 126 (41)

Since the discovery of the Cygnus object, continuous efforts have been made to obtain further identifications, and at the present time between 50 and 100 radio sources have been related to peculiar and distant photographic objects. The most distant source identified is in Boötes at 4,500 million light years. Many of these are cases similar to the Cygnus galaxies—showing two members apparently in a state of close interaction. For some time it was widely believed that these pairs of galaxies were cases of collisions in which one galaxy was in process of passing through another. However it has not been possible to arrive at any satisfactory theoretical estimate whereby such a collision process could give rise to the relatively great output of energy in the radio part of the spectrum. At the moment the tendency is to believe that the pairs of galaxies represent the division of a single nucleus—a view consistently held by the Russian astronomer Ambartsumian since the initial discovery. p 126 (40)

In 1962 and 1963 the situation was still further complicated by the discovery that some of these radio sources seemed to be related to star-like objects and not to extragalactic nebulae. For some months it was thought that these objects might actually be stars of an unusual nature in the Milky Way, but in the spring of 1963 information obtained with the 200-inch telescope showed that they were, in fact, a hitherto unrecognized type of distant galaxy. The characteristic of these galaxies is that they possess a nucleus which is of unusual mass and brightness—perhaps equivalent to a hundred million suns concentrated in a volume of space smaller than that occupied by the solar system.

These investigations of the extragalactic radio sources have provided a fruitful new avenue of astronomical research involving the close collaboration of the world's largest optical and radio telescopes. Apart from the intrinsic interest of the investigations the work may be of crucial importance to cosmology because of the relative accessibility to the radio telescopes of regions of time and space which may be near the limit, or beyond the range of penetration, of the optical telescopes.

A majestic problem: explaining the universe

So many advances have been made in our observations of the stars and galaxies in recent years that we can now give a reasonable description of the content and arrangement of the universe at least to distances of several thousand million light years. It cannot be said, however, that it is possible to give a similar account of a sound and unambiguous theoretical basis for this observable universe. It seemed possible that Newton's universal law of gravitation must provide the quantitative basis on which a satisfactory theory of the universe could be constructed. However, if we consider the position as it existed in the early years of this century, then it appeared to be impossible to reconcile the observations with Newtonian theory. For example, to consider one obvious difficulty, the observations appeared to indicate that the material of the universe when considered on the large scale was in a static condition and homogeneously distributed throughout space. But on Newton's law of gravitation the entire mass of particles should gravitate into one great spherical mass if the universe was finite or into an infinite number of great masses if the universe was infinite. Many unsuccessful attempts were made to overcome the difficulty by varying the postulates about the condition of the universe on which the theory was based.

A decisive step forward appeared possible when in 1916–17 Einstein applied his theory of general relativity to this cosmical problem. His initial application of the relativistic laws of gravitation and mechanics in place of the Newtonian laws failed to evade many of the difficulties in the classical treatment and he was unable to find boundary conditions which permitted a satisfactory solution of the equations. In 1917 Einstein thought he had overcome the major obstacles by postulating that the universe was a spherical closed space instead of the infinite Euclidean space of the Newtonian theories. This curvature of space produced an unbounded though finite universe, and abolished the infinities where the difficulties with the boundary conditions arise. In order to produce this condition it was necessary to introduce a constant term (the cosmical constant), which, when positive, gave a solution where the density was uniform and the radius finite. Of course at that time it was believed that the universe was in a static condition in which all motions were small compared with the velocity of light.

Almost immediately de Sitter found other solutions of the equations which predicted a static universe only if it contained no matter and in which particles of negligible mass would recede from each other continuously. The subsequent work of Freidman, Eddington and Lemaitre showed clearly that the cosmology based on Einstein's general relativity predicted an unstable universe and that the original static solution of Einstein represented an unstable condition. Hubble's observations, and his interpretation of the red shift as indicative of the recession of the galaxies, therefore appeared to be a triumphant verification of this relativistic cosmology.

For the last 30 years the interplay of the continuous advance in the observations of the universe with the search for a solution of the relativity equations to give an appropriate model universe intermediate between the static Einstein model containing matter and the expanding de Sitter model without matter has been a fascinating exercise, but there is still no satisfactory theoretical basis from which it is possible to predict the past or future history of the universe.

The major observational factors which any theory must include are the apparent large-scale uniformity of matter to our present limits of penetration, and the recession of the nebulae with speeds which increase linearly with distance at least out to the present several thousand million light year limit of our observations. As regards the latter point, the interpretation of the red shift in terms of the high speeds of recession has often been queried. But there has been no satisfactory alternative suggestion within the framework of the known laws of physics which can explain the red shift phenomenon.

It is interesting to mention that Bondi in recent years has pointed out that a paradox established by Heinrich Olbers in the early 19th century must actually imply that the universe is expanding. It is a simple observational fact that, at night, the sky is dark. Olbers' argument was that if we exist in a uniform universe then the number of stars on a hemisphere must increase as the square of their distance from us. The light received on earth from these stars must decrease inversely as the square of the distance and hence the stars distributed over the hemisphere at any distance should send the same amount of light to earth. This should obviously add up to an infinite, or at least a very large, amount of light, and hence the sky at night should be nearly as bright as the sun makes it by day. Olbers' escape from the paradox was to postulate the existence of absorbing matter in the universe but Bondi's argument is that this matter by virtue of its absorption must get so hot that it will in turn make the sky bright at night. In fact, the real escape from the paradox is that the stars and galaxies are receding so rapidly from earth that the amount of light we receive from distant objects is materially diminished. Hence the amount of light from the objects at great distances in the universe converges to a rather small amount.

The arguments in favour of the reality of the expansion of the universe are therefore so convincing that it is now assumed that the phenomenon must appear as a natural consequence of any theory of the universe.

Continuous creation or primeval explosion?

Much of the argument in cosmology has revolved around the reality and meaning of the cosmological constant originally introduced by Einstein so that the equations could be solved to give a static finite universe. The possibility that the constant may be positive, negative or zero means that many theoretical models can be derived from the equations and only a few of these models have been fully explored.

fig 12

If the constant is zero the equations imply an origin from a superdense state. In terms of our present knowledge of the Hubble constant relating red shift to distance the interpretation on this basis is that the universe had an explosive origin from the primeval condensate about 10,000 million years ago. The expansion which we measure today is simply a consequence of the impetus of this initial explosion. If the cosmical constant is negative the model universe contracts from infinity with diminishing speed to a finite minimum and then expands with increasing speed. If the constants are

p 123

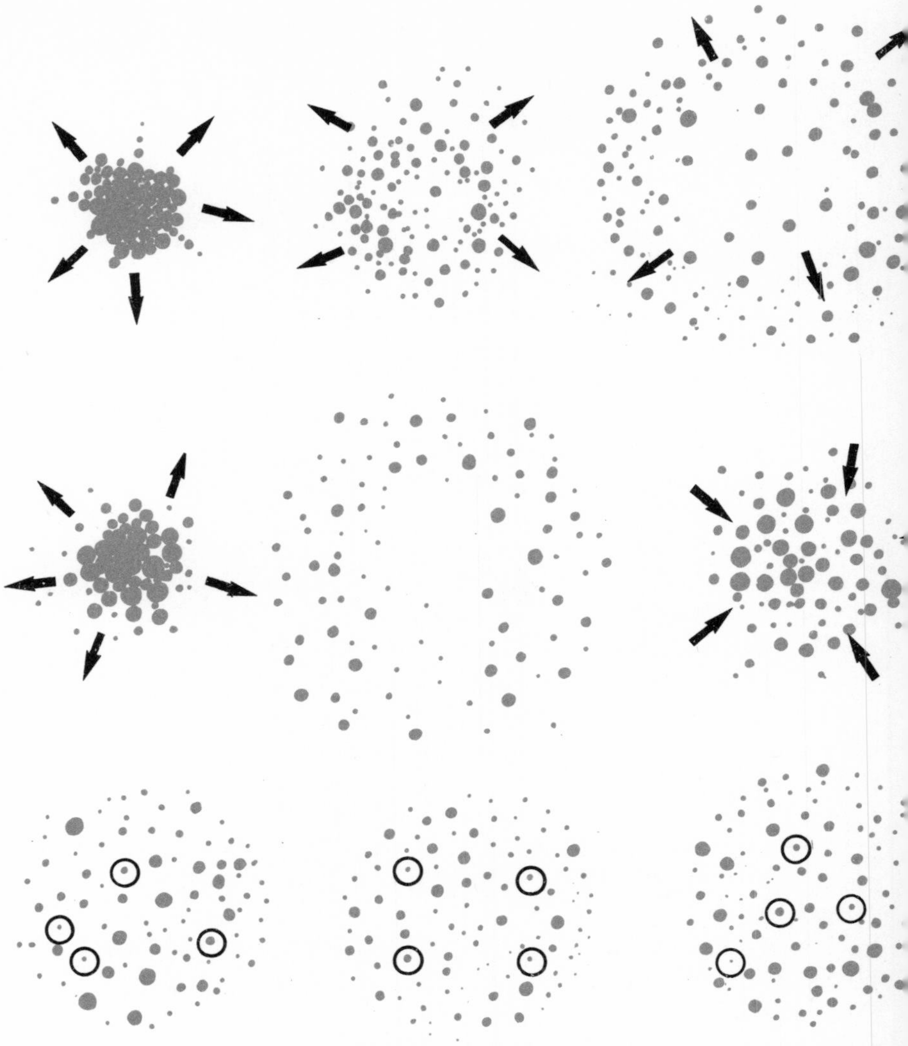

What has happened in the universe? Three theories are being pursued: (Top), a supercondensate, trillions of times denser than water, exploded some 10,000 million years ago and the expansion continued from the initial impetus of this explosion. On this theory, the distribution of galaxies should be denser towards our present limits of observation. (Centre), the universe is pulsating, expanding to a maximum and then contracting again. Towards the limiting distance, density should be greater. (Below), the universe is expanding, but new matter (ringed) is continuously created, compensating for the thinning out. Broadly speaking the distribution of the galaxies should be uniform. (12)

correctly chosen the model universe becomes cyclic. The cases with a positive cosmological constant have been thoroughly investigated by Lemaître. In his theory the entire material of the universe was concentrated in a primeval atom 50,000 million years ago. The size of the universe at this initial moment was about the size of the solar system today and the density in the conglomerate must have been trillions of times greater than that of water. This atom exploded and distributed the material over a great volume of space. Ten thousand million years ago the impetus of the explosion was exhausted and the primeval gas of the universe settled into a nearly stable condition occupying a volume of space with a diameter of perhaps 1,000 million light years. The clusters of galaxies then began to form from this primeval gas, and the force of repulsion associated with the positive value of the cosmical constant became greater than the force of Newtonian attraction between the clusters of galaxies, and so the expansion of the universe began.

The evolutionary theories of general relativity have a common feature in that they imply a changing condition of the universe with time, and that singular conditions occur in their past history which—except in the possible case of the cyclical model—require the creation of the entire material of the universe in a finite past epoch. The difficulties in this conception, coupled with an earlier numerical difficulty about the time-scale of the universe, led a group of cosmologists, in which Hoyle, Gold and Bondi were prominent, to the idea of the perfect cosmological principle in which the universe is considered to exhibit uniformity not only in space but also in time. In order to achieve such timelessness it is necessary to postulate the continuous creation of matter. On this view the primeval hydrogen atoms are in process of creation at all time. From these atoms the galaxies form and the rate of formation is balanced to compensate for the thinning out of the galaxies as a consequence of the expansion of the universe. In Hoyle's treatment the field equations of the steady-state universe have been developed as a special solution of the equations of general relativity. In the treatment by Bondi and Gold the use of the field equations has been avoided.

The predictions of the various evolutionary model universes and the steady-state theories are so divergent that it might seem to be a rather easy matter to decide between them by observing the universe which they are supposed to describe. In fact, the observational problem is tantalizing in the extreme and no decisive results have yet been obtained. Some of the relevant considerations may be summarized as follows.

1 Twenty years ago the value of the Hubble constant derived from the existing red shift–distance relationship indicated that the singular initial condition of high density in the evolutionary theories occurred only 3000 to 4000 million years in the past. But there was evidence that the earth, the sun and the stars must be much older—4000 to 5000 million years. Hence it appeared that the evolutionary theories could not, in any case, give a sufficiently long time-scale for the universe and this was one of the major factors which gave the impetus for the development of the steady-state cosmologies in which the time-scale difficulties disappeared. In fact, about 1950, it was realized that there had been a mistake in the identification of certain classes of Cepheids and the consequent revision of the distance-scale of the universe changed the Hubble constant to a value which places the initial condition in the evolutionary theories in an epoch of about 10,000 million years ago. Therefore, the arguments about the possible time-scales as a decisive factor do not apply.

2 In the evolutionary theories it was necessary to presume that the elements were formed by processes which occurred shortly after the initial explosion or disintegration of the atom. Since no singular moment of formation occurs in the steady-state theory, the adherents of this cosmology were compelled to develop other ideas to account for the formation of the elements. This was done with remarkable success in terms of the build-up or 'cooking' of the elements in the interiors of the stars. However, this mechanism is not a special privilege of a star in a steady-state universe and in fact these new ideas for the build-up of the elements saved some of the models of evolutionary cosmology from a serious difficulty in element-building. Thus again there is no argument in favour of any particular cosmology.

3 Because of the singularity in the evolutionary models it seems that most of the galaxies in the universe would be about the same age. In the steady-state cosmology, clearly galaxies of all ages will be found at any moment in the history of the cosmos. Thus if galaxies older than the average could be found this might be a decisive test in favour of the steady-state cosmology. There are two troubles. Firstly the excess of old galaxies must be expected to be small since the expansion of the universe will have removed the majority from our field of view. Secondly, as we have seen, we are not certain about the nature of the evolutionary sequence of the galaxies, and until this matter can be cleared the idea

does not seem likely to offer a decisive test between the various theories.

4 Perhaps the clearest test between the evolutionary theories as a whole and the steady-state cosmologies would be to determine the spatial density of galaxies (that is the number per unit volume of space) as a function of distance from the Milky Way. Broadly speaking it is evident that throughout all space the steady-state cosmology predicts that this spatial density will remain constant, whereas the singularity in the evolutionary cosmologies implies that in an earlier epoch the galaxies must have been more concentrated than they are today. The penetration of the telescopes to distances of a few thousand million light years means that we can study the state of the universe in those early epochs. The linearity of the red shift and the counts of galaxies fail to reveal any striking change in the condition of the universe at least to distances of 5000 million light years. However, this degree of penetration would in any case be insufficient to reveal the significant changes in the predictions of the cosmologies.

It is now well established that classes of peculiar objects exist—such as closely interacting galaxies—which although faint optically have an unusual output of energy in the radio wave part of the spectrum. Many thousands of unidentified radio sources can be detected with modern radio telescopes and it seems probable that the majority of these are at distances of cosmical significance, many perhaps beyond the range of the optical telescopes. Unfortunately there is no known method of measuring the distance of the radio sources and hence the spatial density–distance relationship cannot be determined directly. Nevertheless, statistical treatments of the problem on the general assumption that the fainter radio sources are further away have been carried out by Ryle and his colleagues in Cambridge and by the astronomers of the Radiophysics Laboratory in Sydney.

The early Cambridge results showed a striking effect indicating that the density was not uniform but that there was an excess of faint sources over that to be expected in a uniform distribution. This, of course, is in conflict with the steady-state cosmology. The Australian results did not show this effect and in recent years there has been a violent conflict of opinion about the interpretation of these radio source counts. The present position is that the more recent Cambridge results show a lesser but still significant departure from the situation to be expected in a steady-state universe, but it cannot be said that there is, as yet, any degree of unanimity over the interpretation of the result.

There is hope that the position may be resolved as more detailed information is obtained about the individual radio sources in this large sample. In particular, the measurements of the angular diameters and structure of the radio sources which are now proceeding may be expected to give data which will largely compensate for the inability to measure the red shift. Indeed at this moment it may be said that these radio methods offer the most promising avenue for the observational tests of the cosmological theories.

Towards a solution?

On page 104 reference is made to the new limit of penetration into the universe set by the optical identification of a radio source in Boötes as a cluster of galaxies at 4500 million light years with a recessional velocity of 83,000 miles per second or 46% of the velocity of light. On page 107 mention is made of the discovery in 1962 and 1963 that some of the strong radio sources were associated with star-like objects. These objects were at first thought to be peculiar blue stars in the Milky Way, then the measurement of the red shifts of some of these 'stars' showed that they were extragalactic at considerable distances, but at that time the most distant of these objects, with a red shift of 60,000 miles per second, was considerably nearer than the most distant identified radio galaxy in Boötes.

Subsequently there have been dramatic developments in connection with these blue objects. They are known as 'quasi-stellar radio sources' or conventionally as 'quasars'. At the Assembly of the International Astronomical Union in Hamburg in August 1964 Maarten Schmidt of Palomar announced that he had identified a total of 13 quasars and had measured 2 more red shifts, one of which, for the source known in the Cambridge Catalogue as 3C 147, indicated a recessional velocity more than half that of the velocity of light, making it the most distant object yet studied in the universe. In Texas in December of 1964 Schmidt announced the identification of 21 more quasars and early in 1965 he published the red shift measurements for 5 more. All these five measurements were of red shifts even greater than that for 3C 147; the largest, for the quasar 3C 9, indicated a recessional velocity 75% of that of light. More recently Schmidt's measurements confirm an earlier suggestion of the Russian astrophysicist Shklovsky that the red shift of the quasar 3C 286 was 80% of that of light. These great red shifts can only be interpreted in terms of distance if the cosmology, and in particular the deceleration parameter, is specified. If the red shifts are truly cosmological then on any cosmology the distances of these quasars must be in the region of 7 to 8 thousand million light years.

The qualification is necessary because during the summer of 1965 suggestions arose that the quasars may be objects resulting from the explosion of the nucleus of our own and other nearby galaxies. In this case the red shifts would be real but would be actual velocities as distinct from cosmological effects, and the distances of the quasars would be millions as distinct from thousands of millions of light years. This suggestion has arisen because there are many peculiarities in the quasars—for example the fluctuations in their light output, the nature of their radio spectrum, and the increase in the strength of the radio emission by several per cent per year—which make an interpretation in terms of distant cosmological objects exceedingly difficult.

The subject was even further complicated by the publication by Sandage in 1965 that he had discovered many other objects similar in appearance to quasars, but not strong radio sources, which were believed to be distant galaxies of a hitherto unrecognized type—quasi-stellar galaxies or Q.S.G.'s.

Ideas on the quasars and the Q.S.G.'s are changing rapidly as new experimental facts are accumulated. If, indeed, the cosmological interpretation of the red shifts is confirmed then it seems certain that a vital step will have been taken towards a solution of the cosmological problem.

The new and astonishing knowledge of the universe
gained by astronomers in recent years, centres round two great achievements in precision engineering—the larger and larger optical telescopes culminating in the 200-inch Hale reflector on Mount Palomar and the great radio telescope assemblies of which the 250-foot reflector at Jodrell Bank is the largest completely steerable example in the world.

In the photograph opposite, the observer sits in the prime focus cage of the 200-inch telescope, with his back to the incoming light. In front of him, at the end of the tube of steel girders, is the giant mirror, the observer's cage reflected in it as a black circle, and its centre pierced by a tube to allow twice-reflected light to pass to the Cassegrain focus. The mirror is more than two feet thick and weighs over fourteen tons. It was ground and polished from a 22-ton block of glass to a parabolic shape, with tolerance measured in millionths of an inch. Its reflecting surface is an extremely thin layer of aluminium, about 1000 atoms thick, deposited on its front surface to avoid absorption of light by the glass. Light from the stars reaches it through the space between the cage and the surrounding girder, an aperture large enough to give it 600,000 times the light-gathering power of the human eye. The whole telescope, a massive 530 tons, is mounted on bearings so true that it can be moved by one hand. It can be set to revolve, against the earth's rotation, for long periods while one faint star is being photographed.

The telescope, which began work in 1947, was twenty years in the making, the dream and endeavour of the American astronomer George Ellery Hale. He did not live to see it finished. (1)

The giant dome of the Palomar Observatory stands a mile above sea-level, its telescope, swung to the vertical, visible through the open shutters. Astronomers have been driven to build their big telescopes in the mountains, not only to avoid the fog and smoke of the towns but also because their light-gathering power is now so great that scattered moonlight and the lights of the cities limit the recording of faint and distant objects. The projected 236-inch Russian telescope is to be placed, after a long search for the most suitable site, at a height of 6000 feet in the North Caucasus. These great instruments may well have reached the limiting size, for small movements in the atmosphere set the image twinkling, and the nights are relatively few when conditions are stable enough for the resolving power and light-gathering capacity of the telescope to be used to its maximum. (2)

To map the stars, a telescope is required which gives high definition over a wide field of view. To produce the famous *Palomar Sky Atlas*, a 48-inch Schmidt-type telescope was used, with a concave spherical mirror and large-diameter lenses to minimize distortion of the image. The photographic plate, which must be curved, is situated centrally in the telescope at the focus of the mirror. In the photograph left centre, the astronomer is inserting the plate-holder into the telescope. He looks towards the aperture; the mirror is behind him. (3)

The elements which make up the stars, and much more information on their history, temperature, relative movement and distance, can be discovered by analysing the light which reaches us—by studying the lines in their spectra. Large telescopes therefore include spectrographs as an essential part of their equipment. In the photograph on the left (below) the astronomer looks into the spectrograph eyepiece of the 200-inch telescope; he is at the Coudé focus, which the light reaches after a third reflection through the side. As the telescope moves, this focus remains at the same place, the heavy equipment need not be moved, and greater accuracy can be achieved by keeping it at a constant temperature. (4)

The blazing magnificence of the Orion nebula is revealed by the 200-inch telescope. What the naked eye knows as the middle 'star' of Orion's sword is seen under this powerful magnification to be the brilliant spectacle opposite—a vast cloud of gas, glowing in blues and reds, with hot stars shining through it. It lies within the Milky Way, about a thousand light years from the sun. It is thought that ultra-violet light from the intensely hot stars (18,000°C or even higher) excites the rarefied gas of the nebula to emit the radiation in the visible spectrum. It is strange to think that this vivid cloud consists of a gas so thin that each cubic centimetre contains only a few hundred atoms. This 'dense' nebula is in fact a million times more rarefied than the best vacuum obtainable on earth. (5)

The radiation which streams from space

can be studied only in part by earth-bound instruments. Of the long range of wavelengths, shown in metres on the scale which runs across these pages, only two bands reach the earth, through two 'windows' in the protecting atmosphere. The first, the narrow band of visible light, bordered by some ultra-violet and infra-red radiation, brings the energy, light and warmth which maintain life, and is the source of all that man has discovered about the universe through most of his history. The second, a longer range from a few millimetres to 30 metres, is the band, known only in recent years, which is being studied by the radio telescopes.

But the new space technology has enabled scientists to examine the whole range before it is stopped. The first obstacle is the dust and atmospheric turbulence which limits the powers of even the large mountain-top telescopes (the observatory shown is the McDonald, at Fort Davis, Texas), and the water vapour which stops a large part of the infra-red radiation. This is overcome by telescope-carrying balloons rising to 15 miles or so. Princeton University's Stratoscopes (which are erected for flight and initially raised by a small launch balloon) have taken infra-red spectra of the Moon, Mars, Jupiter and several stars and direct photographs of the sun and planets. At greater heights, circling 500 miles above the earth (in true scale it would be far above the drawing), America's series of Orbiting Astronomical Observatories, accurately 'pointed' for long periods, are transmitting ultra-violet and visible spectra of the stars and nebulae.

The short X-rays and the ultra-violet rays are scattered by ionized atoms at a high level and reach barely below the 20-mile ceiling of the stratosphere. They have been measured by instruments in sounding rockets (the one shown is the British 'Skylark') at heights from 60 miles upwards and at higher levels by many orbiting satellites.

The long-wave end of the incoming stream of radiation includes the wavelengths used in sound broadcasting, which can encircle the earth because they are reflected back to ground level by the free electrons in the high ionized layers. To examine the changes which disturb this reflection, and to study waves of these lengths coming from space (which are themselves reflected and absorbed by the layers), satellites such as the joint Canadian-American Alouette are being used. This 'topside sounder' circles at about 600 miles, orbiting every 105 minutes. Its instruments are powered by 6,500 solar cells, covering the outer shell of the spacecraft. It measures daily changes in the electron density (by sending out sweeping radio signals), records radio 'noise' from the ionosphere and from outer space, and observes incoming cosmic rays. (6)

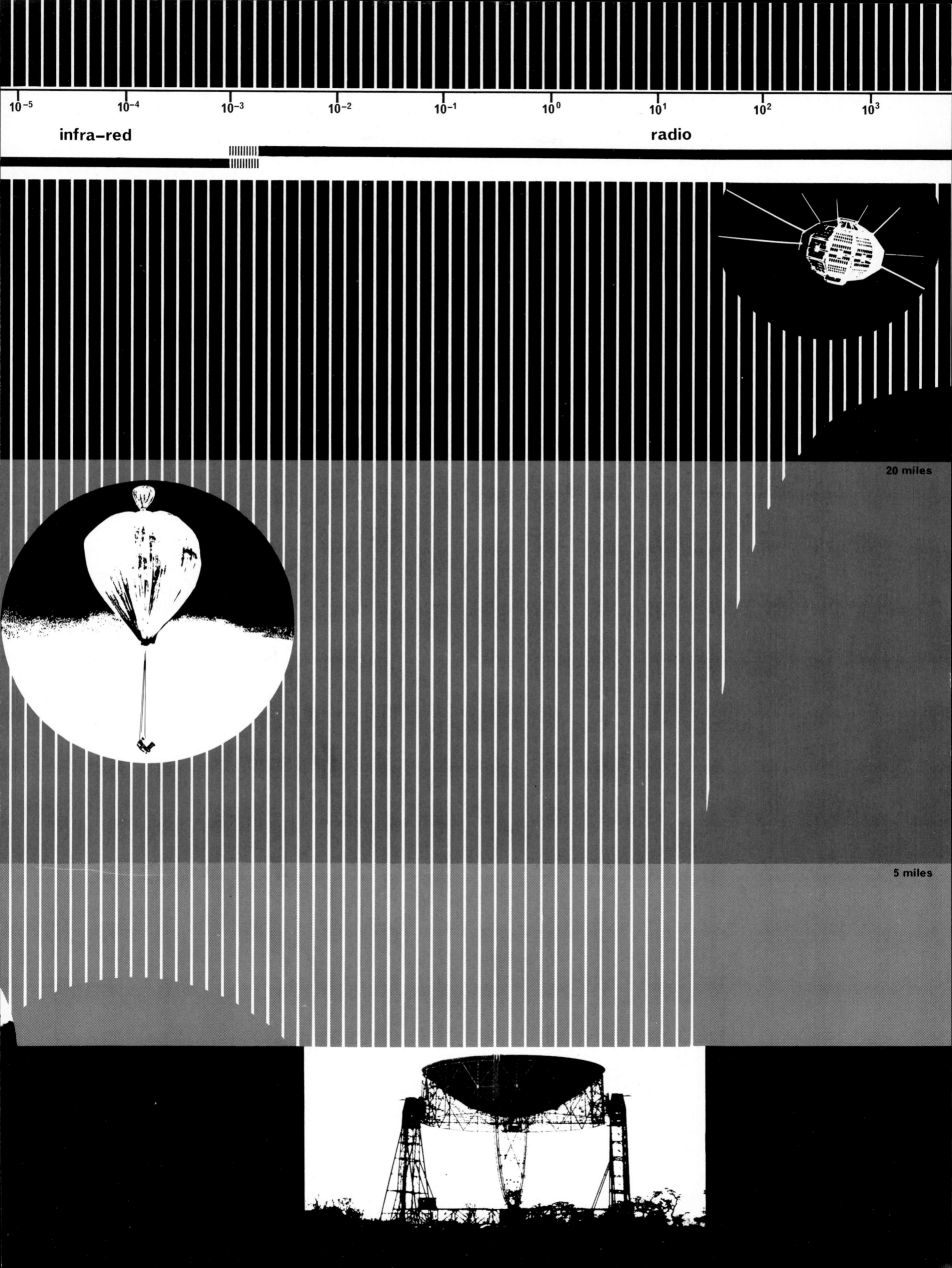

10⁻⁵   10⁻⁴   10⁻³   10⁻²   10⁻¹   10⁰   10¹   10²   10³

infra-red   radio

20 miles

5 miles

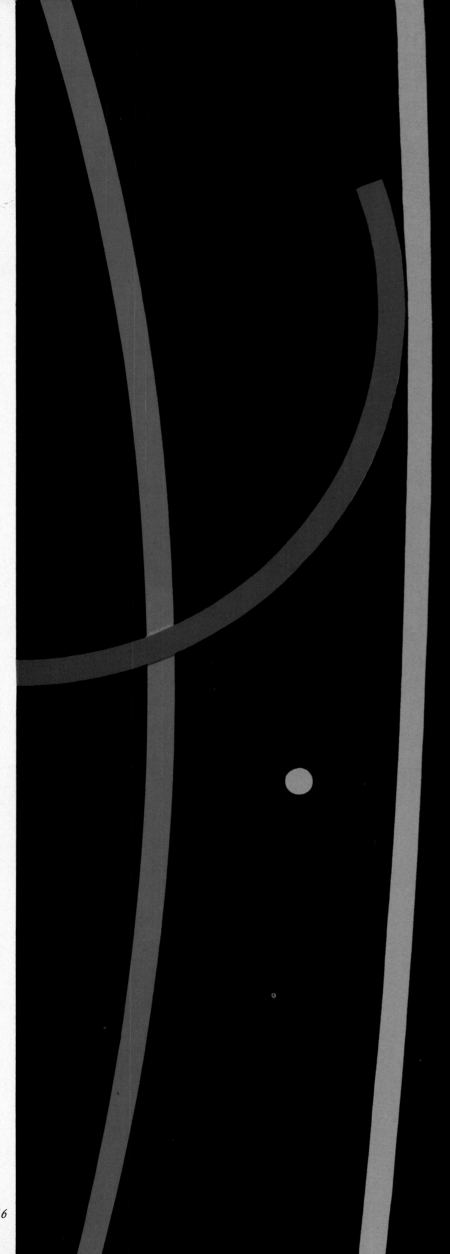

The life and death of a star

can be followed roughly on the famous Hertzsprung-Russell diagram. These two astronomers measured the apparent brightness of a group of stars in the neighbourhood of the sun. As the stars were at distances which varied widely, they reduced their figures to the absolute brightness—the brightness each star would show if it were at the standard distance of 33 light-years—giving a true comparison. They also found the spectroscopic type of each star, which is a measure of its surface temperature. Brightness is not necessarily a measure of the temperature, since cooler stars may be so large as to appear high in the scale, but colour is a rough guide. Red stars (2000°–3000°C) are considered cool; below that, radiation would probably not be enough to make the star visible. Temperature increases through orange, the yellow of our 6000° sun, and white to the searing 20,000° or more of the blue stars. Except in a few cases—the white of Sirius, the red of Aldebaran and Antares—these colour differences are too faint for the naked eye.

When the stars are placed in position on the H–R diagram opposite, with bright stars at the top, faint at the bottom, hot stars to the left, cool to the right, a pattern begins to emerge. The majority occupy a well-defined band, the Main Sequence, running from top left (bright and hot) to faint, cool stars at lower right. The sun, reduced to a very ordinary star of the 5th magnitude, takes a position (arrowed) in the centre. Red giants appear as a branch to the right, yellow supergiants above and white dwarfs to the left below. The sizes of the stars vary so greatly that they cannot be shown realistically on the diagram. A more accurate comparison appears on the left, where the sun (small circle) is shown with the circumferences of the largest red giant, a supergiant and the blue star at the end of the main sequence. The enormous blue star at top left would be a straight line on this scale, some white dwarfs a point too small to see. The red giant Antares, superimposed on the solar system, would extend to beyond the orbit of Mars.

It is thought today that the evolution of a star of the solar type is something as follows. Its origin is a condensation of interstellar gas and dust, cool in comparison and of low density. This contracts from self-gravitation and the pressure of external radiation; the star becomes hotter and denser and moves on the H–R diagram towards the main sequence—a change which may take 50 million years. When the main sequence is reached the internal temperatures and pressure are high enough to begin the conversion of hydrogen into helium, with the release of energy as radiation. Here, almost stable on a very small portion of its track, the star stays for the major part of its life, perhaps 10,000 million years.

After this long time the star, its hydrogen fuel almost exhausted, moves off the main sequence to the right, growing rapidly into a red giant. It is now largely helium, more opaque to the radiation formed internally from the final phases of hydrogen exhaustion. The trapped radiation raises the temperature so far that new nuclear reactions occur in the helium. The star moves to the left, across the main sequence and, its fuel finally exhausted, collapses into a white dwarf. Death has taken the comparatively short time of 20 million years.

This evolutionary history, some of which is as yet uncertain, fits well into the distribution of star qualities revealed in the H–R diagram. The sun has already been on the main sequence for at least 5000 million years; it will probably remain there a further 5000 million before it expands into a red giant and engulfs the earth. (7, 8)

116

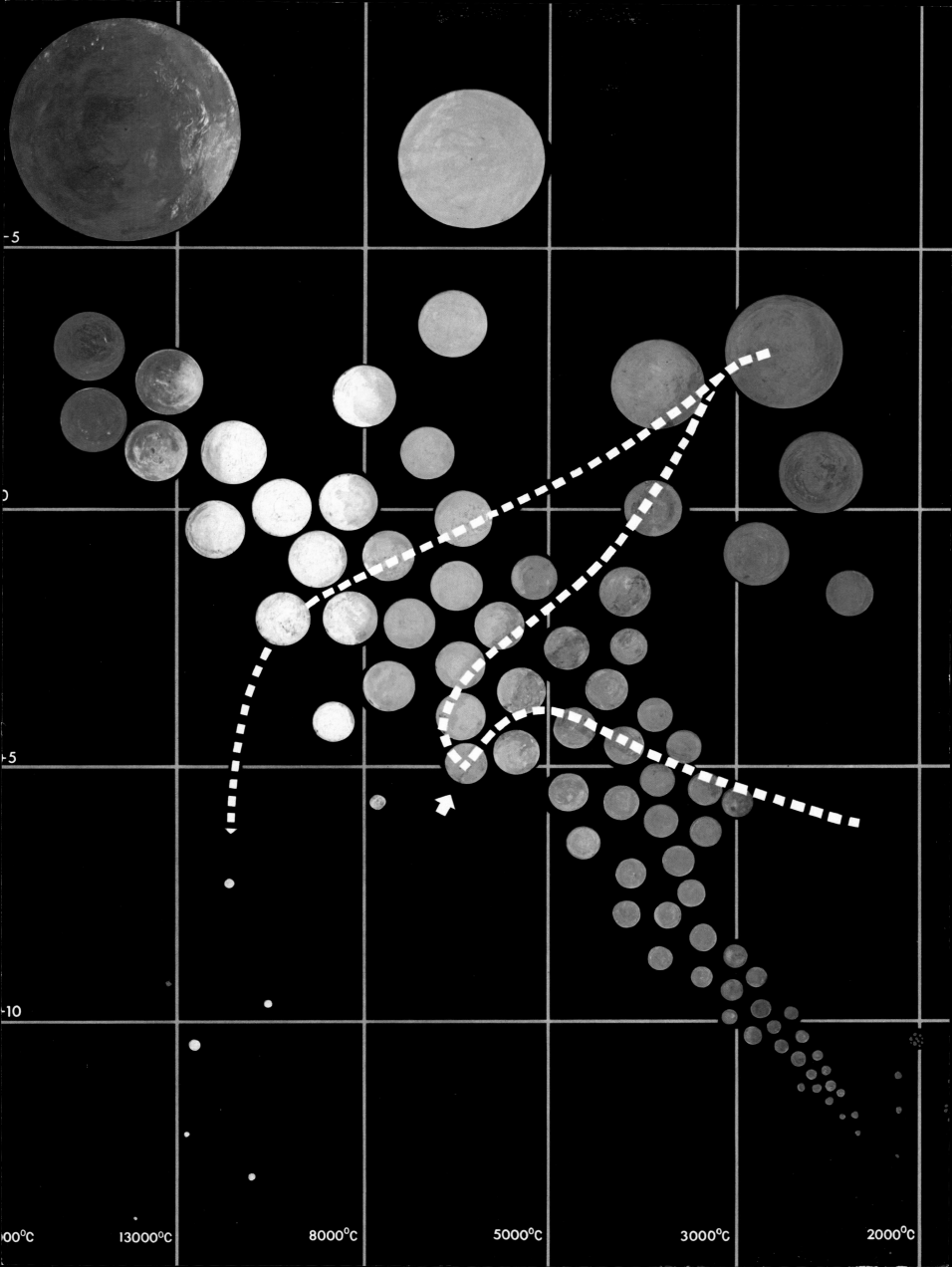

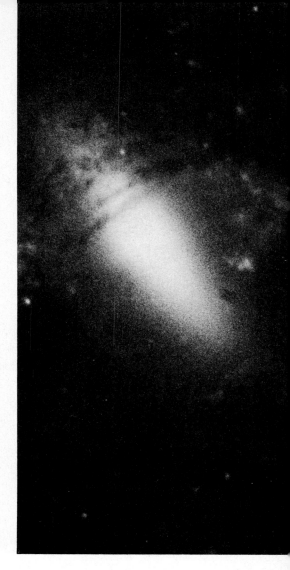

Diffuse, hazy objects which seemed not to be stars were observed by the early astronomers through their telescopes. They called them 'nebulae'—clouds. In 1784 Charles Messier listed 103 of them, and his numbering is still in use today (M31 is Andromeda). Were they part of the Milky Way or beyond it? Were they clouds of rarefied gas or vastly distant, separate star systems? Some showed a spectrum of bright lines, suggesting clouds of gas, others the continuous spectrum of a group of stars.

It was Hubble, in 1925, who settled the question decisively, with the 100-inch telescope on Mount Wilson. Both kinds in fact exist, clouds of diffuse gas, like the one in Orion, which are part of the Milky Way, and vast island star systems, now more usually known as 'galaxies', at immensely greater distances. *One million* galaxies have been photographed at Mount Wilson. Hubble classified them according to their shape; his arrangement, shown above across the two pages, is known as 'Hubble's Tuning Fork'.

Three types emerge. The first, the E-type, vary from the circular E0 (of which NGC (New General Catalogue) 4486 in Virgo is shown), to the elliptical E7 (NGC 3115 in Sextans). These are about seventeen per cent of the catalogued galaxies, and consist predominantly of 'red giants', probably old stars, born perhaps 4000 million years ago in regions where the primeval gas is now exhausted and star formation has largely ceased. A third kind, type S0 (NGC 2685 in Ursa Major), reveals the rudiments of a spiral galaxy. (9, 10, 11)

▶ **Great clouds of darkness,** the obscuring dust of the universe, can be seen in many of the nebulae. In the Horsehead Nebula in Orion (left) the dust rears itself against a diffuse background of hot gas glowing with energy from nearby stars. Some galaxies, seen edge-on, seem to be belted with a rim of dust, as the 'Sombrero' is overleaf. The Milky Way is one of these, the thread of dust clouds being clearly seen in the remarkable photograph on the right. It was taken in the southern hemisphere with red-sensitive emulsion, recording the picture in red light from the Galaxy, which has penetrated the gas clouds which normally obscure the hub and the central parts of the disk around it. (The three dark bars are supports of the film holder.) ◀

The Milky Way is seen to be similar in shape to many galaxies in deep space. On a clear night, the naked eye can distinguish 6500 stars; quite small telescopes reveal vastly greater numbers. The large optical telescopes can photograph about a thousand million; if we could see all the stars in the Milky Way it is estimated they would number about one hundred thousand million. The whole enormous disk is wheeling round the central hub, in the neighbourhood of the sun once in 200 million years. (12, 13)

Type Sa has a large nucleus and tight, undeveloped arms (NGC 2811 in Hydra). (14)

Type Sb has a smaller nucleus and well-developed arms (NGC 3031 in Ursa Major). (15)

Type Sc. The nucleus is insignificant, the arms loose and spreading (NGC 5364 in Virgo). (16)

Spirals make up eighty per cent of catalogued galaxies, and fifty per cent are 'normal' spirals (top), classified Sa, Sb, and Sc according to the size of the nucleus and the development of the arms. In the remaining spirals, the arms develop from a bar of matter which extends the nucleus. They are classified SBa, SBb and SBc, according to the relative prominence of the bar or its arms. Above are shown NGC 4314 in Coma Berenices (left), NGC 1300 in Eridanus (centre) and NGC 7741 in Pegasus.

Younger stars are still being born from the gas and dust in the arms of the spiral galaxies, where a large proportion of main sequence stars are found (as our sun in the Milky Way). The nuclei resemble the elliptical galaxies, containing stars nearing the end of their life. Young stars come later in the 'tuning fork' therefore; it is no longer considered a guide to how galaxies evolve. The number of galaxies is almost beyond comprehension: present estimates put it as at least a hundred thousand million. (17, 18, 19)

Abnormal, shapeless galaxies exist, some three per cent of the total, which do not fit into the 'tuning fork'. Some of them, like the Great Magellanic Cloud below, which is visible to the naked eye in the southern hemisphere, have no nucleus or detectable symmetry. Galaxy M82 (below, left) is exciting astronomers because vast clouds of gas seem to have been expelled from its centre, suggesting a titanic explosion of millions of solar masses still in progress a million and a half years ago. (20, 21)

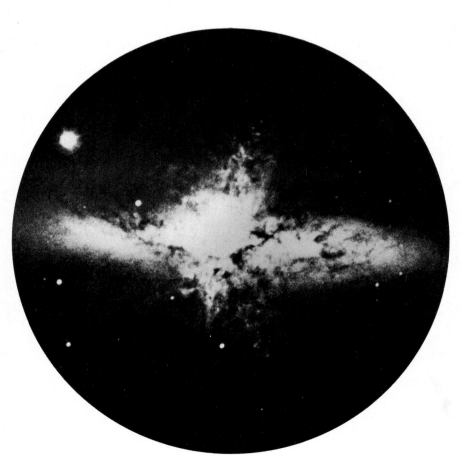

The true brilliance of the galaxies, too faint to be perceptible to the naked eye, is now being recorded in colour by the large optical telescopes, using long exposures and careful colour control. The photographs reveal infinite variety and great beauty, and express directly some of the qualities which have led, through their spectra, to our knowledge of their nature and history.

The 'Sombrero Hat' (M104, top), in the constellation Virgo, is far beyond the Milky Way, 40 million light years distant. It is a tightly bound spiral with a large hub, its rim hidden by a dark dust belt. (22)

The 'Whirlpool' (M51, centre) was the first galaxy in which the spiral shape was established, by the Irish astronomer Lord Rosse in 1850. He also suggested that it was composed of individual stars, not gas, though he did not know that it is outside our own Galaxy, ten million light years away, and receding from us at 300 miles per second. The spreading spiral arms, of Sc type, sparkle with supergiants and show blue and young against the gas-thin spaces between. A long arm stretches out to a companion galaxy, irregular in shape and unusually red in colour. If the Milky Way could be photographed from a distant point in the universe, it would look like the main galaxy here. (23)

The 'Crab' nebula in Taurus (M1, below), lies within the Milky Way, some 4100 light years distant. Astronomers, observing this vast cloud of gas, concluded that it was the debris of a gigantic stellar explosion—a supernova—which occurred about 3000 BC and could first have been observed about AD 1000. In 1921 ancient Chinese chronicles were published describing a star which appeared suddenly in Taurus, where none had been before, and burned so brightly that it shone by day. A Japanese account, discovered in 1934, likened the light to that of Jupiter. The date was AD 1054.

Today, the cloud of matter blown outwards in this titanic death of a star is still seen expanding at the rate of 800 miles a second. It is a strong source of radio 'noise' and also of X-rays, with a magnetic field in which electrons, in the yellow centre, are accelerated to very high energies. The red radiation of the outer filaments is due to hot hydrogen gas at a temperature of about 40,000 degrees.

Two other supernovae have been reported in our Galaxy, one in 1572, seen by Tycho Brahe, and one in 1604 by Johannes Kepler. The remnants of both explosions are radio sources. (24)

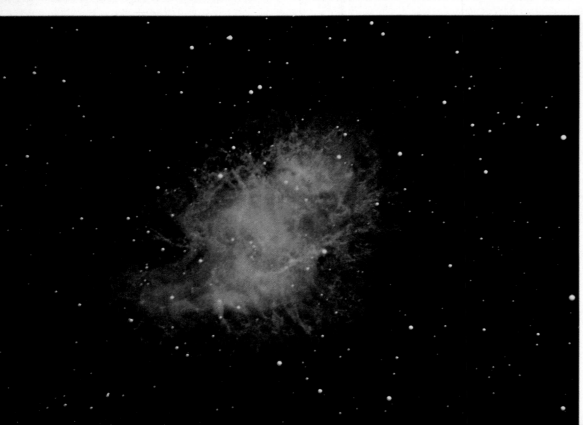

The Andromeda galaxy (M31), seen opposite among the stars of the Milky Way, was the first that was shown to be a separate unit, beyond and outside the Milky Way. This was only forty years ago. It is also the only extragalactic object visible to the naked eye from the northern hemisphere, appearing as a faint, diffuse patch of light in the constellation of Andromeda, below the well-known W-shaped group Cassiopeia. About two million light years distant, the Andromeda nebula is in many ways almost the twin of the Milky Way, being 100,000 light years in length, and containing something like 100,000 million stars. Colour photography shows up the predominance of blue (young) stars in the spiral arms, and between the arms dust streaks from which new stars may still be forming. In the whitish central hub, star formation has ceased and there are no dust clouds; immediately around this is an area of red giants, near the end of their life-cycle. The two satellite galaxies are of the E-series. (25)

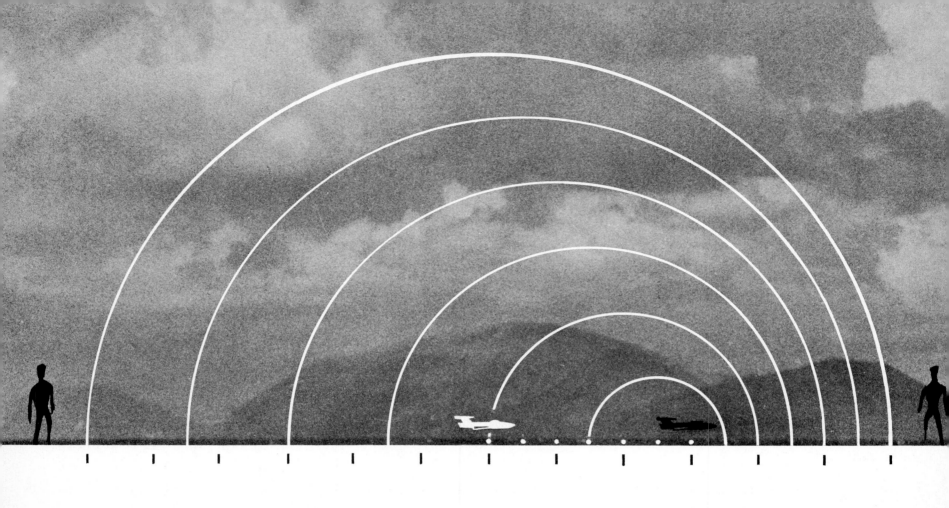

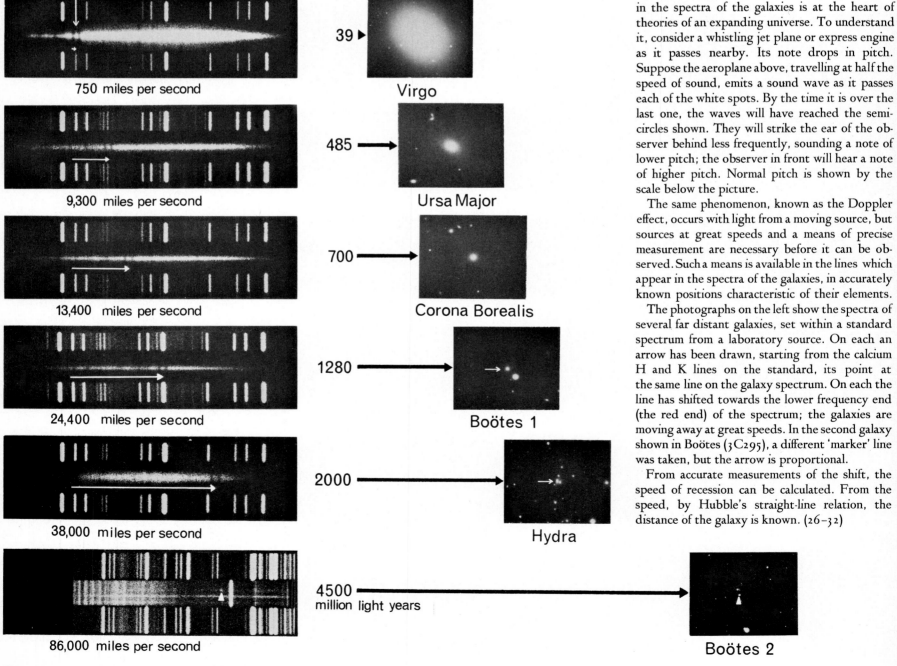

750 miles per second

9,300 miles per second

13,400 miles per second

24,400 miles per second

38,000 miles per second

86,000 miles per second

H+K

39 ▶
Virgo

485 ➔
Ursa Major

700 ➔
Corona Borealis

1280 ➔
Boötes 1

2000 ➔
Hydra

4500 ➔
million light years
Boötes 2

The shift to the red

in the spectra of the galaxies is at the heart of theories of an expanding universe. To understand it, consider a whistling jet plane or express engine as it passes nearby. Its note drops in pitch. Suppose the aeroplane above, travelling at half the speed of sound, emits a sound wave as it passes each of the white spots. By the time it is over the last one, the waves will have reached the semi-circles shown. They will strike the ear of the ob-server behind less frequently, sounding a note of lower pitch; the observer in front will hear a note of higher pitch. Normal pitch is shown by the scale below the picture.

The same phenomenon, known as the Doppler effect, occurs with light from a moving source, but sources at great speeds and a means of precise measurement are necessary before it can be ob-served. Such a means is available in the lines which appear in the spectra of the galaxies, in accurately known positions characteristic of their elements.

The photographs on the left show the spectra of several far distant galaxies, set within a standard spectrum from a laboratory source. On each an arrow has been drawn, starting from the calcium H and K lines on the standard, its point at the same line on the galaxy spectrum. On each the line has shifted towards the lower frequency end (the red end) of the spectrum; the galaxies are moving away at great speeds. In the second galaxy shown in Boötes (3C295), a different 'marker' line was taken, but the arrow is proportional.

From accurate measurements of the shift, the speed of recession can be calculated. From the speed, by Hubble's straight-line relation, the distance of the galaxy is known. (26-32)

The breath-taking rush of the distant clusters of galaxies revealed by the red shift is the same wherever we look in space—away from us, with speeds increasing with their distance. It *seems* as though the universe could be pictured as an expanding balloon, the earth at its centre, the core of a primordial explosion, and the galaxies ranged on its concentric surfaces as it expands. But this geocentric notion has been abandoned by astronomers since the days of Copernicus. To picture the observed expansion, consider the two-dimensional area of the balloon's surface. As it expands, the galaxies separate from one another uniformly; none is at the centre, any one might be our own Galaxy. This, translated into three dimensions (a difficult feat of the imagination) is the expansion which any theory of the universe must take into account.

The fringe of the universe, the greatest distances indicated by the red shift, is an area exciting the attention of both radio and optical astronomers. The red shift of the most distant radio galaxy in the illustration on the opposite page is 86,000 miles per second, indicating a distance of 4500 million light years. Until 1962 it was believed that this represented the greatest penetration of the radio and optical telescopes into the universe, but the discovery of the quasi-stellar radio sources may have radically changed this belief. Red shifts of more than 70 per cent of the velocity of light have been measured for one or two of these newly discovered objects, and if these red shifts are a cosmological effect as is widely believed at the present time, then the distances of the quasi objects must be 7000 million to 8000 million light years. If this view is substantiated then the radio and optical telescopes may now be looking back three-quarters of the way to the birth of the universe, and new possibilities open up for exploring the cosmos at this remote time. (33, 34)

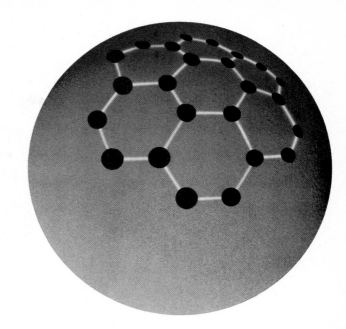

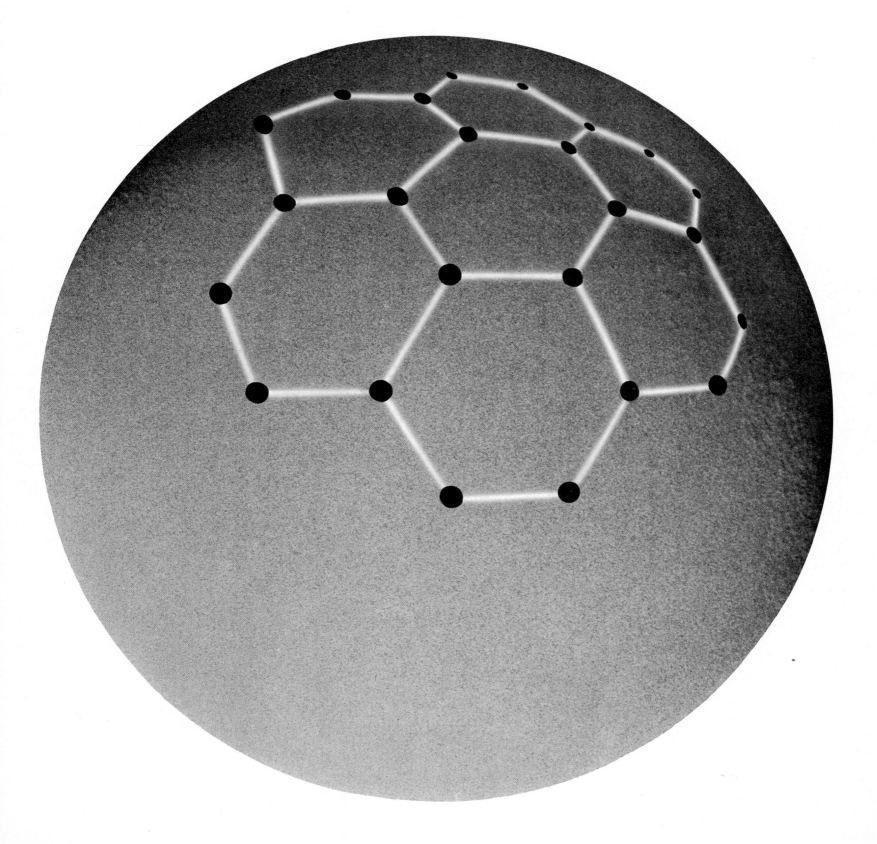

The astonishing distances in space
reached by astronomers in recent years are due
largely to the work of the radio telescopes. These
instruments, or assemblies of instruments, pick up
the faint 'whisper' of waves reaching us from space,
through the 'window' in the atmosphere which
admits wavelengths from a few millimetres to 30
metres. They amplify them, filter out extraneous
'noise' from other sources, register the directions
from which the waves come and record their relative intensities.

Jodrell Bank's great 250-foot reflector
(left) consists of a 'dish' welded from 7000 steel
sheets, one-twelfth of an inch thick, weighing 80
tons. The dish is supported on a cradle weighing
800 tons and the whole structure is suspended on
trunnion bearings 185 ft. above ground. To move
the dish to point higher or lower in the sky, the
27 ft. diameter racks from the 15-inch gun tur-
rets of the battleship *Royal Sovereign* are
mounted in the two supporting towers; to
move it sideways the towers run on a circular railway track pivoted in the centre of the
girder which joins their bases, the only place at
which the structure is fixed to the ground. The
semicircular hoop girder which reaches down to
this point stabilizes the dish against winds. At the
centre beneath the bowl a small laboratory is
suspended so that it remains upright whatever the
tilt. The whole moveable structure weighs 2500
tons. (35)

At the focus of the dish, on which the reflected waves are concentrated, stands the dipole
receiving aerial, supported on a 62½-foot mast
(below left). The operator has reached it by the
hydraulically operated platform on which he
stands, his head opposite the thin crossed rods of
the aerial (in the right-hand picture he is working on
the rods themselves). Above the aerial rests a box
containing the early stages of some of the high-
frequency receiving apparatus, placed there to
avoid loss of strength in conveying impulses
through the long cables to the control room on the
ground. (36, 37)

On the other side of the world, the
Parkes radio telescope in the Goobang Valley,
New South Wales, points its 210-ft. bowl to the
zenith of the evening sky. It is fully steerable, the
world's largest after Jodrell Bank, and sweeps wide
sections of the Southern sky invisible to astronomers in the north.

These giant telescopes, and the other assemblies
in America, Russia, Britain, South Africa, Australia and elsewhere, are tailored for the work they
have to do. Some are designed specifically to track
spacecraft and to receive and record the information they send back. Some have bounced radar
signals off the moon and Venus, an accurate
measure of their distances. But the main purpose
of the large telescopes is to locate the sources of
radio emission in the galaxies and to study its
nature. The various kinds of radiation from the
Milky Way (to which the contribution of the stars
themselves is small) are now well known, as are
emissions of similar intensity from the nearer extragalactic nebulae, but different causes must be
responsible for the large numbers of point sources
which have been discovered at greater distances.
Some of these, strong in the radio spectrum, are so
faint optically as to have been unknown until the
200-inch telescope was directed to them; some are
the intensely energetic quasars and some are so
distant as to be at the limits of the known universe.
(38)

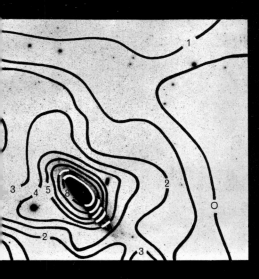

This radio map of Andromeda (above) was built up by the Jodrell Bank telescope, which was patiently scanned hundreds of times across the galaxy. When the intensity records were plotted, lines of equal strength came out like 'contours' of the emission. Numbered in units of increasing intensity, and superimposed on a negative optical photograph of the galaxy, the 'contours' clearly show how the general galactic radiation concentrates on the visible region but is not confined to it. The source however is not the stars, but the interstellar gas which surrounds them. (39)

A remote point source of strong radio emission in the constellation Centaurus has been traced to the strange-looking galaxy at top right, photographed by the 200-inch Palomar telescope. Its light, obscured by the huge broken belt of dust clouds, was originally thought to come from two colliding or closely interacting galaxies, but it is now thought more likely that the galaxy is one in which violent events have taken place in the nucleus resulting in the emission of strong radio waves. For example, one theory suggests that its state of evolution is such that it contains an abnormal number of exploding supernovae, similar to that which produced the Crab Nebula. (40)

The second strongest source in the sky lies in the constellation Cygnus, the Swan. No supernova remnant or other unusual object appears in our Galaxy in that area, but a prolonged exposure of many hours with the 200-inch Mount Palomar telescope in that part of the sky revealed this peculiar object. At first it was believed to be an example of two spiral galaxies in a state of collision and the red shift indicated a distance of 50 million light years. The idea that the strong radio emission resulted from the collision of the galaxies was abandoned some years ago, and it is now thought to be one of the most outstanding cases where some violent events have taken place in the nucleus of the galaxy. The discovery of this peculiar object in Cygnus rapidly led to the association of more of the localized radio sources with these strange distant galaxies visible on the photographs taken with the large optical telescopes. (41)

5   The assault on the atom

P. T. Matthews

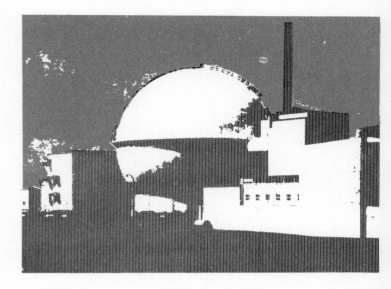

The assault on the atom

In previous chapters we have considered only matter in bulk, as it appears in the solids of dry land, the liquids of the oceans, and the gases of the atmosphere. For a deeper insight into its nature, we turn to the analytic notion of the Greeks. According to this idea, to understand matter we must take it to pieces, and then take the pieces to pieces until finally we come to the constituent parts, which are so simple that they defy further analysis. This process was carried a long way by the chemists of the 19th century, who showed that matter in all its variety of forms is made up of just 92 different types of identical atoms, or elements, just as a wall is made up of identical bricks. The alternative names, atom or element, both imply something too small to be divided.

This simple idea arose from observations and measurements of the quantities of substances taking part in chemical reactions. For example, water is formed from two parts, by volume, of hydrogen and one part of oxygen. This observation led to the idea that water consisted of molecules, each made up of two atoms of hydrogen and one atom of oxygen. But although there is twice as much hydrogen in the water as oxygen, the oxygen weighs 8 times as much as the hydrogen. In other words, the basic brick, or atom, of oxygen must weigh 16 times as much as that of hydrogen. One of the differences between the 92 elements was that each had atoms of different, and characteristic, atomic weight.

A hundred million to the inch: the atom

Note that, so far, no one knew how big the atom was, nor what its actual weight was. Atomic weights were simply measured in terms of the weight of a hydrogen atom. In the late 19th century, several methods were used to get an idea of the size of atoms. One method was to put a small drop of oil on the surface of water, where it spread until it was only one molecule thick. In this way an estimate of the length of a long oil molecule could be made, and knowing the number of atoms it contained, a rough figure for the size of an atom could be calculated. The results suggested that atoms, imagined as round solid lumps, had a diameter of 10^{-8} cm. (The shorthand 10^8 means 1 followed by eight zeros, or one hundred million; 10^{-8} is the inverse of this number.) Later investigations by more sophisticated methods confirm this value. Atoms are very small indeed. In terms of size, an atom is to a golf ball as a golf ball is to the whole earth.

Having discovered the size of an atom, we can find its mass simply by weighing a known volume of the element and dividing by the number of atoms. Thus 1 cubic centimetre contains about 10^{24} atoms (1 followed by 24 zeros,

or a million million million million). One cubic centimetre of silver, one of the heavier elements, weighs a little more than 10 grams. Thus the mass of an atom is about 10^{-23} gram.

By the turn of the century, it was already realized that these tiny atoms are not in fact indivisible, and that their structure is electrical in nature. This discovery was made through the study of the passage of electric current through gases, a phenomenon which is used nowadays in familiar neon lighting. At ordinary pressures little or no current will pass through a gas. But when the pressure is reduced to about one hundredth of normal atmospheric pressure, an electric current can be made to flow fairly readily. In a typical apparatus of the type used 60 or 70 years ago, the two metal plates A and C are connected to a high-voltage supply. When the pressure in the gas is reduced by the vacuum pump a current flows through the gas. To find out how this current is carried, pinholes were drilled through the metal plates. A simple experiment shows that whatever it is emerging from the pinholes, the stream can be bent by a magnet, or by an electric field—a sure indication that the stream consists of electrically charged particles.

fig 1

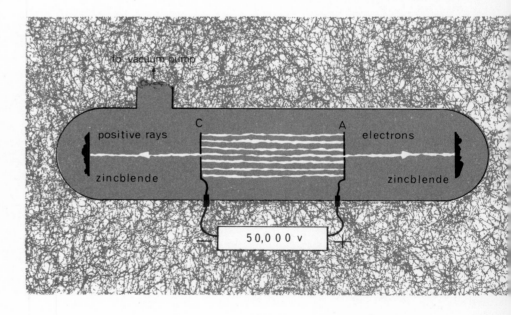

The atom, only about one hundred-millionth of an inch in diameter, can still be divided. This was discovered at the turn of the century, from the phenomenon used today in neon lighting tubes. Two metal plates, each with a pinhole through its centre, were sealed into a closed tube, and a vacuum pump greatly reduced the number of atoms of gas in the tube. When a high voltage was connected across the plates, a current flowed between them, and two thin streams of charged particles passed through the pinholes and flashed on the zincblende. The atoms had split into positive ions and negative electrons, and each was attracted by the plate of opposite charge. (1)

There followed a whole series of experiments by J. J. Thomson and others to discover the properties of these mysterious particles. The picture that finally emerged was a remarkable one. The atoms of the gas, far from being indivisible, are readily broken up into fragments, which carry an electrical charge. The negatively charged particles are attracted to the positively charged plate (A), where a few of them escape through the pinhole. Similarly, the positively charged particles go to the negatively charged plate, and again some escape. In rushing towards the appropriate metal plate the atomic fragments jostle and collide with the unbroken atoms, causing them too to break up.

By examining the particles escaping through the pinholes, it was possible to discover the properties of the fragments of the atoms of different gases. The beam of particles escaping through the hole in the positive plate must carry a negative charge themselves, since unlike charges attract. These proved to behave identically, whatever gas the tube contained. Measurements made by J. J. Thomson in 1897 on the way this beam was deflected by electric and magnetic fields showed that, whatever the gas used, these negative particles always have the same ratio of electric charge to mass. Notice that this experiment did not establish that these particles are all of the same mass and the same electric charge. All Thomson could say for certain was that if some particles are larger than others, the large ones carry proportionately more electric charge. Nevertheless, the experiment led to the idea of the *electron*—a subatomic particle assumed to be contained in all atoms.

A few years later, in 1909, an American, R. A. Millikan, succeeded in measuring changes in the electric charge carried by tiny oil drops. These were always whole-number multiples of a certain small unit. He assumed, rightly, that this charge is that carried by a single electron. Knowing the charge carried by the electron, and Thomson's value for the ratio of charge to mass, the mass could easily be calculated. It proved to be only about one 2000th of the atomic weight of hydrogen.

Since the whole atom is neutral, the removal of an electron leaves the rump of the atom—called an ion—with an equal but opposite electric charge. These positively charged fragments are attracted to the negative metal plate and some escape through the pinhole drilled in it. Sure enough, experiments showed that the 'positive rays', as they were called, vary in property according to the gas in the tube.

Proton sun and electron planets?

All this led to a new picture of an atom as something which had a central core like a pudding with one or more tiny marble-like electrons embedded in the surface. The adhesive force is the electrical attraction between the opposite charges on the electron and the core—the same force which attracts fluff to a fountain pen which has been vigorously rubbed with a cloth. Note that the core was assumed to be roughly the same size as the atom itself, since it was taken for granted that solid matter is reasonably solid!

This idea was exploded in 1911 by the New Zealand physicist Ernest Rutherford, who was working at Manchester University on radioactive elements. Some of these elements, when they break up, emit energetic alpha-particles. These are doubly charged helium ions, with a mass about four times that of hydrogen (and, consequently, about 8000 times that of an electron).

Rutherford directed a collimated beam of these alpha-

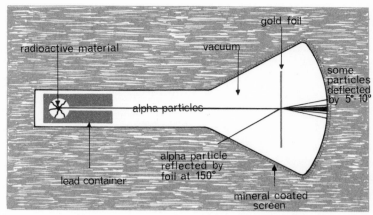

The atom is emptier than the solar system. This was shown by Rutherford, who directed a stream of alpha-particles, given off at high speed by radioactive elements, onto extremely thin gold foil. In total darkness, he watched the tiny flashes made as the deflected particles struck a mineral-coated screen. Most particles passed straight through the foil, but some were spread into a narrow pencil, and a few bounced back, deflected by 150°. This can only mean that the atoms of gold have a concentrated central nucleus extremely small and, like the alpha-particles, positively charged. Most alpha-particles passed through the atom too far away from the nucleus to be repelled by its charge; some, passing nearer, were deflected a little. A few, making a direct hit, bounced back—so few, in fact, that the nucleus must be minutely small in relation to the space within the atom. (2)

fig 2

particles onto a thin gold foil, and studied the deflections produced. These deflections were detected by allowing the particles subsequently to strike a mineral-coated screen. On striking the screen the particles make tiny flashes, which may be seen by the human eye, if the experimenter has first been conditioned by spending about twenty minutes in total darkness. It was observed that most of the alpha-particles shot right through the gold foil, but some were deflected by 5° or 10°. A few even bounced back, deflected through as much as 150°.

This effect could not possibly be explained on the basis of the Thomson atom. The interaction between the doubly charged alpha-particles and the gold could only be the electrical attraction of the electrons in the gold atoms, or the repulsion of their cores. But the light electrons would be simply brushed aside by the much heavier alpha-particles, and could not possibly play an important role. On the other hand if the atomic cores were about the same size as the whole atom, then positive charges would be fairly evenly spread through the volume of the foil. Their repulsive forces would tend to cancel each other out, and would produce only small effects. However, if the atomic core is in fact a highly concentrated nucleus, it is possible for an alpha-particle to pass close to one nucleus and relatively far from all the others. Since the repulsive force between electric charges falls off as the square of the distance between them, close encounters of an alpha-particle with a nucleus produce large deflections, while less close encounters produce only a small deflection. Thomson's diffuse puddings are thus replaced by hard scattering centres, off which the alpha-particles bounce whenever they score direct hits. Rutherford was able to deduce, from the proportion of alpha-particles which bounced back, that the gold nuclei are concentrated in a volume of radius about 10^{-12} cm.; that is, about 1/10,000th the size of the atom. This is tiny, even on an atomic scale.

Rutherford developed his theory of the atom, imagining it almost exactly like a miniature solar system, the negatively charged electrons circling like planets around the massive central positively charged nucleus, which takes the place of the sun. The gravitational attraction between the planets and the sun is replaced by the electrical attraction between the opposite charges on the electrons and the nucleus. The atom is even emptier than the solar system, the nucleus on this scale being somewhat smaller than the sun. From the point of view of distribution of *mass*, solid matter is no more solid than a few wasps flying about in St Paul's cathedral. It is the combined effect of the electrical forces which gives matter its solidity, and prevents, for example, a man from walking quietly through a closed door, like the best of ghosts!

On this picture, the simplest atom is hydrogen, consisting of a single electron orbiting around a nucleus with charge equal and opposite to that on the electron, usually represented by the symbol *e*. This hydrogen nucleus is another elementary particle like the electron, called the *proton*. Its mass is 1840 times that of an electron. The other ninety-two different types of atom differ primarily in the number of electrons. In a normal atom the charge on the orbiting electrons is balanced by the number of protons in the nucleus. So if we arrange the elements according to their atomic weight, this amounts to listing them according to the number of electrons. (Since a helium atom normally has two electrons, the alpha-particles of the Rutherford experiment are, in fact, just helium nuclei.)

Why a 'solar system' does not work

There are two general features of this picture of an atom which are still totally wrong. In the first place an electron circling in an orbit is an accelerating charge, which, as we saw in an earlier chapter, should give off energy in the form of radiation—it should act as a miniature transmitter. It is easy to calculate that the planetary electron in a hydrogen atom should give up all its energy in a brief flash of light and, in 10^{-10} second, coalesce with the proton or nucleus. Of course, nothing of the sort happens.

A more subtle defect of the model is that the frequency or wavelength of the emitted radiation should be related to the period of the electron in its orbit. As the energy of the orbit decreases continuously with the emission of radiation, the frequency of the radiation should also vary continuously. In fact, atoms do emit and absorb radiation. But a given element only emits and absorbs light of certain quite definite frequencies. It is because of the definite frequencies absorbed and given out by the atoms that objects have distinctive colours. The light given out by an element consists of a mixture of these definite wavelengths which are characteristic of the element, and can be used as a means of analysis. The characteristic wavelengths in sunlight, for example, tell us what elements are present in the sun.

A brilliantly successful, but thoroughly unsatisfactory, answer to both these difficulties was proposed, in 1913, by a young Danish physicist, Niels Bohr, who was working with Rutherford in Manchester. In the Bohr theory the purely classical Rutherford atom was supplemented by two *ad hoc* rules. These stated, firstly, that an electron in an atom could not move in an orbit of arbitrary energy, like a planet, but could only be found in a certain discrete set of energy levels. The higher the energy, the more the electron moves out under the action of the centrifugal force. Thus the radius of an orbit increases with the energy, and a discrete set of energy levels would imply that only a discrete set of radii were physically permissible. When moving in one of these allowed orbits, the energy of the electron would be constant, so radiation, which is the emission of energy, would be impossible.

fig 3

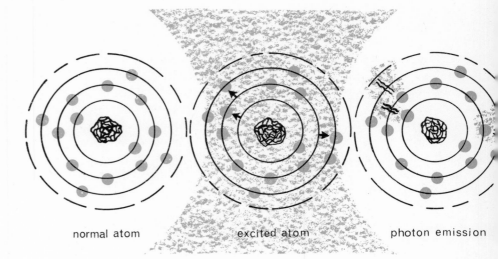

normal atom   excited atom   photon emission

The famous Bohr atom was both brilliantly successful and thoroughly unsatisfactory. It postulated that the orbiting electrons in Rutherford's miniature solar system could have certain permitted energies only, which meant they could occupy certain orbits only—the greater the energy the farther out the orbit. Incoming radiation 'excited' the atom, lifting electrons instantaneously to higher orbits; as the electrons jumped back, radiation was emitted. The theory gave the right size for the atom and predicted exactly the correct wavelengths for the emitted radiations. But it had fatal flaws; Bohr's electrons, for instance, could not radiate while orbiting—contrary to well-established experimental fact. (3)

However, Bohr's second rule was that an electron could make instantaneous jumps from one allowed orbit to another, the change in energy of the atom being balanced by the emission or absorption of radiation. If an electron is in one of its outer orbits it is said to be 'excited'. It emits radiation by cascading down through its allowed energy levels, like a ball rolling down a flight of stairs. The energy is given off in a series of discrete lumps corresponding to the gaps between the steps. Thus the energy of the emitted radiation, or photon, and consequently also its frequency, has a discrete set of allowed values. On this model the whole atom is stable, since once it reaches its lowest allowed level, or ground state, no further radiation is possible.

This theory was brilliantly successful in that Bohr's formula for the allowed frequencies of emitted radiation exactly fitted observation. Also the radius of the orbit corresponding to the lowest energy level is about 10^{-8} cm., giving correctly the size of the atoms. The constant *h*, introduced by Planck in connection with radiation and photons, plays an important role in both these crucial results.

A particle, a wave—a wave, a particle

At the same time the theory was thoroughly unsatisfactory, because it made absolutely no sense. The rules which Bohr imposed on Rutherford's model do not simply supplement the classical theories of Newton and Maxwell. They flatly contradict them at a very fundamental level. According to Maxwell, an electron in an orbit is accelerating and *must* radiate. This was a well-established experimental fact. It is also basic to Newtonian mechanics that a particle with a well-defined orbit traces out a continuous history, and *cannot* jump suddenly, and discontinuously, into a different orbit. This was a fantastically paradoxical situation, but not the only one of its kind.

A similar situation arose as a result of experiments carried out with beams of electrons by Davisson and Germer of the Bell Telephone Laboratories in the United States, in 1927. When the electrons were fired at a nickel crystal, they did not behave like miniature bullets. Instead they were deflected at certain preferred angles, thus building up a

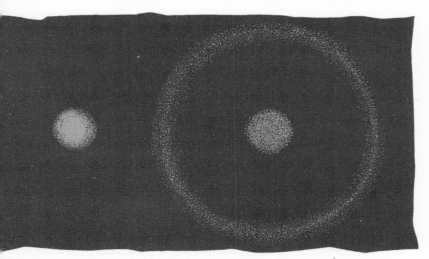

Today's atom is less precise. Scientists have realized that we cannot simultaneously know exactly where an electron is and measure its precise momentum. For the only way we can discover these is to strike the electron with photons of light, which changes both the quantities we are trying to measure. This means that even the notion of an orbit becomes impossible. The dilemma has been resolved, and the flaws of the Bohr atom removed, but we are left with the conception shown above (only roughly to scale) of the single electron in the simplest atom—hydrogen. The lowest Bohr orbit becomes a spherical region, the next, 'excited', orbit two main regions, in which the high probability of finding the electron is indicated by the density of the shading. (4)

pattern, exactly analogous to the diffraction pattern produced when monochromatic light is reflected from the surface of a fine grating.

Now diffraction is essentially a wave phenomenon, related to the blurring of the shadow as the wave passes round the sharp edge of an object. The situation was complementary to that faced by Planck, who had shown that radiation, classically regarded as waves, must sometimes be treated as a stream of particles, called photons. Already in 1924 the French physicist, Prince Louis de Broglie, had suggested that waves should be associated with electrons. He had further postulated that the particle properties, energy and momentum, and the wave properties, frequency and wavelength, should be related in the same way, both for electrons and photons. This conjecture predicted the wavelength to be ascribed to electrons. If the spacing of the atoms in the nickel crystal (about 10^{-8} cm.) was interpreted as the mesh of the grating, the standard theory of the diffraction of light could then be used to calculate the preferred angles in the Davisson-Germer experiment. The results fitted perfectly. They again involved Planck's constant in an intimate way, but again demanded a chaotic, and apparently arbitrary, mixing of well-defined classical concepts.

The answer to all these puzzles—the particle aspects of radiation, the wave aspects of electrons, and the blatant inconsistencies of the Bohr atom—was provided by quantum mechanics, which was developed by Schrödinger, Heisenberg and Dirac in the late 1920s.

Beyond our certain knowledge

Physics is concerned with the correlation of the results of quantitative measurements into physical laws. On the basis of these laws the development of a physical system can be predicted, and checked, again against the results of observations. It is the tacit assumption of classical physics—in particular of the theories of Maxwell and Newton—that these observations do not themselves influence, or appreciably disturb, the development of the observed system. It is conceivable that for systems which are small enough, this is no longer true. Indeed the notion of a photon strongly

p 70

p 75

fig 4

suggests that this is so. The simplest observation is to look at something. To do this one must shine light on it. This means one must strike it with photons. Owing to the diffraction patterns produced, the position of an object can only be determined to an accuracy comparable with the wavelength of the light used. For precision measurement, one therefore needs light of very short wavelength, which, according to Planck, means striking the object with photons of high momentum. If the object is as small as an electron this appreciably disturbs the electron's momentum. There is no escape. The minimum amount of light is a single photon. One may decrease the disturbance of the momentum by using photons of lower energy, but this increases the wavelength and the accuracy of the position measurement goes down. The tacit assumption of classical physics, that the position and momentum can both be measured with arbitrary precision, is simply not true for electrons. The observations produce mutual disturbances, which render these ideal measurements impossible. This restriction on the possible accuracy of mutually disruptive measurements is known as the Uncertainty Principle, and quantum mechanics is a refinement of Newtonian mechanics, which makes allowance for this uncertainty.

Planck's constant, h, appears in all this as the absolute measure of 'smallness'. It is a unit of 'action', which is the product of 'length' and 'momentum'. Its absolute value is about 10^{-27} erg-secs. The typical action of a system is the product of the significant length and the appropriate momentum. (In the diffraction of electrons, for example, these are the crystal spacing and the momentum of the electrons respectively.) When this product is comparable with, or even smaller than h, the disturbances accompanying observations are appreciable, and quantum mechanics is essential. This is the case for atoms, chemical reactions between atoms, and electron diffraction. For the motion of electrons in discharge tubes, the typical action is large compared with h, and classical theories are adequate.

One consequence of this is that for a particle satisfying quantum mechanics the notion of an orbit is impossible, since this implies an exact knowledge of both position and momentum. The best one can hope for is some probability distribution which determines these properties of the particle within certain limits.

If an electron of well-defined momentum is confined in a perfectly reflecting box, the function which determines this probability distribution turns out to be just the wave suggested by de Broglie. But the frequency must be such that an exact number of waves fit into the box, just as a violin string can only vibrate with frequencies such that an exact number of waves fit into its length (giving rise to the various harmonics). This implies that only a discrete set of momenta are possible for the electron, and consequently that it may take on only a discrete set of energies.

An electron in a hydrogen atom is also confined to a certain region by the electrical attraction of the proton. Again only certain energy values are allowed, which correspond to probability distributions which 'fit' this region. The region is less precisely defined, and the definition of an allowed fit is more complicated, but the important point is that the possible energy levels coincide precisely with those given by the Bohr model. But the Bohr orbit, which led to all the inconsistencies, is now replaced by a probability distribution. The radius of the lowest Bohr orbit appears in Schrödinger's theory as the radius of the spherical region in which an electron in the ground state is almost certain to be found. Thus quantum mechanics also predicts correctly the size of an atom. Since the electron is charged, the probability distribution may be regarded as a charge distribution. But it does not change with time. The charge distribution is *static*, and it is now perfectly consistent with Maxwell's theory that it does not radiate. It is also quite consistent that there should be a finite probability for transitions from one level to another. When this happens there is a sudden change in the charge distribution, which naturally produces radiation. Thus the Schrödinger theory reproduces all the satisfactory features of the Bohr model—the energy levels, the atomic size, and the mechanism of radiation—but, by replacing the classical orbits by a probability distribution, it removes all the inconsistencies with the well-established theories of Newton and Maxwell.

One final point is required to understand the structure of an atom. When a dozen balls are rolled down a staircase, all of them end up at the bottom. One might think that in a many-electron atom all the electrons would settle, similarly, in the ground state. But it was found by Wolfgang Pauli that no two electrons can have exactly the same probability distribution. This he enunciated in his famous Exclusion Principle. When combined with the Schrödinger theory this shows that there is room for just two electrons in the ground state, corresponding to the two possible orientations of the electron spin. In the first excited state there are eight possible configurations, and so on. As electrons are added to make up more and more complicated atoms, the possible states are filled up in an orderly way. When all possible states for a given energy level are filled, the electrons form a closed 'shell' of charge, which is of great importance in determining the chemical properties of the elements. This is discussed in later chapters.

p 137

p 160
(fig 3)

This was the situation in 1930. It was a remarkably rosy one, and many scientists felt that they were near the end of the logical quest set by the analytical approach. There were only two types of fundamental force in nature—gravitational and electromagnetic. There were only three types of particle—the proton, the electron and the photon. These were considered to be structureless points. All matter was made up of 92 elements, whose atomic structure was well understood in terms of protons and electrons and the electrical forces between them. The residual electrical forces between atoms also provided a basis for chemical bonds and chemical reactions. Gravitational forces control the motion of neutral matter in bulk.

The only fundamental question still not explained was the structure of the atomic nuclei themselves. It is this problem which has been engaging physicists for the last thirty years. Their studies have already produced a violent technical revolution in military affairs, and an equally violent potential revolution in man's social and industrial capacity. At a more sophisticated level, they seem to call for a similarly profound revolution in our thinking about fundamental physics. We turn now to these topics.

Source of supreme power: the nucleus

The nucleus of a particular atom, with a given number of orbiting electrons, must contain the same number of protons to balance the charge. However, it turns out that, apart from hydrogen (at least in its normal form), the masses of the atoms, and consequently the atomic nuclei, are roughly double the value attained by multiplying the mass of the protons by the number of protons required to make up the nuclear charge. It was thought, at one time, that the extra

fig 5

mass might be made up by adding equal numbers of protons and electrons to the nuclei, to make up the mass without altering the charge. However, there was no good reason why the nuclear electrons should be confined within a distance of 10^{-12} cm., while the atomic electrons are free to roam over the relatively vast range of 10^{-8} cm. This difficulty was cleared up in 1932, by James Chadwick of Cambridge University, who discovered that when beryllium nuclei are bombarded with alpha-particles, some of them turn into carbon nuclei with the emission of heavy neutral particles of almost the same mass as a proton. These neutral particles, in turn, can cause the emission of protons from nuclei which they subsequently strike. The newly discovered particle was called the *neutron*. Nuclei are made up of protons and neutrons—enough protons to make up the charge, and then a roughly equal number of neutrons to give the observed total mass.

The chemical properties of an element are determined by the number of orbiting electrons, and hence by the number of protons in the nucleus. The atomic weight depends on the total number of particles—protons and neutrons—in the nucleus. Now a few neutrons more or less should not change the chemical properties of the atom. This has indeed been found to be the case. An instrument called the mass spectrograph, developed by F. W. Aston, uses electric and magnetic fields to sort out atoms according to their mass. Aston was able to show that most of the common elements do not consist entirely of identical atoms. All the atoms of a given element have the same number of protons in their nuclei, but there may be a few neutrons more or less than usual, and a corresponding difference in atomic weight. Different nuclei of a given element are called *isotopes*. An isotope is specified by giving the chemical symbol for the element, writing the charge (or number of protons) as a superscript, and the approximate mass in nuclear units (or total number of protons and neutrons) as a subscript. Thus two isotopes of uranium are $^{92}U_{238}$ and $^{92}U_{235}$. Natural uranium contains 99 per cent $^{92}U_{238}$ with a little less than 1 per cent $^{92}U_{235}$. There are three isotopes of hydrogen, $^1H_1$, $^1H_2$, and $^1H_3$. The nucleus $^1H_1$ is just a proton, $^1H_2$ is a proton and a neutron bound together to form what is called a deuteron, the nucleus of 'heavy hydrogen'. The isotope $^1H_3$ consists of a proton and two neutrons, and is called a triton, the nucleus of 'super-heavy hydrogen'. Except for the very lightest atoms, the different isotopes have identical chemical properties. However, different isotopes may

p 142
(3-5)

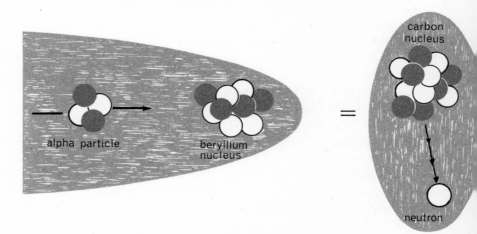

A second heavy particle in the nucleus of the atom was discovered by James Chadwick in 1932. He directed a stream of fast alpha-particles onto nuclei of beryllium. After the collisions, carbon nuclei remained and a new particle was ejected—with almost the same mass as a proton and with no charge. He named it the neutron. Protons and neutrons, in roughly equal numbers, together make up the nuclei of all atoms. (5)

behave very differently in specifically nuclear reactions such as that observed by Chadwick. In the notation introduced above, this can be written,

$$^4Be_9 + {}^2He_4 \rightarrow {}^6C_{12} + {}^0n_1$$

beryllium + helium → carbon + neutron

(alpha particle)

(Note that the total charge (upper suffices) and the total number of nuclear particles (lower suffices) remain unchanged in the process. These are very general rules.)

Ten thousand times smaller, a hundred million times stronger

We must now face the basic question of what holds the nuclei together. They consist in part of protons, packed together at a distance of less than 10^{-12} cm. This is smaller, by a factor of $10,000$, than the distance between the electrons and protons in an atom. They, therefore, *repel* each other electrically with a force which is $(10,000)^2$, or 10^8, times greater than the force holding the electrons together in an atom—a hundred million times stronger than the forces operating in chemical reactions. There is also a gravitational attraction between the protons, but this can easily be shown to be negligibly small. Since the nucleus holds together, unchanged by even the most violent chemical explosion, some other completely new and specifically nuclear force must be acting, which is even stronger than the powerful electric repulsion. Also, since neutrons are bound tightly in the nuclei, it is reasonable to suppose that the same force operates between protons and neutrons, and between pairs of neutrons.

This rather simple argument is the key to the understanding of all modern nuclear technology. It stems from the very tiny size of the nucleus, even on an atomic scale. This is the physical origin of the factor of a million, which turns up repeatedly in various connections in technical applications of the nuclear force—the megatonnage of H-bombs, the mega-deaths of textbook nuclear wars, or the relative efficiency of uranium to coal as a civilian fuel.

When a match is struck a chemical reaction is set off. The phosphorus atoms in the match head re-arrange themselves under the action of their electrical interactions (chemical bonds), to form new molecules with the oxygen in the air, and give off energy as heat. According to Einstein, energy is conserved in the reaction, the heat given off being balanced by a small difference between the mass (or rest energy) of the atoms present before and after the reaction. However, for all chemical processes, the mass difference is so tiny that this is not of much practical importance. But the nuclear force, because it is so large, results in a mass difference of appreciable size. The mass of a heavy nucleus, like that of uranium, is about 1% lighter than the sum of the masses of its constituent nuclear particles. The apparent loss of mass, or mass defect, of the nucleus is accounted for, as Einstein's theory predicts, by the cohesive energy holding the nuclear particles together. This amount of energy would have to be supplied to break the nucleus into its constituent parts.

The stronger the forces holding the nucleus together, the greater the mass defect. Measurements show that the medium-sized nuclei, containing about 100 particles, are the most stable. This at once suggests a new way of releasing energy. For if a large atom can be split in half to make two medium-sized ones, the difference in energy between the original and product nuclei will be released. The amount of energy released in this way is very large compared with that

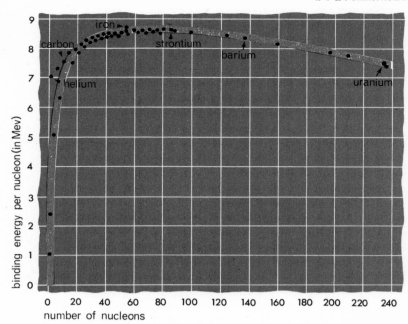

The amount of energy required to remove a proton or neutron from a nucleus (the particle's 'binding energy') is also the energy which would be released if the particle returned to the nucleus. For the lightest nuclei it is low, rising quickly to a maximum for nuclei of medium weight such as strontium or iron and falling off again for an element as heavy as uranium. If a heavy nucleus can be split, or light nuclei combined, to form nuclei of middle weight, then in each case energy will be released—for most energy is released in assembling the particles to form middle-weight nuclei. Where does the energy come from? It is converted from mass as the nucleus forms under the strong nuclear forces. The energy released in such reactions is about one million times greater than in chemical reactions involving similar quantities of material—hydrogen bombs compared with TNT. (6)

produced by chemical reactions, such as the burning of coal. The breakdown (or fission, as it is called) of one pound of uranium nuclei into smaller nuclei of about half uranium's atomic weight releases as much energy as burning three million pounds of coal.

Since it is the medium-sized nuclei which are the most stable, energy is also released when smaller nuclei join together to form medium-sized ones. This process of building medium-sized nuclei from smaller ones is called fusion. It is in this way that the sun produces energy, linking protons together to form more complex nuclei.

Nuclear fission put to work

Nuclear technology is concerned with the harnessing of these enormous forces, and putting to specific uses the vast energies released. It is one thing to realize that a nuclear force is available for technical exploitation; it is quite another to see how this can be done. The technical breakthrough occurred in 1939, when Lise Meitner and Otto Hahn discovered that the process of fission actually takes place fairly readily, when a uranium nucleus is struck by a slow neutron. The large uranium nucleus splits into two roughly equal parts, almost as if it were a drop of liquid breaking up. In the process, apart from the two major fragments (medium-sized nuclei like barium and strontium), a number of neutrons also are emitted. On average each fission produces about three neutrons. This gives the obvious possibility of a chain reaction in a lump of uranium, in which the neutrons, emitted from one fission, trigger the fission of other nuclei. In this way a 'family tree' of fissions can build up and the energy-releasing process does not fizzle out, but may grow rapidly.

The discovery of fission was made just before the start of World War II, and physicists on both sides, particularly in

fig 6

p 142
(2)

America, Britain and Germany, realized the fantastic military possibilities of nuclear explosions. In Britain and the United States a start was made on making some nuclear explosive. The two combined their efforts in a single programme after 1942.

Although the primary objective at that time was military, the first man-made release of nuclear energy was in a controlled nuclear reactor. This was built in a squash court in an obscure corner of Chicago University in 1942, under the direction of Enrico Fermi. This reactor was the prototype of all subsequent models, particularly those being built to generate electricity in Britain today.

There were two main difficulties to be overcome. As has been said, the fission process is most effectively induced by slow neutrons, moving at about one mile per second. The neutrons that appear as fission products are moving about ten thousand times too fast. Somehow they have to be slowed down. Suppose a number of billiard balls are placed on a billiard table and one of them is given a high velocity. At each subsequent collision some of its momentum will be transferred to another ball. After a number of collisions all the balls will be moving comparatively slowly. This was the principle employed. To be effective the neutrons must bounce around in a medium—or *moderator*—which is made up of nuclei of comparable mass, and of an element which does not absorb the precious neutrons and thus take them out of the fission-producing cycle.

The protons in the hydrogen of ordinary water are ideal from the point of view of mass, but they absorb the neutrons to form deuterons. This can be avoided by using heavy water as a moderator, in which the hydrogen is replaced by deuterium (that is hydrogen with the deuteron isotope as nucleus). This has been employed in subsequent models, but the original Chicago reactor used very pure graphite (carbon) as a moderator. To prevent the neutrons from escaping before each parent fission could produce on the average at least one fission child, the reactor had to be of considerable size—about 500 tons. The rods of natural uranium fuel were buried, in the form of a cubic lattice, in the vast pile of graphite moderator—hence the alternative name 'pile' for a nuclear reactor.

p 150 (38)

p 144 (14–16)

p 141 (1)

Having seen how to arrange the uranium so that the fission reaction would keep going, the second problem was to devise some means of control to prevent the reaction from getting out of hand. This was done by inserting, in the pile, control rods of boron or cadmium, which are very effective neutron absorbers. If the fission chain starts to go too fast, the control rods can be inserted a bit deeper and neutrons absorbed. As the reaction dies off, the control rods can be slightly withdrawn.

From the point of view of civilian power, the important end product of a nuclear reactor is the heat which comes from the buffeting of atoms by the fast-moving fragments of the broken uranium nucleus. The heat is usually carried outside the reactor by water under pressure or by steam, gas, or molten metal. Usually the heat is used to raise steam to drive an electrical power station. In these stations the nuclear reactor simply replaces the coal or oil furnace.

p 146–7 (21)

Fuel for a power-hungry world

The implications of nuclear power supply have hardly yet begun to be felt. The world resources of chemical fuels—coal and oil—are limited to a few hundred years' supply, assuming that there is no suddenly increased demand for fuel from countries at present underdeveloped. If their standard of living is ever to be raised, nuclear fuels are destined to play an absolutely vital part in a power-hungry world.

p 150–1 (39–40)

Since the operation of the Chicago pile, there have been improvements in the details of reactor design, but not in the principles. The reason why the original pile was so big, is that only the rare isotope $^{92}U_{235}$ takes effective part in the reaction, so that natural uranium is very low-grade fuel. Much smaller piles operating more efficiently at a higher temperature can be made if the fuel is enriched by increasing the proportion of the U_{235}. When natural uranium is used in a pile, some of the neutrons are captured by the U_{238} which leads to the formation of plutonium ($^{94}Pu_{239}$), an element which occurs in nature in almost undetectable traces, and, like U_{235}, is a good fission fuel. Reactor fuels may also be enriched by including plutonium extracted from the fuel elements of older piles. With enriched fuel one does not need to be so careful to make the neutrons effective in order to set up a self-sustaining reaction. They do not need so much slowing down, and the whole structure can be much smaller. Such a reactor is called 'fast' since it operates with fast neutrons. A reactor which is deliberately designed to convert non-fissile material such as U_{238} into nuclear fuels such as plutonium, so that more fuel is produced than the reactor uses, is called a 'breeder'. Breeder reactors and fast reactors of various kinds have been built in the United States, the Soviet Union and Britain.

One serious drawback to fission reactors is their radioactive waste. The nuclei in the fission products emerge from the violent nuclear reaction in a highly excited state. Their constituent nuclear particles subsequently re-arrange themselves into a more 'comfortable' position under the action of the powerful nuclear forces, giving off energy in the form of photons, electrons, neutrons and alpha-particles. The process is very similar to the emission of photons by excited atoms, but since the forces involved are far greater, the photons, in particular, are also much more energetic. They are usually called gamma rays and have an extremely damaging effect on living tissue.

p 145 (17–19)

p 148–9 (22–37)

The time taken for a lump of a given isotope to radiate half its surplus energy is called the half-life. During a further half-life, half the remaining energy will be given off, and so on. Half-lives can vary from fractions of seconds to thousands of millions of years. The isotopes which constitute the greatest danger are those with the longer half-lives, since the short-lived ones can be stored in a safe place until the radiation is given off. The others can be kept in thick concrete tanks, or dumped in containers in deep parts of the ocean, but no really satisfactory solution has yet been found to this problem of disposing of them.

p 145 (20)

Power from the sea
for ten thousand million years

We have seen that medium-sized nuclei are the most stable, and that energy is also released when small nuclei coalesce to form larger ones. If these 'fusion' reactions, which have been made to take place explosively in the hydrogen bomb, could be controlled, their social implications as a source of power would be far greater than that of nuclear power produced by fission. The reason is the abundance of the light nuclei compared with heavy ones. Using deuterium nuclei contained in all water (including sea water), it should be possible to extract power from water, weight for weight, more than a million times more effectively than from coal or oil—and there is no shortage of sea water even for the most highly industrialized and world-wide society one can imagine.

A typical heat-producing fusion reaction is to make two deuterons combine to form either a helium isotope and a neutron, or a triton and a proton. In the notation described above,

p 142
(6·7)

$$^1H_2 + \ ^1H_2 \rightarrow \ ^2He_3 + \ ^0n_1 + energy$$
deuteron + deuteron → helium + neutron
$$^1H_2 + \ ^1H_2 \rightarrow \ ^1H_3 + \ ^1H_1 + energy$$
deuteron + deuteron → triton + proton

Using these reactions there is enough deuterium in the sea to supply the world's present power demands for ten thousand million years. Furthermore there would be no problem of getting rid of radioactive waste.

These reactions can be made to take place easily by firing deuterons from an accelerator at others contained in a suitable target. But there is no net gain. For although some of the deuterons will react to produce a burst of energy, the great majority will be lost through alternative reactions. The energy produced by successful impacts is always far less than that used to run the accelerator.

Some way is needed of recovering the energy of the unsuccessful deuterons and feeding it back into the system to produce further fusion. One method is to heat a collection of deuterons to a very high temperature, about 100 million degrees Centigrade, in a gas at very low pressure (about 10^{15} particles per c.c. compared with 10^{28} per c.c. in water). At these temperatures a proportion of the deuterons jostling together will be moving as fast as those produced by the accelerator: fast enough to overcome the electrical repulsion between them. A proportion may produce a fusion reaction. The rest will not, but their energy is not lost (as was that of the unsuccessful deuterons from the accelerator) but merely transferred to other deuterons with which they collide, perhaps giving them enough energy to succeed where they themselves had failed in overcoming the electrical repulsion.

So the problem is one of obtaining a sufficiently high temperature and containing the extremely hot gas in something which neither melts nor carries away the heat. At such temperatures the atoms are stripped of their electrons, and the gas, which is called a 'plasma', behaves in certain characteristic ways.

The most hopeful approach to the problem of containing the hot plasma is to use magnetic forces to form the container. One approach uses a toroidal apparatus—the shape of a motor tyre inner tube—to contain the gas. A heavy current is set up in the plasma round the inside of the tube, and this induces magnetic fields, circling the current, which tend to drive the plasma rapidly away from the walls of the apparatus, into the centre of the tube. This 'pinch' effect can, in principle, both create the high temperature and at the same time keep the hot plasma away from the walls of the material container. The snag is that the whole system is not stable, since any irregularity produces forces which tend to drive the hot plasma back against the walls, rather than restoring the desired 'pinch' effect. These deficiencies may possibly be corrected by using different geometries, and it is probable that the solution will be found, using the general principle of the 'magnetic bottle', in which the hot plasma is contained by magnetic fields, which are set up by currents in conductors outside the plasma itself. Conditions of temperature and plasma density falling short of those required by a factor of about one thousand had already been ob-

fig 7

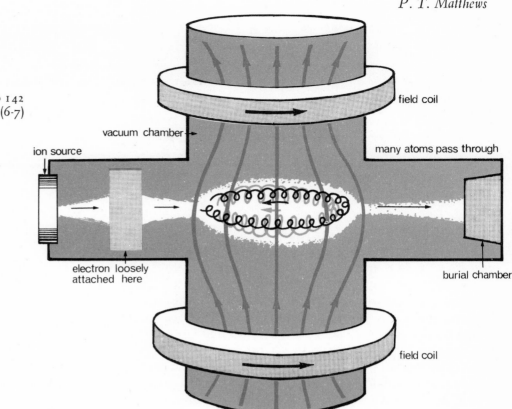

P. T. Matthews

The world's fuel problems would be solved at once if the fusion reactions which explode in the hydrogen bomb could be controlled as a source of power. The fuel, deuterium ('heavy water'), is available in vast quantities from the sea, but a temperature of a few hundred million degrees Centigrade must be achieved before the particles are moving fast enough for the reaction to continue. Many ways are being tried, the most hopeful being those in which the highly rarefied fuel is isolated by magnetic fields, long enough for its temperature and density to build up until the energy released by the reactions exceeds that fed into the system. In a recent 'magnetic bottle' experiment (top), ions with electrons loosely attached were fired at speeds equivalent to a temperature of 300 million degrees Centigrade into a bottle-shaped magnetic field produced in a vacuum chamber. The particles were trapped by the field, ions and electrons spiralling in opposite ways. But before the density was high enough, particles spilled out from the field and reached the walls. In the 'magnetic well', additional conductors carry currents which so change the shape of the magnetic field that its strength increases in all directions from the central region—and should resist more effectively the spread of the hot plasma. (7)

tained in 1965 by such methods. It is surely only a matter of time before this most far-reaching of all present-day technical problems is solved.

Knocking the nucleus to pieces

We have had rather a long digression on nuclear technology. Just as the most sophisticated motor-car design throws little light on the chemical forces involved in the combustion of gasoline, so this technology has given virtually no new insight into the detailed workings of the nuclear force. This is a problem for fundamental physics, and is the key to a deeper understanding of the structure of matter. We return to this our main theme.

Experiments to study nuclear structure are all modelled on Rutherford's experiment described above. The essential ingredients are a beam of electrons or nuclear particles, a target of nuclei or subnuclear particles, and some detection device for observing the results of the collision.

As a source of beam particles, Rutherford used naturally ejected alpha-particles. Today experimenters use protons (or sometimes electrons), which are accelerated artificially by means of electric and magnetic fields. To study the nuclear force it is best to see it operate in its simplest form, which is between just two nuclear particles—protons or neutrons.

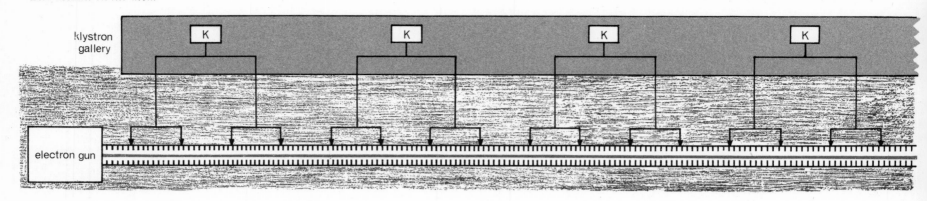

(We shall refer to these particles collectively as nucleons.) The nuclear force holding the nucleons together is very short-range. It is extremely strong when the nucleons are less than 10^{-12} cm. from each other, but dies off very rapidly outside this distance. To investigate the specifically nuclear interaction of two protons, it is necessary to shoot them at each other with considerable momentum, otherwise they are simply pushed apart by the purely electrical repulsion between their positive charges, before they are sufficiently close for the short-range nuclear force to start to operate.

Thus the accelerator is to the nuclear physicist as the telescope is to the astronomer. It is his one method of observing the nucleus; and the larger the accelerator (that is, the more energetic the beam of charged particles it produces), the more deeply can he penetrate through the powerful repulsive electrical forces to the region in which the essentially nuclear force dominates. The development of accelerators began in about 1930 with the work of Cockcroft and Walton. The charged particles from a suitable source were accelerated by passing them through an electric field produced by a high-voltage generator. This type of accelerator is satisfactory only up to a limited energy. The big accelerators of today however are based on a principle of cyclical acceleration invented by Lawrence in California. Instead of attempting to accelerate the particles in a single step, he used a magnetic field to force them into a circular path, and speeded them a little more each time they passed across the gap between the D-shaped electrodes.

The biggest proton accelerators work on this cyclical principle, although various methods are used to reduce the size of the magnet required, and to correct for the changing mass of the particles as their speed approaches that of light. Proton accelerators are now operating at Brookhaven Laboratory in the United States, and in the co-operative European Laboratory, CERN, outside Geneva, which accelerate particles to an energy of about 30,000 million electron volts (1 electron volt is the energy an electron gains in a potential of 1 volt). For convenience physicists write 1 MeV for 1 million electron volts and for 1 thousand million electron volts either 1 GeV (G for giga) or, in the United States, 1 BeV (B for US billion).

Rutherford examined the interaction between the alpha-particles and nuclei in his gold foil target, by studying the directions in which alpha-particles were found to be moving after collision. The modern nuclear physicist does the same. But in addition he measures the energy of the particles, and also examines their nature. The particles which emerge from a collision need not be the same as those which collided in the first place, as was shown for example in Chadwick's discovery of the neutron. While Rutherford had to sit in a dark room, counting the minute flashes of light (15 to 40 a minute) on a fluorescent screen as each alpha-particle hit it, various kinds of automatic counters are now available which can count up to 10 million per second.

p 153 (47)

An interesting particle accelerator recently in operation is not circular but stretches for two miles in a straight line—the linear accelerator built by Stanford University. It uses pulsed beams of high-energy electrons, 360 per second, to study the electro-magnetic properties of protons, neutrons and other nuclei and determine, in particular, their shape and size. The accelerator tube, a copper pipe in 960 10 ft. sections, 4" in diameter, runs through a concrete underground chamber, with sensitive remote-controlled alignment and cooling mechanisms. It is reduced to a high vacuum. Above ground, protected by 25 feet of earth, runs a manned chamber housing 240 klystrons producing powerful radio microwaves. Each klystron feeds the waves through pipe waveguides, to four tube sections (in stage two of the operations 960 klystrons are planned, one to each section).

The electron pulses are shot into the accelerator by an electron gun and ride through the 2-mile tube on the crest of the waves, steadily increasing in energy. At the end, they enter a 'beam switchyard', where large electromagnets deflect them at choice to any of several research areas, housing the targets, bubble chambers, and other analysing equipment. The wave-speed is controlled, typically to the velocity of light, by disks inserted transversely in the copper tube, reducing the diameter of the electron path to ¾ inch. How can an electron gun, even if the copper tube is exactly straight, shoot electrons without loss at the sides for two miles? The problem largely disappears, for under the theory of relativity, an observer travelling with the electrons would see the pipe greatly foreshortened, because everything approaches the observer with nearly the velocity of light. At an energy of 30 BeV the 10,000-ft. pipe would seem to be 22 inches only, and the precision required to shoot electrons through a ¾-inch pipe of this length is less, for instance, than that necessary to produce the picture on a television screen. (8)

p 153 (45)
p 156 (49–52)
fig 9

Alternatively the nuclear collision can be made to take place in photographic emulsion, or in a bubble chamber. In both cases the charged particles leave visible tracks, and the whole event is recorded photographically. A recently developed method of making charged particles visible is the counter-controlled spark chamber. A high voltage is maintained between two metal plates, so that a spark is just on the point of passing between them. If a charged particle passes across the gap between the plates, a spark runs along its track. A whole series of metal plates are arranged in a pile and the sparks produced by charged particles are photographed.

The simple proton grows complex

Before considering the results of experiments with high-energy proton beams and sophisticated detection apparatus, it is interesting to try to work out what we may reasonably expect. Consider a thought-experiment in which two nucleons suddenly materialize at a certain distance apart. According to the theory of relativity, no message or influence can pass from one nucleon to the other at a speed greater than that of light. The simplest way to ensure this is for the mechanism of their interaction to be the exchange of yet another particle. The nucleons interact like football players, who pass the ball between them whenever they are close enough to do so, each one changing direction in the process. The observer, who cannot see the details of the mechanism,

p 152–3 (41–6)
p 154–5 (48)
fig 8

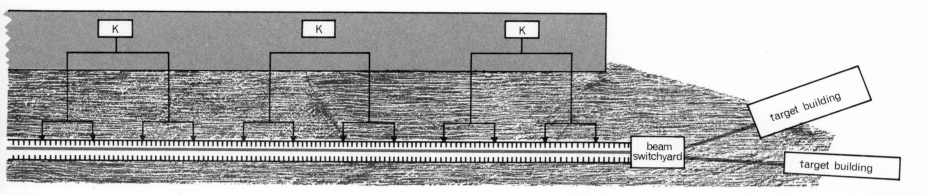

will notice merely that they affect each other's motion, whenever they come within range, and will see that there is a short-range force operating between them.

Note that the range of the force is directly related to the mass of the exchanged particle. A football may be passed over a distance of some yards. But the players must come within a foot of each other if they are to exchange cannon balls. The Japanese physicist Yukawa suggested in 1934 that this might be the mechanism of the nuclear force, and from consideration of the range, predicted that the exchanged particle should have a mass about three hundred times that of an electron. This sort of middle-sized particle is called a *meson*. A very important consequence of this theory is that if the protons collide with sufficient energy (about $1/2$ GeV), instead of coming out of the collision, like two billiard balls, with the same kinetic energy, a meson may be produced and all three particles emerge quite slowly

from the collision. If the football players go fast enough a pass may be dropped, and the ball, as well as the players, may appear from the mêlée.

It was not until 1947 that this remarkable and qualitative prediction was confirmed, since physics of this fundamental nature was brought to a complete standstill by the war. It was not in fact necessary to wait for the construction of a sufficiently powerful machine, since there is a continuous stream of high-energy protons entering the earth's atmosphere in cosmic rays. C. F. Powell and his group at Bristol University used the newly developed photographic emulsion technique. It was found that when cosmic ray protons collide with nuclei in the emulsion, they frequently produce Yukawa's particles, now called pi-mesons. Shortly after, pi-mesons were produced by artificially accelerated protons in America, and since then their production and subsequent reactions with other particles have been studied extensively under laboratory conditions. All the qualitative features of Yukawa's theory have been amply confirmed.

p 143
(8)

p 156
(52)

Matter and anti-matter

Another general theoretical prediction which has been confirmed by high-energy machine physics is that concerning anti-matter. By combining the requirements of quantum mechanics and relativity, Dirac was able to show that an electron must be regarded as a small top able to spin in either direction. (This has already been mentioned above in connection with the Exclusion Principle.) At the same time, he showed that corresponding to *any* charged particle there should be an 'anti-particle' of the same mass, but opposite charge. When particle and anti-particle meet, they annihilate each other, most of their mass (or rest energy) being carried off as kinetic energy by lighter particles. Anti-electrons, or positrons, were discovered by Anderson soon after Dirac made his prediction. When they annihilate, they turn into very energetic photons; they disappear in a flash of electromagnetic radiation. Anti-protons were first produced with the use of the high-energy proton accelerator at Brookhaven, USA, relatively recently. When proton and anti-proton meet, they annihilate to produce an average of about five pi-mesons and a lot of kinetic energy. Notice that in this process about three-quarters of the rest mass originally present turns into kinetic energy, compared with less than one per cent in a fusion reaction. Thus, in proportion to the weight of fuel involved, an H-bomb explosion is a damp squib compared with nucleon—anti-nucleon annihilation.

p 156
(49)

p 143
(9)

p 143
(10)

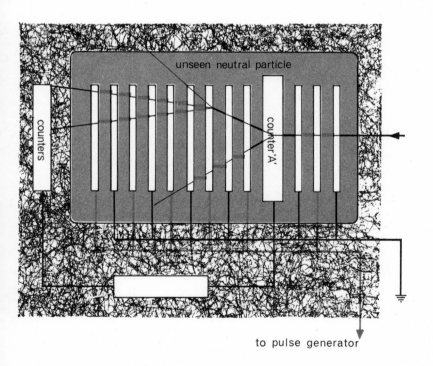

to pulse generator

The charged particles which are knocked out of nuclei can be examined in a spark chamber, which consists of a series of thin metal plates immersed in the inert gas neon. In the drawing above, such a particle has entered the chamber and interacted with a target nucleus in counter A, yielding a charged secondary (below) and a neutral particle which has then decayed into two charged particles and a second neutral. The neutrals had no effect, but as the charged particles passed through the gaps, they released electrons from the atoms of neon. Meanwhile the 'event' in counter A has triggered the circuits into applying a high voltage pulse to alternate plates; the released electrons, moving under the high voltage, collide with neon atoms and release more electrons until the gas suddenly becomes conducting and bright sparks pass. These, photographed, reveal the path of the particles. If many particles enter the chamber, the circuits select for pulsing only those events previously 'programmed' as interesting—a choice which must be made in a ten-millionth of a second. (9)

The 'strange particles'

However, apart from confirming these qualitative predictions, experiments with cosmic rays and high-energy accelerators have produced many completely unexpected results. Already in 1947, G. D. Rochester and C. C. Butler obtained evidence that in some nucleon–nucleon collisions in cosmic rays, not only pi-mesons are produced, but other particles as well. By 1962 over thirty sub-nuclear particles had been identified and the number is now over one hundred. These consist of *hyperons*, which are heavier than nucleons, and other mesons, which are lighter than nucleons, but heavier than pi-mesons. There is also a group of light particles, called *leptons*, which include the muon and neutrino along with the electrons. These particles were so unexpected that some of them are technically known as 'strange'.

p 143
(13)
fig 10

In the light of this development, one may say that the objectives of the nuclear scientist and the nuclear technologist have become almost diametrically opposite. The technician works with nuclear reactors and nuclear weapons, whose basic purpose is to turn rest mass into kinetic energy (heat) in an economic manner, in the sense that far more available energy comes out than is put in. The scientist, on the other hand, with high-energy machines uses vast quantities of available energy in the form of electric power to accelerate protons. The kinetic energy of the protons is then turned into rest mass in the form of rare types of sub-nuclear particles, whose properties he can then study. Economically the pure scientists' activities are, of course, absurd, at least in the short run. Nothing comes out, but the satisfaction of a quite irrational thirst for knowledge. But we should stress that it is a thirst for an understanding of the physical universe at its most general and fundamental level, which in the long run provides the basis of our industrial civilization.

The reason why these sub-nuclear particles are only seen under the exceptional circumstances of very high-energy collisions, is that all, with the exceptions of the proton and electron, are unstable, most of them disintegrating—or decaying—into lighter particles. The half-lives of these very unstable particles are usually of the order of 10^{-8} to 10^{-10} second.

This kind of decay was first observed in its pure form in the beta-decay of a neutron, which is slightly heavier than the proton. When free it decays, with a half-life of about eleven minutes, according to the scheme

p 143
(11)

$$n \rightarrow p^+ + e^- + \bar{v}$$
neutron → proton + electron + anti-neutrino

The neutrino produced by the decaying neutron is a fascinating particle. It was proposed on theoretical grounds by Pauli, and was postulated to have no mass and no electric charge, like the photon, but to carry a spin like the electron and proton. A few years ago its existence was directly established experimentally, and recently experiments have been carried out with neutrino beams.

The form of spontaneous nuclear radioactivity, in which electrons (called beta-particles) are thrown out of the nucleus, is due to one of the neutrons, which is not very firmly bound, decaying in this way. If the neutron is tightly bound in a nucleus this sort of decay is impossible. But it may happen that a bound proton goes through the reverse process

p 143
(12)

$$p^+ \rightarrow n + e^+ + v$$
proton → neutron + positron + neutrino

The reason why there are only 92 elements in nature is that as more protons are added to a nucleus, the long-range electrical repulsion, which operates between all the protons present, builds up faster than the short-range nuclear attraction, which is only effective between neighbouring pairs. For more than 92 protons, it is always energetically favour-

able for a proton to convert to a neutron by positron emission, thus losing one charge and forming an isotope of an element one place lower down the periodic table. Unstable elements, with charges greater than 92, can be formed by bombarding heavy elements with neutrons or protons. Plutonium, used in nuclear reactors and as a nuclear explosive, is one very important example.

'Left-handed' forces of decay

The half-life of any unstable system is a very sensitive function of the available energy. The free neutron has a relatively long life because it is only slightly heavier than its decay products and, consequently, very little energy is available for the decay reaction. In fact, on a nuclear scale even half-lives of 10^{-10} second are very long. Times must always be measured in units of the natural period appropriate to the system. Thus human times are measured in days or years, which are the natural periods of the Earth's spin and its orbital motion, respectively. The natural period for a sub-nuclear particle—the period of oscillation of a nucleon in a nucleus—is about 10^{-23} second. If we call this a 'nuclear year', the half-lives of even the short-lived particles are still more than a million million nuclear years. All these decays seem to have a common origin, but it is evident from these long half-lives that they cannot be a result of the 'strong' nuclear interaction, which holds the nuclei together, and through which the strange particles are produced, and particle–anti-particle pairs annihilate. There must be a further natural force, which is generally known as the 'weak' nuclear interaction. It is a curious disruptive influence which lurks in these otherwise stable particles, and which gives rise to a very small probability (on the nuclear scale) of their spontaneous disintegration. This leads to these tiny lumps of matter in its most ephemeral form.

This weak interaction has a very remarkable property. The everyday world looks essentially the same whether viewed directly or in a mirror. But there are certain special features which appear different. Clocks conventionally go round in a particular direction. People greet by shaking their right hands; screws are generally constructed with a right-hand thread. These rather subtle effects of 'handedness' appear reversed in the mirror, and provide a distinction between the real world and its reflection. To show 'handedness' or helicity, a system requires a certain amount of complexity. It has always been assumed that the basic laws of physics, and the basic stuff out of which the physical world is made, must be such that no distinction is made between left-handedness and right-handedness, and that the same laws would be found if all experiments were done looking at the apparatus in a mirror. This is certainly true of gravitational interactions. It is also true of Maxwell's electromagnetic theory, and of the 'strong' nuclear interactions.

It was discovered in 1957, in experiments carried out at the instigation of T. D. Lee and C. N. Yang, two Chinese physicists working in America, that this is not true of the weak interactions. In neutron decay, for example, the electron always emerges spinning in a left-handed direction about its line of flight in the rest system of the original neutron. In a mirror, this would appear as a right-handed spin, giving a sure way of distinguishing between the original and its mirror image. Since then, many other effects which define a definite 'handedness' have been found in weak interactions.

There is a further qualitative way in which the ideas of the

P. T. Matthews

	name	symbol	mass (MeV/c²)	charge	spin	hypercharge
	Photon	γ	0			
Leptons	Neutrino	ν_e	0	0	$\frac{1}{2}$	
	Mu-neutrino	ν_μ	0	0	$\frac{1}{2}$	
	Electron	e^-	$\frac{1}{2}$	-1	$\frac{1}{2}$	
	Muon	μ^-	105	-1	$\frac{1}{2}$	
Mesons	Pi-zero	π°	135	0	0	0
	Pi-meson	π^+	140	$+1$	0	0
	Anti-pi-meson	π^-	140	-1	0	0
	K-meson	K^+	495	$+1$	0	$+1$
	Anti-K-meson	$\overline{K}^-$	495	-1	0	-1
	K-zero	K°	500	0	0	$+1$
	Anti-K-zero	$\overline{K}^\circ$	500	0	0	-1
	Eta	η°	550	0	0	0
Nucleons	Proton	p^+	938	$+1$	$\frac{1}{2}$	$+1$
	Neutron	n	939	0	$\frac{1}{2}$	$+1$
Hyperons	Lambda	Λ°	1115	0	$\frac{1}{2}$	0
	Sigma-plus	Σ^+	1190	$+1$	$\frac{1}{2}$	0
	Sigma-minus	Σ^-	1190	-1	$\frac{1}{2}$	0
	Sigma-zero	Σ°	1190	0	$\frac{1}{2}$	0
	Xi	Ξ^-	1315	-1	$\frac{1}{2}$	-1
	Xi-zero	Ξ°	1315	0	$\frac{1}{2}$	-1

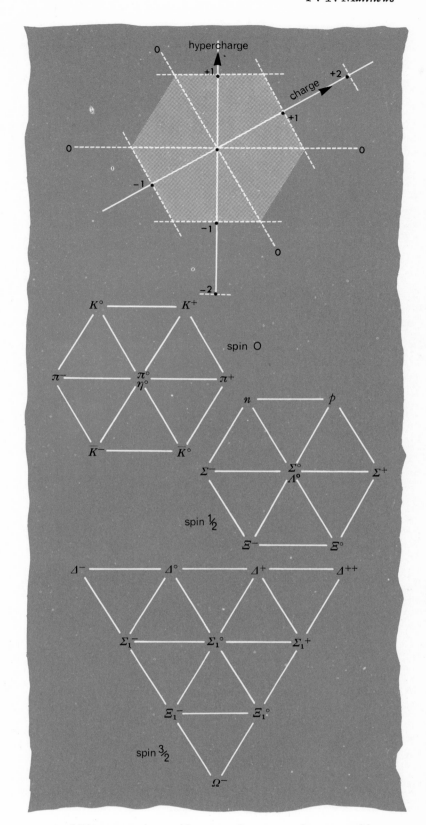

When, around 1930, scientists had discovered the proton, the electron and the photon, they could feel that the simple, ultimate constituents of matter were within their grasp. For all physical phenomena could be explained in terms of these three—except those that might be involved in the structure of the nucleus itself. Today the tiny distances of the nucleus (about a million-millionth of a centimetre) have been broken open, by bombardment with the fast cosmic rays and the high-energy particles of the giant proton accelerators—and more than 100 sub-nuclear particles have been revealed. It is the scientists' present task to reduce this new multitude to order and understanding.

The principal particles are listed in the table above, in the order of ascending mass, with their names and the symbols used to denote them and the charge they carry. They group roughly into light, medium-weight and heavy particles, and for each exists an anti-particle of opposite charge (three only are listed)—except for one or two of zero charge from which an anti-particle is not distinguishable. The first four and the protons are stable, all the others, when freed by collision, decay into the lighter particles in the table, the neutron slowly, the others on our time scale very quickly indeed—in thousandths or millionths of a millionth of a second.

In seeking order in this complexity the scientist endeavours to find qualities which, in strong nuclear interactions, are conserved—the same in net total before and after any nuclear reaction. Electric charge is one. Every known particle carries either the charge on an electron (-1), or an integral multiple of this, usually ± 1 or zero, and the net charge on the fragments is unchanged in any nuclear reaction. Another such quality attributable to the particles is known as hypercharge, again usually plus or minus one, or zero. A third quality, spin, is one form of the angular momentum which remains unchanged after any interaction. It can be minus or plus, clockwise or anticlockwise, and can take integer quantum values 0, 1 or half-integer, $^1/_2$, $^3/_2$, etc.

As theory marched with experiment, patterns began to emerge from these conserved qualities. One can group together all particles of the same spin and plot their properties with charge and hypercharge as axes (top figure). The heavy particles, nucleons and hyperons, all of spin $^1/_2$, fall into a hexagon (third figure). The eight middle-weight particles and anti-particles of spin 0 fall into a similar hexagon (second figure). The theory allows for ten-particle groupings in pyramid shape as well as hexagons. Nine particles, all of spin $^3/_2$, discovered by

1962, fell into appropriate positions on such a pattern, but one particle was missing, at the point of the pyramid; it had to be negatively charged (-1), have a hypercharge -2 and spin $^3/_2$ and even its mass, a heavy 1685 MeV/c², could be specified—and the conditions under which it should appear were deduced. In one of the most dramatic experiments of recent years, early in 1964 with the great Brookhaven synchrotron, the missing particle was discovered, fitting the predicted qualities precisely. Its name is omega minus.

Scientists are convinced now that their probing is in the right direction, but they are faced with a position analogous to that revealed by Mendeleev's Periodic Table of the elements, and the 'elementary' particles—the basic stuff of the universe—still escape them. It will be noticed that one shape is fundamental to both the hexagons and pyramids—the equilateral triangle. Could it be that the fundamental pattern of matter is revealed by these triangles, representing just three basic particles? Theory suggests so: the whole multitude of sub-nuclear particles can be constructed from these three and their spins can be explained. The 'quarks', as they are called (from 'Finnegans Wake': 'Three quarks for Muster Mark') must be a new physical reality, with fractional electric charges, very heavy on a nuclear scale, their forces enormously strong. In the quest for the true heart of matter, the hunt for the quark is on. (10)

1930's have proved too naïve. The first elementary particles to be discovered were the proton and electron, and these were assumed to be structureless points. However, the meson-exchange mechanism of nuclear forces implies that a nucleon, when it is by itself, is continually emitting and reabsorbing mesons. It is as though the keen football player juggled by himself with footballs, when there was no one around to pass to. The strength of the coupling implies that he is good at it, and there are several balls in the air at any time. This means that each protonic core is surrounded by a cloud of mesons, and that there are a number of mesons in the cloud at any instant. The proton is thus not a point, but consists of quite a complicated structure. This structure has been directly observed in experiments pioneered by Robert Hofstadter at Stanford, USA, in which beams of high-energy electrons are deflected by target protons. The experiment is identical, in principle, to that by which Rutherford showed that the nucleus was much smaller than expected. Though the effect has not been directly confirmed by experiment, it is now generally believed that all strongly interacting particles are complicated structures, with radii comparable to that of the proton.

fig 8

The elusive stuff of matter

More recently it has been found that the particles listed on page 139 are only the ground states of a whole spectrum of sub-nuclear entities. These group themselves into multiplets of nearly equal mass in much the same way that the atomic states form multiplets of equal energy, which give rise to the regularities in the periodic table. The strong interaction splits into a super-strong part for which these groups of particles have exactly similar properties, and medium-strong interactions which distinguish between different members of the groups. This theory of strong interactions, which began in 1959 with a Japanese team under Y. Ohnuki and was developed by N. Ne'eman in London and M. Gell-Mann in the USA, is based on the group theory of Unitary Symmetry. It was confirmed in 1964 by the discovery of a new particle, the omega minus, of mass 1685 MeV/c². This has very remarkable properties which had been precisely predicted on the basis of the theory in 1962.

fig 10
p 156
(50–1)

This completes a summary of the main features of our present knowledge of the basic stuff of the universe. Anything which ever happens, which can be expressed in physical or chemical terms, is a consequence of some combination of the five natural forces—gravitation, electro-mag-

netic, strong, medium-strong and weak nuclear. The two former are of long range. Gravitation dominates the motion of neutral bulk matter in the universe, in particular the solar system. Electric forces hold the electrons in the atom and are responsible for the inter-atomic molecular binding forces of all chemical reactions. The strong and medium-strong nuclear forces are short-range (10^{-13} cm.). They hold the nuclei together, against the electrical repulsion of the closely packed protons, and are responsible for the production of pi-mesons and strange particles in nuclear collisions. The weak nuclear interactions are also short-range, and cause the disintegration—or decay—of the great majority of the sub-nuclear particles.

This is a very remarkable synthesis, but it is very far from the simple picture which seemed to be emerging in 1930, and it is far too complicated to be regarded as the answer to the analytic search for basic substance which is so simple it defies further analysis. It is clear that it is no longer reasonable to regard the sub-nuclear particles as *elementary* in this sense. Certain regularities have been found in the strong interactions which suggest that the strongly interacting particles may all be made of three basic 'quarks', with fractional electric charge and enormously strong binding. However, even if they are discovered it will throw no light on the leptons or the weak interactions, and there will still be many fundamental questions unanswered. Why do the particles have the particular masses which they do? Why has the situation turned out to be so complicated, just when we thought we were reaching the ultimate in simplicity? Is the situation really complicated, or are we making it appear so by looking at it the wrong way (like interpreting the paths of the planets as geocentric rather than heliocentric motions)? Are we even right in expecting simplicity in the ultimate, or is all the wisdom of the Greeks to be outdone in the end by the old adage—

> *Big fleas have little fleas upon their backs to bite 'em,*
> *Little fleas have lesser fleas and so ad infinitum!*

Most physicists would agree that the pressing need at the moment is for a really brilliant new idea though the recent discovery of unitary symmetry in strong interactions is very encouraging. The situation is still reminiscent of that in chemistry, when the Periodic Table was known, but nothing of the dynamics of the atom which give an understanding of the possible energy levels. New concepts of comparable depth and originality seem necessary to give answers to these problems.

A revolution in human life

bringing great benefits or violent destruction as man himself decides, is the clear promise of the studies of the atom during the past thirty years. That tiny piece of matter, of which a million million million go to make a pinhead, is revealed as holding enormous power—as much energy in the pinhead as could be obtained by burning 5000 tons of coal. For the purposes of war, this energy is already released; it is the aim of scientists and engineers throughout the world to harness it, to ease the problems of the life of peace.

The silent source of atomic power is quite different from anything the world has known. In the photograph opposite, one is being built on the coast of Kent, Dungeness 'A'. Beneath this surface, sealed in steel and thick concrete, is the radioactive core, where the splitting nuclei are thrown into violent agitation—which is what we know as heat.

Through each of the protruding round-capped pipes a huge, but extremely precise, mechanical loader will insert and replace the rods of natural uranium which are the source of the nuclear fuel. There are 121 such pipes emerging at this surface, each containing an average of 32 channels for uranium, each channel holding 7 fuel rods—a total of 27,132 fuel rods to be inserted.

Through each of the flat-topped pipes, numbered systematically in white, a winding device will lower or raise the control rods of boron steel which will keep the chain reaction at the desired pitch and prevent it running away. Through each of the white upstanding tubes, samples of the circulating gas can be drawn off from any channel and tested for radiation leaks from burst rod containers. The whole will be roofed by removable concrete slabs, above which the loader will run. (1)

The enormous energy in the atom is tapped in large quantities if neutrons are caused to strike the heavy nuclei of the unstable form of uranium, U_{235}. The nuclei split into medium-weight nuclei, giving off great energy and shooting out more neutrons – an average of three per collision. Some of these will split other nuclei, and if the quantity of uranium is large enough to prevent too many neutrons escaping, a chain reaction will build up in millionths of a second—producing the great heat and massive radiation of the atom bomb. In the controlled production of power from natural uranium, owing to the high proportion of the stable U_{238}, the neutrons have to be slowed down to produce a chain reaction in a pile of reasonable size. This is done by allowing them to collide with graphite nuclei. Graphite does not absorb neutrons, but boron does. The neutron flux, and hence the rate of burning, can be controlled by rods of boron, which can be inserted or withdrawn as required. (2)

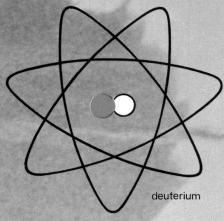

hydrogen

deuterium

tritium

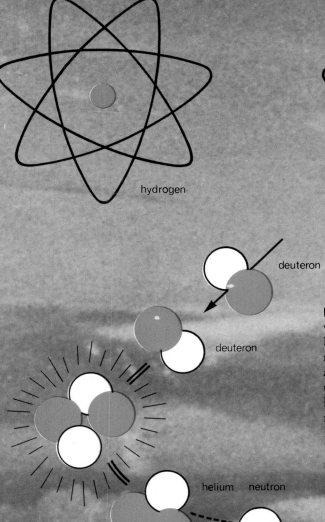

deuteron

deuteron

helium   neutron

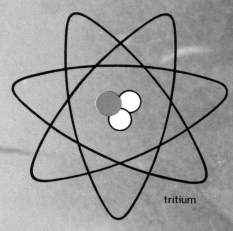

deuteron

deuteron

proton   tritium

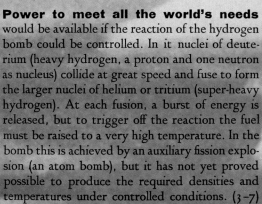

Power to meet all the world's needs would be available if the reaction of the hydrogen bomb could be controlled. In it nuclei of deuterium (heavy hydrogen, a proton and one neutron as nucleus) collide at great speed and fuse to form the larger nuclei of helium or tritium (super-heavy hydrogen). At each fusion, a burst of energy is released, but to trigger off the reaction the fuel must be raised to a very high temperature. In the bomb this is achieved by an auxiliary fission explosion (an atom bomb), but it has not yet proved possible to produce the required densities and temperatures under controlled conditions. (3–7)

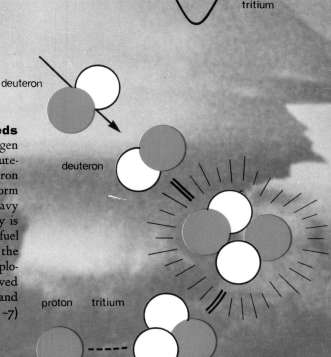

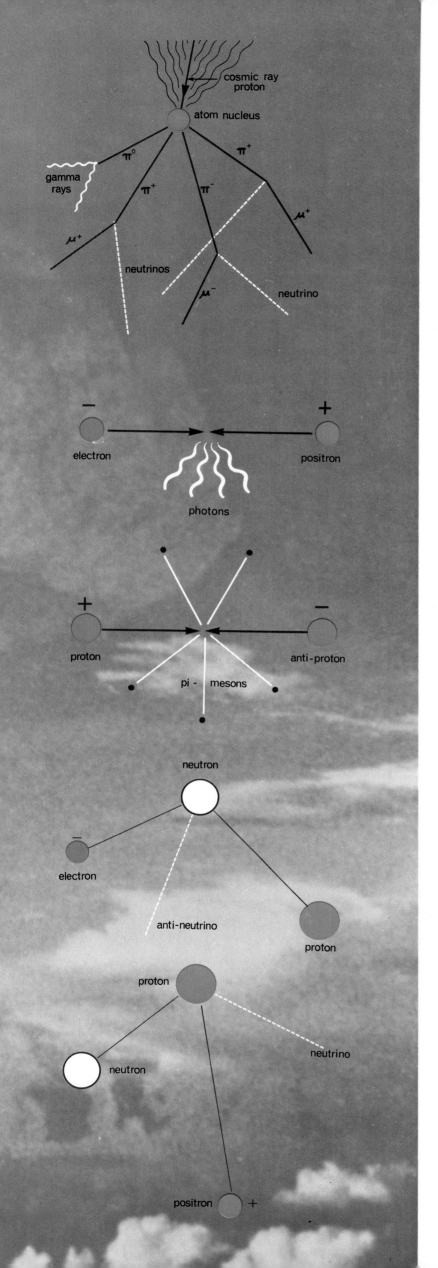

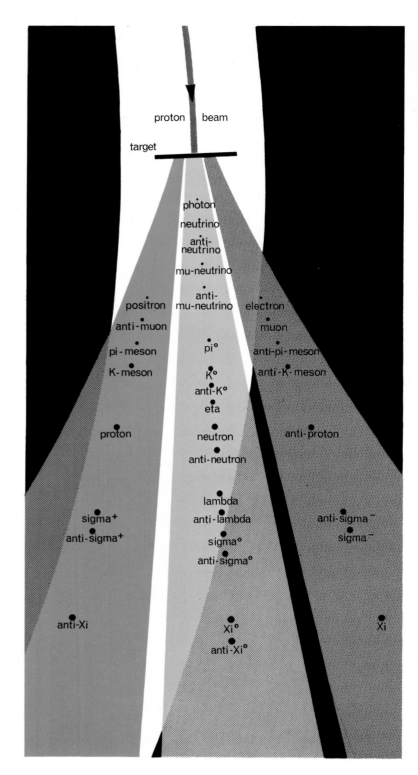

The powerful nuclear forces are at work, holding protons and neutrons together, when the distance between them is less than a million-millionth of a centimetre. To study these, the scientist must bombard nuclei with particles fast enough to penetrate the strong electrical repulsion from the charged protons. Theories that new particles were involved were first confirmed by a study of nature's fastest-moving masses, the cosmic particles from space. Balloon-borne instruments recorded on photographic emulsion the effects of collisions with nuclei of the emulsion (top left). Tracks of new particles appeared, named pi-mesons (π), which decayed rapidly into lighter muons (μ), gamma rays and the fascinating neutrinos, which have spin but no mass and no charge and leave no tracks in the emulsion.

The giant man-made accelerators have now revealed over 100 subnuclear particles. The principal ones are shown above—the collected results of many experiments in which fast protons have struck target nuclei. The charge on the emergent particles would be revealed by a magnetic field, positively charged spreading out to the left and negative to the right, while particles with no charge would continue undeflected. For every charged particle there exists an anti-particle of the same mass but opposite charge. When the two meet they annihilate one another (left, centre). Thus electron and positron give a flash of radiation, while proton and anti-proton annihilate with the release of pi-mesons and about 50 times more energy, weight for weight, than the hydrogen bomb. Most of the particles decay into lighter ones. Free, or loosely bound, neutrons decay into an electron, a proton and an anti-neutrino, and bound protons may reverse the process (left). (8–13)

The hot heart of a nuclear power station consists of long rods of natural uranium. Those being adjusted above (some of the 27,132 in each Dungeness 'A' reactor), are encased in a magnesium alloy with spiral fins to give maximum surface for the transfer of heat to the circulating gas. The rods are surrounded by graphite (to slow down the neutrons) assembled in blocks such as the one being inserted below, shaped and slotted to ensure rigidity. The fuel rods are inserted, and renewed while fission is in progress, by loading machines of which the 400-ton, 57-ft. giant (right) at Trawsfynydd, Wales, is an example. It hangs from a travelling crane above, reaching down to the charge floor 45 feet above the core itself. Three hoists, of which two are visible (white cylinders), equipped with three-pronged grabs, insert or remove the rods one at a time through standpipes. The hoist TVH also lowers a TV camera which can view the core when the reactor is shut down. The control rods of boron steel are driven in and out by individual motors. (14, 15, 16)

◀

Strict safety precautions are essential against the invisible and insidiously dangerous radiation given off with great energy from the violent nuclear reactions and often persisting for long periods—fast-moving alpha-particles, neutrons and electrons and highly penetrative and damaging photons (or gamma rays). In the photograph above, a Russian scientist uses a Geiger counter in routine tests for radioactive leakages at a reactor station in the Baltic Provinces. The 85-ton monster (right) protects workers in 'hot' nuclear areas in Nevada. The operator, protected by thick lead and glass shields, can swing his cabin round and lift it on extending legs 25 feet above the ground. His mechanical arms lift and carry parts and perform intricate operations on nuclear power and propulsion systems. (17, 18)

'Master-slave' manipulators must be used for work in a radioactive area. The operator (left), whose pistol-grip handles are the 'master' end, looks through a window which is in fact a tank containing zinc bromide solution—equivalent in protection to concrete four feet thick. (19)

Taking no chances, the Americans removed 2000 tons of topsoil in 8000 barrels (over 1000 are waiting below on Palomares beach) from Spain to their waste dump in South Carolina. Four H-bombs had fallen from a crashed B-52; they were unarmed and protected, but exploding detonators had ruptured the shell-casing and allowed the radioactive contents to scatter. (20)

The world's most powerful nuclear station will be Dungeness 'B'. At its heart (shown yellow) is the cylindrical concrete pressure vessel, sealed internally with a water-cooled membrane of mild steel. Within it, in the bell-shaped steel cylinder, are the fuel and control rods housed in graphite and shielded by two layers of steel with carbon between (not shown). The fuel is uranium dioxide, enclosed in stainless

steel tubes, in clusters of 36 within graphite sleeves stacked 8 high in each channel—over 118,000 fuel rods in all. When the reaction starts, the nuclei are thrown into violent movement, raising the temperature to as high as 800°C. To draw off this heat and use it to provide power, four circulating pumps (three are shown in white) drive the inert gas carbon dioxide into the inner cylinder, under pressure and heated to

320°C. Some of the gas rises to the top and passes down, round the graphite and control rods, to keep them close to inlet temperature, then the total gas passes up the hot elements, emerging into the (green) space above at 675°C. The hot gas descends through four boilers (two are shown, in purple), passing pipes fed with demineralized water which it converts into steam. This, at 565°C, passes away in pipes (light blue) to drive the normal turbo-generators of an electrical power plant. The current (red lines) runs through transformers to the switch room and then underground to the grid. Above the massive concrete cylinder stands the giant loading machine which, working through standpipes and by remote control, extracts used fuel and replaces it with new, serving also a twin reactor behind. (21)

Intense radioactivity can be induced in many common elements by a small increase or decrease in the number of neutrons in their nuclei. Such radioactive *isotopes* are identical in their chemical properties with the stable form, but may behave very differently in nuclear reactions. They are produced as by-products of the atomic energy reactors and may emit alpha-particles, neutrons, electrons or short-wavelength, highly penetrating gamma rays, radiation which has many uses in the modern world. In the first photograph (right) such isotopes are being taken in lead containers from a small reactor at Harwell. In the second (far right) a scientist, shielded behind a perspex screen, his hands protected by synthetic rubber gloves, is purifying insulin impregnated with radioactive iodine. (22, 23)

The dangerous radiation needs careful handling at all times. On the right, two ounces of cobalt-60, a highly radioactive isotope for medical use, are being delivered at the London Clinic. It must be packed in a two-ton lead container and even then tested periodically for leakage. Far right, engineers at Vauxhall Motors manoeuvre, from a safe distance, the gears into a car back-axle. The gear components have been made radioactive in a reactor. After assembly and extensive running tests, the lubricating oil will be run off and examined for radiation. The amount detected, from minute traces of metal in the oil, is a measure of the wear the components have undergone. (24, 25)

More penetrating than X-rays, gamma rays are much used for the quick detection of internal flaws. Radiation from an isotope of gold penetrates the plastic casing of a telephone receiver, and throws shadows of the metal parts. The moon-man-like probe carries caesium-137, giving off gamma rays, at the end of its proboscis. The rays will pass through steel, registering flaws on a photographic plate on the other side. When not in use, the probe is withdrawn into the container (26, 27)

Packages on a production line pass across a beam of radiation from a radioactive source. The beam is so adjusted that if the package is properly filled, little or no radiation passes through it. If it is only partly filled, sufficient radiation—that which would have been absorbed by the missing contents —passes through to the detector, setting in motion a device which throws the faulty package off the production line. Leaks in underground pipelines can be detected by including a little radioactive solution in the liquid passing through, when radioactivity collects outside the break. It can be detected with precision from the ground level above or by passing a probe (far right) along the pipe. (28, 29)

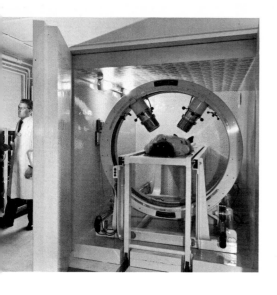

Medicine makes many new uses of radioactive isotopes, apart from the traditional direct bombardment and destruction of diseased areas by the high-energy particles and gamma rays. On the left, a patient, with a suspected brain tumour, has been treated with chlormerodrin 'labelled' with mercury-197. The marked substance collects in the tumour and is revealed by this scanned picture on an X-ray. On the far left, an isotope of such elements as calcium, iron or copper has been administered to a patient. The two detector heads scan the whole body, following, by the movement of the radioactive element, its path of spread and the period for which it is retained in the body—information useful in diagnosis. (30, 31)

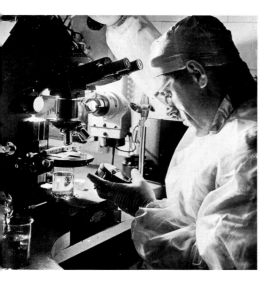

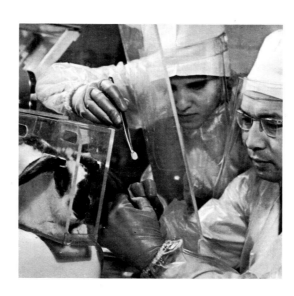

'Labelled atoms'—radioactive traces inserted in living tissue—are useful in studying its subsequent history. In the photograph far left, a scientist at a Kazakh radiological laboratory is working on the problem of introducing radioactive iodine into the molecules of thyroid gland cells. As he watches, with suitable detectors, the progress of these molecules, he can study the formation of hormones in the gland. Left, at the same laboratory, scientists study the healing of wounds by labelled atoms inserted into the tissue of a test animal. (32, 33)

A hornet eats honey from the tip of a thin glass tube. The honey has been labelled, at Brookhaven National Laboratory, with radioactive barium. Using special detectors, scientists can study the use of food by the hornet's body. Research on the effects of nuclear radiation on natural cycles of growth, and therefore on our natural resources, can be undertaken in the gamma ray and neutron radiation from a small outdoor reactor. A student at Emory University, Georgia (left) examines a buckeye plant with abnormal, radiation-damaged leaves. (34, 35)

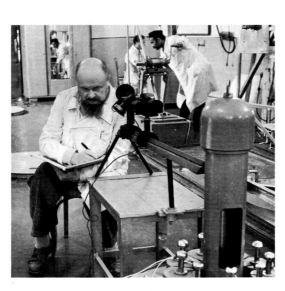

Food can be kept for a year without refrigeration if it is first exposed to a radioactive source. Here, in the U.S.A. (far left), broiler chickens, handled by 'master-slave' arms, are being irradiated. Left, Sergei Zakharovich Pashinsky, chief engineer of a Russian gamma ray plant, offers his visitors 100-years-old wine. Winetasters commend it, but in fact it is from a recent vintage, its maturing speeded by gamma rays. At this plant, radio-canning is studied. Ready-packed foods are sterilized quickly and economically by being passed through a chamber in which they receive a controlled dose of radiation. (36, 37)

In the 'swimming pool' reactor, the uranium fuel elements, enriched with U_{235}, are suspended in a tank of purified water. The photograph (left) shows the small research reactor 'Lido' at Harwell, where a movable trolley carries a framework supporting a reactor core about the size of a tea-chest. The output of heat is the equivalent of 200 kilowatts. In research, the core can be moved towards aluminium windows set into the walls of the tank, permitting experiments on the shielding powers of various materials—one task was to assist in the development of nuclear propulsion units for submarines. The water serves both to slow down the neutrons as graphite does, and as a shield.

The ghostly blue and purple glow is an interesting phenomenon first noted by the Russian physicist P. A. Cherenkov. The gamma rays emitted from the reactor accelerate electrons of the water molecules to very high speeds, faster indeed than the speed of light in the tank, for although light travels through empty space with a speed not attainable by matter, in transparent media such as water, glass or mica it travels more slowly. The excited electrons give off light concentrated in the blue regions of the spectrum, which reaches the eye in a 'shock wave' effect—much as sound waves reach the ear when an aircraft crashes the sound barrier. (38)

The space engine of the future will be driven, we must expect, by nuclear energy. Indeed America has already sent one reactor-powered satellite into a circular orbit 700 miles up. When the craft, launched by rocket, reached its orbit, a radio command from earth started a sustained chain reaction in the core of its reactor. The satellite, shown (right) being assembled, carries the reactor (shown uncovered) at its nose and a converter of heat into electricity in the white cone. On further commands from the ground, batteries, recharged by the reactor, started an experimental ion engine (carried below). A small amount of gas (such as caesium vapour) was ejected into the main chamber of the ion engine. There, positive ions from the gas spiralled under the influence of strong electric and magnetic fields until they were finally ejected at high speed out of the exhaust. By reaction, as in a rocket, the craft was propelled forward. The thrust developed is very small, but once above the atmosphere and beyond the earth's pull, the engine, applied continuously, could accelerate a craft to 100,000 miles per hour. Since it absorbs minute quantities of fuel, very long journeys are possible. In the photograph above, such an engine is being tested; from the engine's exhaust on the left, a beam of ionized particles streams into the test chamber. (39, 40)

More speed is added (below left), at the European consortium's laboratory of CERN near Geneva, by a linear accelerator, shown with its cover (which maintains the vacuum) removed. The proton beam passes through the holes seen along the axis of the cylindrical electrodes. As the proton jumps across each gap between two adjacent electrodes, it is accelerated by an electric field, reaching 50 million electron volts as it emerges. (42)

Speeds almost that of light are reached at the next stage, a huge circular tunnel round which the protons travel many times per second. The most powerful under construction, accelerating pulses of ten million million protons to 70,000 million electron volts, is shown (right) at Serpukhov, near Moscow. Within the tunnel, which is sunk below ground level and is almost a mile round, is a ring of 600 magnets, some groups of which are seen below (looking like railroad carriages) in their aligned positions. These serve to bend and focus the proton pulses, to keep them in their narrow channel with a minimum of loss. Interspersed between the magnets are 53 accelerating stations, which boost the speed of the protons as they circle the ring. (43, 44)

The smallest things we know require for their study huge works of precision engineering. We can break into the heart of atomic nuclei only by bombarding them with other nuclei or nuclear particles of high energy, moving with almost the speed of light. Massive installations such as those shown on these pages have been built simply to produce these high-energy particles. At Brookhaven National Laboratory on Long Island, the bombarding protons start their journey from a Cockcroft-Walton generator (above), a proton gun in which an electric field from a high-voltage generator provides a first acceleration to 750,000 electron volts. (41)

The two-mile-long linear electron accelerator built by Stanford University is shown nearing completion in the photograph below. In the foreground is the entrance to the underground accelerator housing with, behind the wall, the electron 'gun' which shoots the electrons into the accelerator. On the surface, stretching into the distance, is the klystron gallery, source of the radio energy which speeds the electrons. Twenty-five feet beneath it runs the accelerator. At the top of the picture is the underground beam switchyard and the area which will contain the target buildings with their sophisticated detecting and analyzing equipment (bubble chambers, particle counters, detectors, spark chambers and analyzers). The accelerator uses electrons and positrons as bombarding particles, lifting them to energies not possible for these particles in the circular accelerators, and accelerating a greater number of particles at one time with the consequent larger number of collisions per pulse. Because of their small mass, electrons subjected to even a moderate accelerating field rapidly reach a very high speed; after the first few feet they will be travelling at .995 of the velocity of light and will keep an almost constant speed for the rest of the journey—the added energy appearing primarily as a very rapid increase in mass. (47)

At top speed, and at the height of their energy, the protons are deflected to strike a target. As in Rutherford's experiment, some of them are stopped abruptly by direct collision with a nucleus. The nucleus is shattered and fast sub-nuclear particles emerge. To identify these, examine them and measure their energy, they can be directed into a bubble chamber, a massive tank of liquid hydrogen such as the one shown above, built by the Rutherford High Energy Laboratory at Harwell, Berkshire, and being mounted for operation at CERN. To coincide with the entry of a pulse of particles, the pressure on the hydrogen is suddenly relieved, with the result that a track of tiny bubbles will form along the path of charged particles passing through it. At the precise moment that the tracks are formed, a flash of light illuminates them and they are photographed from several angles. Then the liquid hydrogen is re-compressed; this erases the tracks and the chamber is ready for the next pulse. The nine ports in the oval face of the vacuum tank will contain the lamp housings. The particle beam is finally absorbed in concrete outside the chamber. (45)

For a single experiment, hundreds of thousands of photographs may be required. When developed, they are projected on large screens in scanning machines to select those showing events of interest. The selected photographs are then passed through measuring machines (the one being operated below is at CERN). Data from the tracks are then fed into a computer. (46)

The search for basic particles which might be the physical reality from which all matter is made is the major endeavour of sub-nuclear physicists to-day. It can only be pursued further by building accelerators of greater power. In both Europe and America plans are being prepared for these: in Europe specifications have been drawn for a proton accelerator of 300 GeV, more than four times the energy of the largest in construction at present. It is illustrated on these two pages.

According to one design, the particles will begin their journey from a proton 'gun', which will shoot them into a linear accelerator (centre enlargement). From this, already at an energy of 200 million electron volts, they will pass round and round a small 'booster' ring, which will accelerate them to 8000 million electron volts. At this energy, they will be deflected by magnets into the main ring. Here, after many circuits, their energy is planned to reach 300,000 million electron volts, when they could be deflected out of the ring into the experimental hall. The booster ring is to be some two-fifths of a mile round, the main ring over $4\frac{1}{2}$ miles, the total distance over 5 miles–a distance which the protons will travel something like 40,000 times. The whole journey will take one second.

The main ring will be composed primarily of electromagnets (grey rectangles) in 864 units (top right), with 6 accelerating stations (red circles) and 12 main access points (red rectangles). The protons will enter the ring in pulses, building up to 30 million million protons per pulse, and travel in a high vacuum elliptical tube of stainless steel, 10 cm × 6 cm. It will be the task of the magnets to keep the protons moving smoothly round the ring, with a minimum of loss by spreading. They will therefore bend the beam gradually, and by a system of alternate focusing and defocusing, confine it to the centre of the tube. At each accelerating station (top, left), the pulses will pass through guides carrying electromagnetic waves at radio frequency, synchronized with the pulses to give each a boost of energy, and to maintain the protons in bunches much as traffic lights, by holding fast cars while slow ones catch up, bunch the cars of varying speeds.

The whole journey of the protons will take place some 50 feet underground, to prevent external radiation. When the beam is deflected out of the ring by 'chopper' magnets it will pass, still underground, to be directed at will into several channels, leading to different experimental halls waiting to receive it. Immediately inside the experimental hall it will strike the target and the emergent sub-nuclear particles will continue, within magnetic channels and shields of steel and baryte, in directions dependent upon their energy, to enter finally bubble chambers or other devices in which they can be studied. (48)

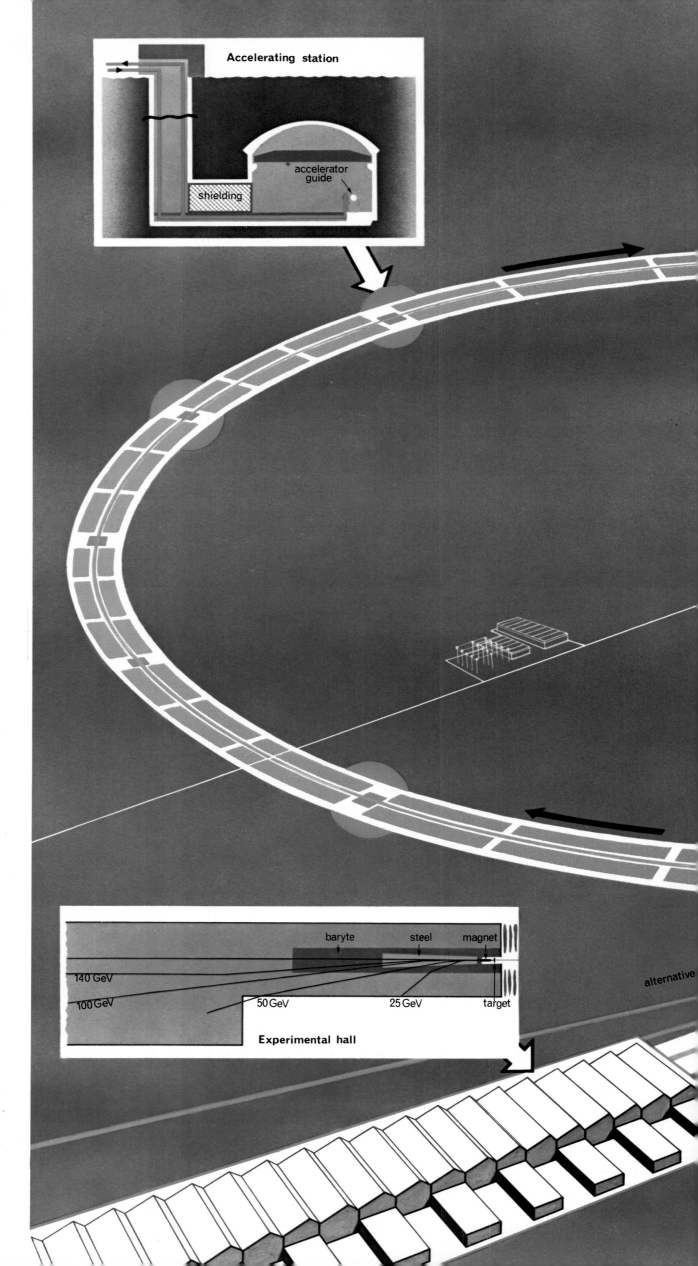

Accelerating station

accelerator guide

shielding

Experimental hall

baryte   steel   magnet

140 GeV

100 GeV   50 GeV   25 GeV   target

alternative

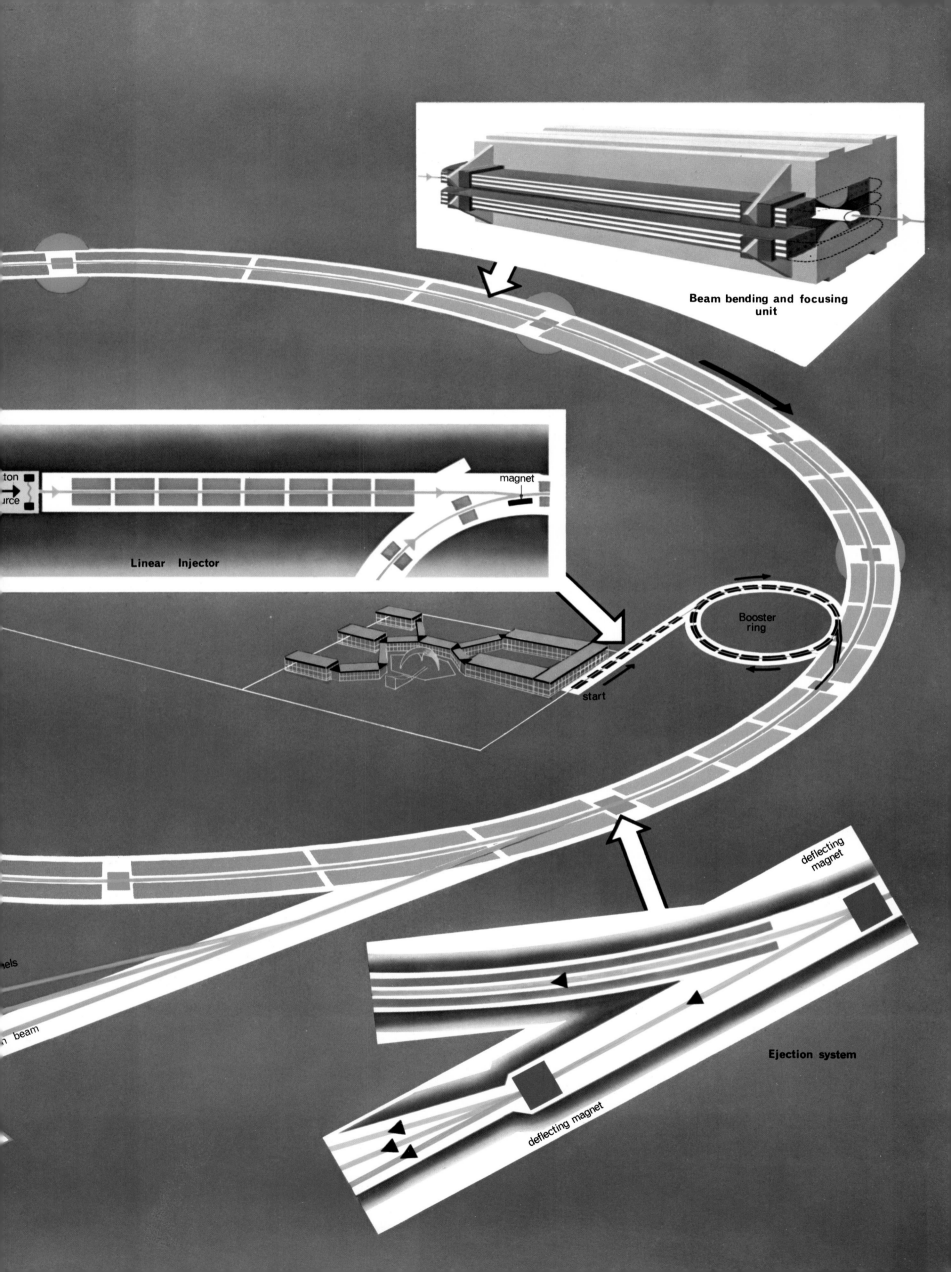

Beam bending and focusing unit

magnet

ton
urce

Linear Injector

Booster ring

start

deflecting magnet

els

beam

deflecting magnet

Ejection system

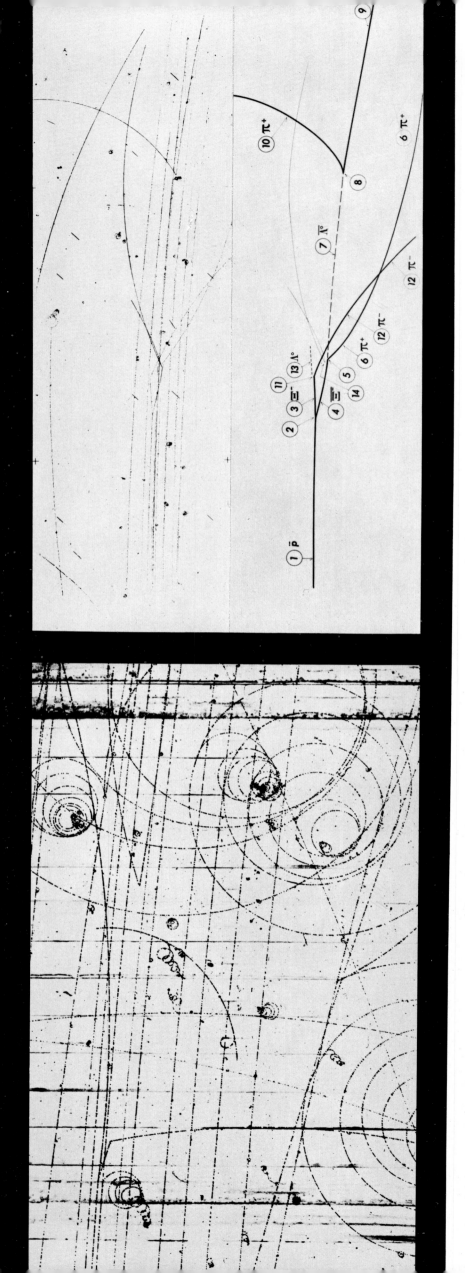

When nuclei are smashed by collision with high-speed, high-energy particles, the results are revealed by tracks in photographic emulsion or in bubble or spark chambers. The collision on the right took place in emulsion carried to 90,000 feet by a research balloon. A cosmic particle, a nucleus of carbon, enters the emulsion at the top. It collides with a nucleus of silver or bromine and produces some 200 mesons which shoot forward, about half of them within an angle of $1\frac{1}{2}°$ — indicating that the energy of the cosmic ray was about 10 million million electron volts. In addition the target nucleus is shattered and scatters in all directions, in many cases passing out of focus.

In bubble chambers, tracks are similar in appearance to those in emulsion. The length of a track can reveal the particle's lifetime; since a strong magnetic field surrounds the chamber, a particle's charge, mass and momentum can be determined from the curvature of its path. But particles carrying no charge do not produce tracks — their presence must be inferred when they decay into new charged particles which suddenly appear. Typical tracks from CERN are shown on the left (top). An anti-proton (1) has entered the chamber and collided with a hydrogen nucleus, a proton (2). They annihilate one another and the mass and energy are transformed into two heavy particles, xi (3) and anti-xi (4). After a short time these decay into various pi-mesons and a lambda (13) and anti-lambda (7) which, having no charge, do not show tracks (dashed lines). Finally (8) the anti-lambda decays into a pi-meson (10) and an anti-proton (9).

The tracks which revealed the predicted particle omega minus at Brookhaven are shown left and analysed below. A negative anti-K-meson enters the picture from the bottom (1). At (3) it collides with a proton, producing the omega minus, a positive K-meson (2) and a neutral K-zero (dashed line). The omega minus decays (after a lifetime of approximately one ten-thousandth of a millionth of a second) into a negative pi-meson (4) and a xi-zero. The latter decays into a neutral lambda and a pi-zero (not shown) which decays instantaneously into two gamma rays (7 and 8) which in turn each convert into an electron-positron pair. The lambda travels a few centimetres and then decays into a negative pi-meson (5) and a proton (6). Other anti-K-mesons pass through (parallel lines) and electrons of low energy spiral in coils. (49–52)

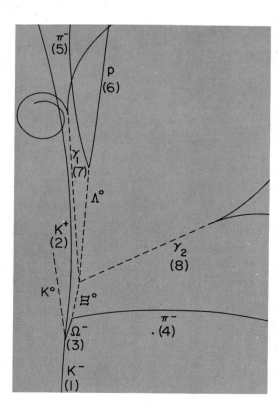

6 The architecture of matter

M. A. Jaswon

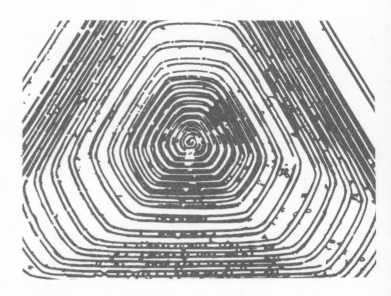

The architecture of matter

Two Greek philosophers, Democritus and Leucippus, were the first to question the way in which matter is constructed. They asked what would happen if one continued to subdivide a piece of matter into progressively smaller parts. It was inconceivable, they held, that one could go on chopping away indefinitely. At some stage, the matter must be reduced to hard, indivisible 'atoms' which cannot be further divided.

Although the concept was right, it remained no more than a bold idea. The Greeks were 2000 years ahead of their time, and there was no possibility of carrying out experiments to prove their thesis.

These experiments had to await the work of John Dalton, who showed in 1808 that any gas was composed of a great number of identical atoms, that these atoms had definite physical attributes such as mass and volume, and that the nature of the atom varied from gas to gas. A few years later, the Italian chemist Avogadro extended Dalton's theory by suggesting that the effective unit of structure was not necessarily a single atom, but could be a combination of two or more atoms termed a molecule. Avogadro's hypothesis illuminated some hitherto baffling facts concerning the volume relations of reacting gases, but fifty years elapsed before it became fully established. With Mendeléef's introduction of the Periodic Table of Elements in 1869, the modern scientific era began.

This approach to atomic theory is, of course, very different from that of the last chapter, which was concerned primarily with the properties of the individual atom. The atomic theory, in that sense, was a product of the early 20th century, brought about by observations of the light produced when an electric current passes through rarefied gases, and by the study of atomic fragments thrown out by radioactive substances, or torn off by strong electric fields.

In this chapter, we are concerned with the integration of these two approaches: to discover the arrangement of atoms in matter; to relate atomic properties with those of the substance in bulk; and to use the new knowledge to create materials with specially desirable properties, such as synthetic diamonds and plastics.

Matter can exist as a solid, a liquid or a gas, depending on the temperature, and all three states must be explained in terms of the ingredient atoms. The behaviour of gases can be readily explained by a very simple theory in which the individual gas atoms (or molecules) behave as though they were very small but quite perfect billiard balls. All the billiard balls move independently of one another and are in constant motion. Occasionally a ball meets another ball, and the collision obeys the ordinary laws of mechanics.

The motion of the atoms in the gas increases as the temperature increases. One result of this is that the atoms which happen to collide with the container do so with more speed. If the walls of the container are fixed, these more violent collisions represent an increase of pressure. If the walls are free to move then the heavier collisions push them back and the gas expands.

Thus, the simple billiard ball theory explains the behaviour of gases, especially when they are far removed from the temperature at which they liquefy. There are two important points to notice about this 'kinetic' theory. First, it is a statistical theory. We do not follow the individual fate of the atoms; we do not attempt to calculate the speed and direction of each of the miniature billiard balls. We simply concern ourselves with their average behaviour.

The success of the kinetic theory depends on the fact that the individual gas particles go their own way, completely independent of all the others, except during the brief moments of collision. Is this an acceptable assumption? The particles which make up the gas are normally electrically neutral. But although the total effect is neutral, each atom, as we have seen, is made up of a small positively charged nucleus, surrounded by shells in which the negative charges exist.

The behaviour of the negatively-charged electrons in these shells is governed by quantum mechanics rather than by classical mechanics. Fluctuations in the positions of the electrons mean that momentarily the atom appears to have one side more negative than the other. It becomes a temporary 'dipole'.

When this happens to two atoms fairly close together, the positive side of one attracts the negative side of the other. If

fig 4

fig 1

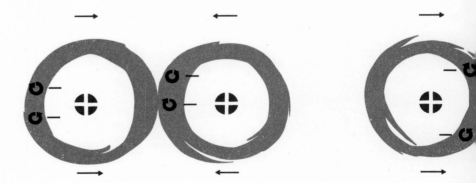

The helium atom consists of two negatively charged electrons in rapid motion relative to a positive nucleus. At times, two electrons appearing on the same side will give that side a negative bias and the other side a positive bias. If with two atoms a 'positive' side and a 'negative' side are sufficiently close together (left), the atoms will attract one another. If the temporary charges are the same (right), they will repel one another. These are the weakest interatomic forces (the 'Van der Waals' forces), and the forces which hold all molecules together. (1)

M. A. Jaswon

the atoms are sufficiently close together so that the attraction is strong enough, the pull of one atom may affect the distribution of electrical charge in the electron shells of the other so that the attraction is enhanced.

Molecules attract one another in the same way (and in no other way), by means of these temporary dipoles. Occasionally when several atoms combine to form a molecule (for instance in water, where two atoms of hydrogen combine with one of oxygen) the interaction between the atoms gives the molecule a permanent electrical lopsidedness. In these cases the forces between the molecules are very powerful. The dipole molecules of water are attracted to one another (and to other polar molecules) much more strongly than are non-polar molecules like benzene. This explains why water and benzene will not mix. If the two liquids are shaken together, the water molecules attract each other, squeeze out the benzene molecules, and coalesce into a separate layer.

The attractive forces between atoms are of several different kinds according to the number of electrons in the outer shell of the particular atoms involved. We shall discuss this further on a later page. In those gases which behave in the way described by the kinetic theory, the interaction between the atoms must be small. These conditions exist where the atoms are a considerable distance apart (that is the pressure is low) and where their average energy is large (that is the temperature is high).

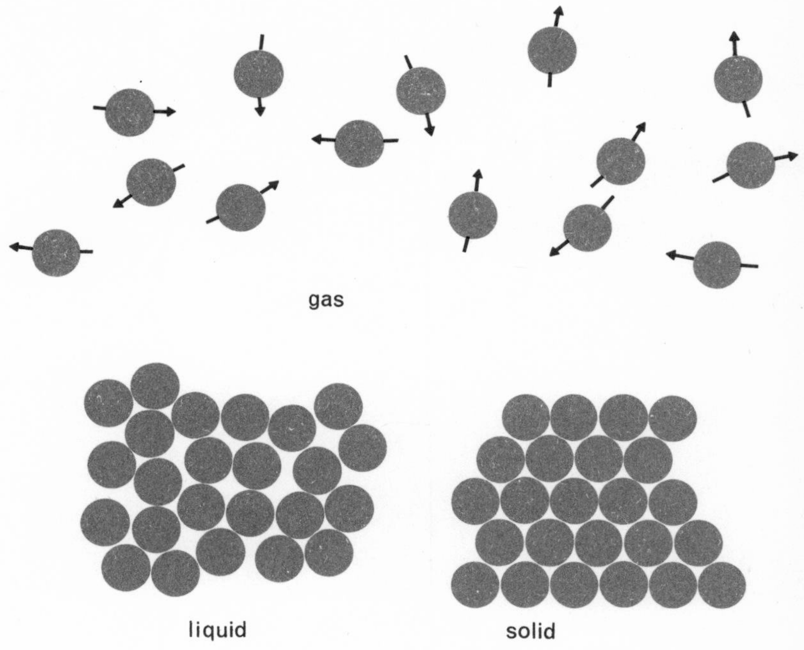

In random assembly: the liquids

Now suppose the temperature of this gas is reduced. The violent haphazard motion of the atoms begins to be quelled. As the atomic storm produced by the high temperature abates, the steady pull between the atoms begins to make itself felt. Now we can squeeze the gas easily to force the molecules closer together. But the simple law relating pressure and volume given by the kinetic theory now no longer holds good.

At some lower temperature still, the motion of the atoms has slacked off sufficiently for the attractions between atoms to have an over-riding effect. The gas becomes a liquid. Something can be learned about the condition of the atoms in the liquid from a few simple observations.

First, while it is fairly easy to squeeze the atoms of a gas closer together, it is exceedingly hard to compress a liquid. From this we must assume that the atoms are packed in the liquid almost as tightly as they will go. Yet the liquid will flow to fill a container. The atoms must be sufficiently free to move over one another. The force between them is very strong. If we pour a thin stream of the liquid it breaks up into small spherical droplets, the most compact shape into which the atoms can draw themselves.

In spite of these forces holding the liquid together, some atoms obviously escape. If we leave a saucer of water on the window shelf, it gradually evaporates. Somehow, some of the water molecules have acquired sufficient energy to break through the surface, to escape from the powerful pull of their brothers. We can find an explanation by returning to the concept of the kinetic theory. Within the liquid each particle (atom or molecule) is still exercising a dance, joggling about and bumping into its neighbours, but in a more restricted way than in the gas. And the movement of each particle between collisions will depend not only on the effects of its previous collision, but on the attractions exerted by surrounding particles.

Again, so far as the liquid is concerned, we need only

gas

liquid   solid

The atoms in a gas at low pressure are far apart (compared with their size), in random motion, and have little effect on one another except on collision. In a liquid, the atoms are close together and very difficult to compress further. But a liquid flows; it is probable that the atoms are 'random-packed' like peas poured into a bowl. In solids, the atoms are regularly packed; their outer electron shells can be considered as touching. In both liquids and solids, the atoms still have a restricted movement, becoming more vigorous as the temperature increases. (2)

fig 2

consider the average effect. Suppose the temperature is raised. As the particles jostle more vigorously they will push one another farther apart and the liquid will expand. And because they are moving more quickly and easily, with a little bit more elbow room, the liquid flows more easily: its viscosity decreases.

But we have still not explained how the particles manage to escape from a liquid and cause it to evaporate, even though the temperature is low. Remember that we have been speaking of the average behaviour of the atoms or molecules of this liquid. But if we observe a particular particle, the amount of energy it receives, the speed and direction it attains after a collision is a matter of luck. There is always a chance, even though the temperature is low, that our particle will arrive at the surface of the liquid and at the same time make a collision which hurls it upwards so fast that it escapes the downwards pull of the particles beneath it. The probability that this will happen depends on the temperature and on the strength of the pull between particles.

Although this much is clear about liquids, the actual structure, the arrangement of the atoms or molecules in the liquid, is not yet understood. Recently Professor J. D. Bernal has been working on a theory of liquids based on the simple fact that the random piling of spheres (such as oranges in a barrel) always results in a density about five-sixths that of close-packed spheres. The principle is recognized in the old-fashioned method of selling dried peas and grain by volume.

Most simple liquids take up only a little more space than the corresponding solid. In the case of metals the difference is only about 5 per cent, so the arrangement of atoms in the liquid cannot be greatly different from that in the solid. Bernal's calculations of the random packing of spheres to form a collection of polyhedrons of approximately equal sides gives X-ray scattering coefficients comparable with those obtained from liquids. But the work is still at an early stage.

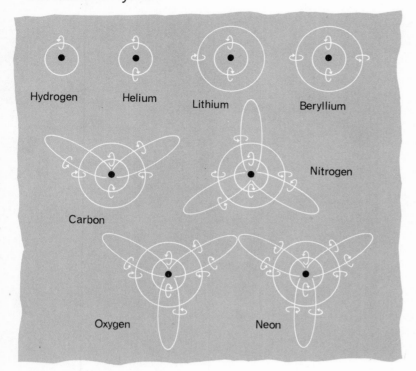

Hydrogen   Helium   Lithium   Beryllium

Carbon   Nitrogen

Oxygen   Neon

	Helium shell			Helium shell	Neon shell			Helium shell	Neon shell	Argon shell			Helium shell	Neon shell	Argon shell	Krypton shell
	Lithium			**Sodium**				**Potassium**								
	Li	2	1	Na	2	8	1	K	2	8	8	1				
	Beryllium			**Magnesium**				**Calcium**								
	Be	2	2	Mg	2	8	2	Ca	2	8	8	2				
								(Here come the ten transition metals)								
	Boron			**Aluminium**				**Gallium**								
	B	2	3	Al	2	8	3	Ga	2	8	18	3				
	Carbon			**Silicon**				**Germanium**								
	C	2	4	Si	2	8	4	Ge	2	8	18	4				
	Nitrogen			**Phosphorus**				**Arsenic**								
Hydrogen	N	2	5	P	2	8	5	As	2	8	18	5				
H 1	**Oxygen**			**Sulphur**				**Selenium**								
	O	2	6	S	2	8	6	Se	2	8	18	6				
	Fluorine			**Chlorine**				**Bromine**								
	F	2	7	Cl	2	8	7	Br	2	8	18	7				
Helium	**Neon**			**Argon**				**Krypton**								
He 2	Ne	2	8	Ar	2	8	8	Kr	2	8	18	8				

A fundamental principle of quantum theory is that any one electron orbit can contain two electrons, provided their spins are paired—i.e. in opposite directions. In hydrogen, the simplest element, a single electron is bound to a single proton in an orbit of the lowest permissible energy. The unpaired electron is available for pairing with similar unpaired electrons—i.e. hydrogen reacts chemically with many other elements. Helium has two paired electrons in the lowest orbit, is un-affected by neighbouring atoms and is chemically inert. The next energy level can contain eight electrons, represented as two in a circular orbit and six in elliptical orbits. When it is complete, the element, neon, is chemically inert like helium. In between are less stable elements which can donate, absorb or share electrons: lithium, for instance, with one of the eight, can readily donate it; oxygen, with six of the eight, can readily absorb two. (3)

The famous Periodic Table of Elements, of which the first four columns are shown above, lists the elements in the order of the number of orbiting electrons. Studied with the orbital diagrams opposite, it explains many of the chemical characteristics of the elements. Each column ends with a chemically inert element —helium, neon, argon, krypton—in which the outer shells have the complete quota of paired electrons. At the top of each column is an element with only one outer electron, readily detachable in combination. So these three have similar chemical properties, as also have fluorine, chlorine and bromine, although these, one electron short, tend to absorb an electron. The build-up of the elements is readily seen from the number of electrons in the outer shells—until calcium is reached, when the fourth shell is kept waiting until the third shell is filled up to a new maximum of eighteen. (4)

In military order: the beautiful structure of crystals

While the structure of liquids is difficult to determine, that of solids is exceedingly symmetrical and, in general, easy to discover. In all crystalline solids (a term which embraces most substances including many which do not have obvious crystals) the atoms are sited on a regular lattice, like a three-dimensional chess board, or a child's climbing frame. Sometimes the external appearance of a crystal will reveal the internal arrangement of its atoms. For instance every grain of salt is a small cubic crystal. If you dissolve salt in water and allow the water to evaporate the crystals formed will still be cubes. If you take a sharp knife and attempt to split the salt crystals, each one will split only in directions parallel to one of the cube faces. The implication is clear: the atoms of common salt (sodium chloride) are arranged on some kind of cubic lattice.

Fortunately, the crystallographer has a still more powerful tool which reveals the internal order of the atoms in crystals. Atoms in a crystal are very close together, mostly between 3 and 10 Ångström units apart (1 Ångström unit = 10^{-8} cm.), which is about the same as the wavelength of X-rays. In 1912 von Laue made the discovery that X-rays could be diffracted by a crystal in much the same way as light is diffracted by a ruled grating or the regular pattern of the weave of fine cloth. Later, Sir William and Sir Lawrence Bragg showed how X-ray diffraction patterns could be used for working out the exact positions of atoms in a crystal. The surprising thing was that the new X-ray method showed that most inorganic solids were crystalline, whatever their

p 170

p 170-1

p. 170 (21-24)

p 172 (26)

fig 7

outward appearance might be. Metals, like iron, copper and gold had relatively simple crystal structures. Tin and cobalt were only a little more complex. And all were made up of interlocking crystals, each almost perfect, each with the same regular lattice, but at a different inclination to the crystals next door. These metal crystals can be seen when a clean metal surface is etched with acid. Occasionally they can be seen on the surface of galvanized iron which has been exposed to the weather, or on a brass door knob which has been etched by sweat from the hands that grasped it.

This discovery that solids are as orderly as soldiers on parade raises again the whole question of the forces which hold the atoms together in this military manner. We have already seen that two atoms at a distance may attract one another. And since the attraction is due to electrostatic forces we would expect it to increase as the distance between the atoms decreased, probably according to a modified square law. But this attraction cannot continue to increase indefinitely as the two atoms approach one another or they would simply engulf one another and become one. Again the mechanism is a complicated one, but is connected with the mutual repulsion between the two positive nuclei.

To express this in more scientific terms, as the two atoms approach each other the potential energy of interaction decreases to a minimum. This minimum is the point where the attraction between them disappears. If the atoms are forced closer together than this neutral point, their potential energy rises steeply and the moment they are released they will spring out again.

Obviously the atoms tend to cluster together until they fall into these troughs or neutral points. The exact form of the crystals depends on the depth and distance apart of the troughs produced by a three-dimensional assembly of atoms interacting with one another.

One thing has to be made clear. The atoms in their troughs are not completely motionless, but are fidgeting, riding up the sides of their 'trough' and falling back again continuously. The higher the temperature, the more thermal energy the atoms have and the farther they stray from their equilibrium position before they are pulled back again. X-ray diffraction photographs even show this effect, for as the temperature increases and the atoms vibrate more wildly about their equilibrium position, so the preciseness of the pattern is spoiled. The X-rays are being diffracted now from a collection of atoms not quite in their appointed places, so instead of the sharply defined directions in which the diffracted X-rays reinforce themselves to produce clear-cut 'lines' on the film, we get a kind of fuzziness, like an out-of-focus photograph. The higher the temperature the more blurred the pattern becomes.

p 172
(23, 24)

fig 5

We have seen that the interatomic forces originate as electrostatic forces acting between charged particles. These forces have relatively little effect on the inner, completely filled electron shells which surround the atomic nucleus, but may profoundly perturb the more loosely bound outer electrons. Quantitative calculations of cohesion present a formidable mathematical problem, which has not yet been exactly solved for even the simplest molecule, let alone a complete three-dimensional array of atoms. Fortunately, an alternative approach has been developed over the past 30 years using the concept of the chemical bond, according to which the energy is partitioned into a number of identifiable factors that can be roughly assessed in any given situation. Utilizing an intuitive mixture of mathematical, physical and chemical argument, great progress has been made in understanding the stability factors at work in different molecules and crystals. But we are not yet in a position to predict what structure would be adopted by a given assembly of atoms.

An exercise in close packing

To start with the simplest case, let us consider atoms in which each electron shell is completely filled. These include helium (its single inner shell filled with the full complement of 2 electrons), neon (inner shell with 2 electrons, outer shell filled with 8 electrons), argon (2 electrons, 8 electrons, and 8 electrons on the outer shell) and so on through the list of inert gases. Their inertness is fundamentally due to the fact that they have filled shells and therefore find it unnecessary to interchange or share electrons with other atoms.

fig 3

The interatomic forces between these filled-shell atoms are rather small and of the temporary dipole type we discussed

above. The force of attraction between these atoms is independent of direction, so if we reduce the temperature (quite a long way because the interatomic forces are so small) until the inert gases solidify, the solid so formed is of a very simple type. The atoms pack together until the electron waves of the outer shells just begin to overlap and the repulsive forces between them overcome the attraction. As a crude analogy, we can look on the atoms as ball bearings of diameter equal to that of the outer electron shell. Now the problem is how to pack these hard spheres so that each one is as close to its neighbours as possible.

The simplest method of understanding this is to try it out with ball bearings or marbles arranged in a tray. The closest method of packing a single layer is to surround each marble with six others. Arrange the marbles in this pattern inside the lid of a box. When the first layer is complete, start building a second layer, placing each marble of the second layer into one of the hollows between a group of three marbles in the first layer. As soon as you have chosen a hollow in which to place the first marble of the second layer, you have fixed the whole pattern of that layer. The three nearest hollows cannot now have marbles in them, because the first one gets in the way. Notice that the centre of each marble in the second layer is displaced with respect to the centres of marbles in the first layer.

Now add a third layer to the structure. Again the marbles fit into hollows produced between each group of three marbles in the second layer. But this time, there is a difference between the hollows. Half of them lie immediately above the centre of a marble in the first layer, the other half do not. So we can build this third layer in two ways, either by choosing to place the first marble in a hollow above the centre of a first-layer marble, or by choosing to place it in a hollow which is not vertically above a first-layer marble.

If we choose the former method, the third layer we have placed on this stack is exactly similar to the first. A fourth layer will be exactly equal to the second. On the other hand, if we choose the alternative method of building the third layer, it is different again from the first layer. If now we build a fourth layer on the third one, we again have two alternatives. It can either be like the first layer, with the centre of each marble immediately above the first-layer centres. Or it can be like the second layer.

So, assuming that we are going to have a regular order of packing throughout the pile, we are limited to two choices: a 1 2 1 2 1 2 pattern in which the third layer is always like the first, or a 1 2 3 1 2 3 1 2 3 pattern in which the fourth layer is always like the first.

p 170
(2-5)

The simpler 1 2 1 2 1 2 pattern is called a hexagonal close-packed structure. It repeats at every third layer, so we can imagine the whole pile being built from individual blocks

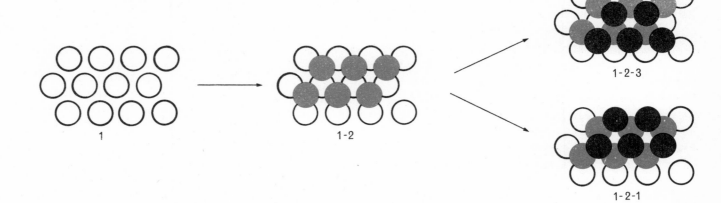

The close packing of atoms held together by weak 'Van der Waals' forces can best be understood by trying it with marbles. On the first, regularly arranged layer, a second layer can be placed in the hollows. For the third layer two arrangements are possible: the marbles can be placed in hollows over hollows, i.e. the positioning (1-2-3) or they can be placed in hollows over the centres of marbles, in which case the new layer is exactly similar to the first (1-2-1). (5)

1   1-2   1-2-3

1-2-1

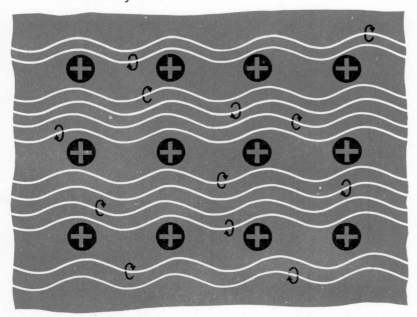

In metals, which in spite of their appearance are made up of many small crystals the spare outer electron is donated to the system as a whole. The positive ions form a close-packed lattice, cemented together by a 'gas' of free electrons equal in number to the ions, and balanced in their spins. They are free to move anywhere within the crystal and surprising results have been obtained by thinking of them in terms of waves. (6)

shaped like a hexagonal tile exactly three layers thick. Its proportions can be worked out by simple geometry. The height of the cell can be shown to be $(8/3)^{\frac{1}{2}} = 1.633$ times the interatomic distance.

The 123123 close-packed arrangement in which the fourth layer corresponds to the first is called face-centred cubic. The four layers do not in this case correspond to the faces of the cube. It is as though we were building a wall with cubic bricks placed in position with one point downwards.

p 170 (6-10)

Which of these two close-packed forms can we expect our complete-shell atoms to adopt? In each case the relationship of the atom with its nearest neighbours is the same: the distance between them is the same and the number of nearest neighbours is 12 in each case. So the choice of one arrangement rather than another must be decided by inter-actions between atoms at greater distances. In fact these forces may extend to atoms at several layer thicknesses. Helium, which only solidifies at a few degrees above abso-lute zero, has a hexagonal close-packed structure, while the other inert gases such as neon, argon and xenon all solidify to form face-centred cubic crystals.

A metal's free-flowing electrons

This simple close-packing occurs also for atoms like copper, which have a single electron in their outermost shell. An important principle in the understanding of the relationship between atoms is this: any atom will donate, accept, share or reject electrons with a view to adopting its nearest available inert gas configuration. Thus atoms with only one or two electrons in their outermost shell are eager to enter a liaison with other atoms which require one or two electrons to complete their outer shell.

A feature of these 'electro-positive' atoms is their readi-ness to give up these extra electrons. But there is here no question of palming electrons off on other atoms which are short of them. For we are now considering what happens when an assembly of atoms of the same kind is formed.

In this case, it is no good the electro-positive atom

attempting to share or donate electrons with a neighbour-ing atom because 6 or 7 extra electrons are needed to fill the outer layer. For instance the lithium atom has three elec-trons. Two fill the inner shell in the helium configuration. One is left over and forms an outer shell. But eight electrons are needed before this shell is full.

fig 6

In these circumstances what seems to happen is that each atom donates its spare electron to the system as a whole, so that the crystal is made up of a collection of positive ions with completed-shell structure cemented together with a 'gas' of free electrons. The electrons can move about any-where in the crystal, no matter how large it may be. Calcu-lations show that this model does lead to a structure that is cohesive. The consequences of the free electron 'gas' are exceedingly important and we shall return to them later. This 'gas' is responsible for the properties that we recognize as metallic, such as good conduction of electricity and heat, and we can now use the existence of a free electron gas as the definition of a metal.

The packing of the metal ions into a crystal is similar to that of the solidified inert gases. Many metals have a face-centred cubic structure—among them copper, silver, gold and nickel. A few, such as cadmium, cobalt and magnesium, have hexagonal close-packed crystals. Other metals, such as lithium, sodium and iron, prefer a different kind of packing, which is not quite so close as the hexagonal or face-centred cubic. In this case, the body-centred cubic, each atom has only eight close neighbours instead of 12 in the close-packed arrangements. But it has a further 6 neighbours which, although farther away than the nearest neighbours, are still not very far away.

p 170 (11-13)

Again, the question of which crystal form is preferred depends on the details of the variation of interatomic attrac-tion with distance. In many cases the difference in energy is sufficiently small for the crystal form to alter with changing temperature. This happens in the case of iron, which is body-centred cubic at ordinary temperatures, but changes to a face-centred cubic form above 900° C.

p 170 (14, 15)

Give and take in common salt

All the crystals we have discussed so far contain only a single kind of atom. But an important class of solid materials contains atoms of different elements in certain definite

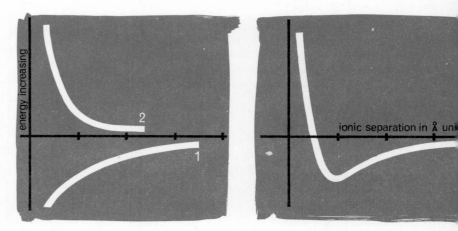

What happens when the Na+ and Cl- ions are brought together? They attract each other with increasing energy as the distance decreases (curve 1), but at a certain point the electrons and nuclei of the filled shells of one atom begin to repel those of the other, also with increasing energy (curve 2). The result of the two opposing interactions is the joint curve (right), showing a point of least energy, at which repulsion balances attraction and stable equilibrium is reached. A minimum occurs similarly when the forces are due to the weak 'Van der Waals' effect. (7)

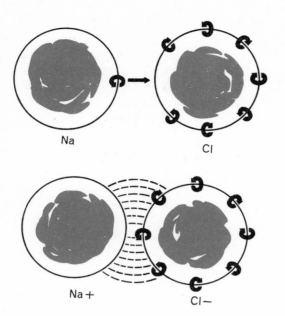

The sodium atom has two completely filled shells and one electron in the third. Chlorine is one electron short of three filled shells. The sodium gives its extra electron to the chlorine, leaving itself positive and the chlorine, with its additional electron, negative. The two attract one another in a powerful bond, to form common salt. (8)

proportions. The simplest of these substances is sodium chloride or common salt, which is made up of equal numbers of sodium and chlorine atoms. Sodium is an electropositive atom, with two completely filled electron shells (as in neon) and one additional electron in the third shell. Chlorine is an electro-negative atom with structure exactly one electron short of the three filled shells of the argon atom.

Using our basic principle that atoms tend to gain or lose electrons to give themselves the nearest inert gas 'filled-shell' configuration, we see that sodium would tend to give up its extra electron, and chlorine would happily receive it, so that a powerful link should exist between the sodium and chlorine atoms. The sodium atom, having lost its electron to the chlorine, has a net positive charge, while the chlorine, having gained an electron, has a net negative charge. These charged atoms are called ions, and the interaction between them is called an ionic bond.

If the sodium and chlorine ions are assembled into a crystal, they arrange themselves so that each ion surrounds itself with the largest possible number of ions of the opposite kind and keeps away from ions of the same kind. The problem is now not simply one of close packing; the ions are arranged at the corners of a simple cubic structure.

The 'rock-salt' structure, as this is called, is the simplest of the ionic crystals. Another simple structure is that of caesium chloride, in which an ion of one kind is at the centre of a cube of atoms of the other kind. But in general the ionic crystals have more complicated structures than the metals.

While metal crystals happily grow together to form the typical polycrystalline structure of ordinary metals and alloys, ionic crystals, because of the selective and powerful nature of the forces operating between the ions, do not easily stick together. The energy involved at the junction between two crystals is large, so in general they prefer to remain separate. One consequence of this is that it is rather easy to grow ionic crystals to large sizes, and the external faces of the crystal usually correspond closely to one or other of the crystal planes. Which planes are chosen depends on the rate of growth in different directions.

fig 9

fig 8

fig 7

fig 10

p 172
(21)

p 171
(17, 18)

p 171
(19, 20)

p 171
(16)

The powerful 'sharing' bonds

A major difficulty confronting chemical theory throughout the last century was to understand how two neutral hydrogen atoms, in the absence of any obvious attractive mechanisms between them, could unite into a stable hydrogen molecule H_2. This difficulty was, indeed, one of the major

factors which delayed acceptance of Avogadro's hypothesis. The modern explanation runs something as follows. Two hydrogen atoms at large separations interact as independent electrostatic units, but at closer distances of approach it has no physical significance to associate a particular electron with a particular proton: each electron belongs to the system as a whole, and therefore moves in a molecular orbit covering both protons rather than in an atomic orbit covering only one. Two paired electrons occupying the same molecular orbit constitute a stable electronic configuration, as confirmed by the celebrated calculations of Heitler and London in 1927.

This kind of link between atoms sharing electrons is called the covalent bond. In the case of hydrogen the covalent bond can link only pairs of atoms, because there is only room in the helium-type shell for two electrons with opposite spins. If two hydrogen atoms approach one another with electrons of opposite spin, they are attracted to form a hydrogen molecule. If the spins are the same, the two atoms are repelled.

This type of covalent bond is very important in the chemistry of carbon, whose outer 'neon' shell has four of its full complement of eight electrons. Each of these four electrons can share living space in its shell with electrons from another atom near by, provided that their spins are appropriately adjusted. For instance methane, a gas frequently found in coal mines, consists of a carbon atom surrounded by four hydrogen atoms each of which shares its electron with the carbon. Thus the carbon has shares in four extra electrons and has achieved, in a sense, a completed 'neon' shell. At the same time each hydrogen has shares in an extra electron from the carbon so that it has a pseudo-helium shell—an admirably cooperative system. The actual arrangement of the atoms in the methane molecule can be shown to be simple. The carbon atom is at the centre of a regular tetrahedron, at each vertex of which there is a hydrogen atom.

This same sharing arrangement is possible between carbon atoms. If we imagine that we replace the hydrogen atoms in a methane molecule with carbon atoms and repeat the structure indefinitely, we have a new type of crystal based on the covalent bond. Every carbon atom shares electrons with its

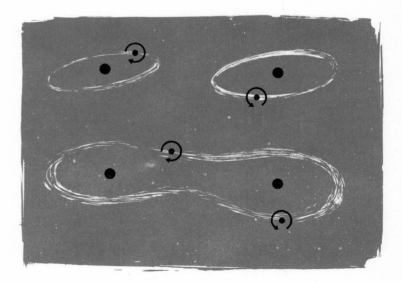

Why do two hydrogen atoms, both neutral, interact to form a molecule H_2, neutral and stable? When they come close together the electrons are shared; each electron belongs to the system as a whole and moves in a molecular orbit covering both protons. But the electrons must have opposite spins; if they had parallel spins, the atoms would repel one another. (9)

four nearest neighbours. This carbon crystal with its perfectly symmetrical system of interlocking directed bonds is exceedingly hard and has a very high melting point (3750°C) because of the powerful cohesive forces. We call the crystals diamond.

Covalent structures similar to diamond are formed by germanium and silicon, whose atoms have similar half-filled outer shells. But in these cases the valency electrons are much less tightly bound, so that the cohesive forces are less powerful and the melting points (1421°C for silicon and 958°C for germanium) are much lower.

The benzene molecule forms an interesting contrast to methane. In this case each carbon lies at the centre of an isosceles triangle linked by directed covalent bonds to two carbon atoms and a hydrogen atom. The pattern is continued to form a closed ring containing six carbon atoms. Note that each carbon has a spare valency electron which appears to take little part in the cohesive process: according to modern views these circulate around the ring and help to keep it plane. All the aromatic compounds of organic chemistry are grounded upon this hexagonal unit.

On replacing the hydrogen atoms by carbon atoms and repeating the pattern indefinitely, we build up an infinite covalent molecule which can be regarded as a two-dimensional crystal sheet. Such sheets do not exist independently in nature, but form the successive layers of the graphite crystal. This layer structure leads to some remarkable properties. For instance graphite behaves as an electrical conductor in directions parallel to the layers, but as an insulator across the layers. Evidently the spare valency electrons, which previously circulated in the benzene ring, can now move anywhere in the crystal sheet: they have become a kind of two-dimensional electron gas akin to that of a metal. Another feature is the ease with which the crystal sheets slide over one another because of extremely weak interlayer forces. The easy sliding of the layers makes graphite useful as a lubricant and a writing material.

The graphite crystal is an example of a structure involving two different kinds of interatomic forces. Within each crystal sheet the powerful covalent forces are at work; while the forces between the sheets are the same weak 'temporary dipole' effect that we discussed in the case of the inert gas crystals. These are known as Van der Waals interactions.

We saw that the most striking properties of metals, their capacity to conduct heat and electricity, can be explained

fig 10

fig 6

fig 11

qualitatively in terms of the electron gas which pervades metal crystals. The gas drifts preferentially under the influence of an applied electric field, thereby producing an electric current; and it enables energy to be transferred rapidly from one lattice region to another, thereby acting as a heat conductor. Ionic and covalent crystals (with the exception of graphite as we saw above) have no electron gas, do not conduct electricity and are poor conductors of heat.

The behaviour of the electron gas is subject to the laws of quantum mechanics (developed in 1926) and the exclusion principle. The electrons do not behave like the simple gas particles in the kinetic theory, for they cannot have *any* energy, but only certain discrete values, and very few electrons can be allocated to each value. This is a very surprising concept. If we imagine a lump of metal, it seems strange that because electrons at one end of the bar happen to have filled a certain energy level, no other electron, even at the opposite end of the bar, can have that same energy.

But we should think of these electrons not as very small marbles, but in terms of waves. The energy of the electron depends on its wavelength: the shorter the wavelength the higher the energy. The only energy levels permitted are those of electrons whose wavelengths are such that a whole number or a whole number plus a half will just fit into the bar of metal.

The electron of lowest energy is one whose wavelength is twice the dimensions of the bar. Two electrons can have this wavelength, one spinning in one direction and one in the opposite direction. The next is a wavelength equal to the dimensions of the bar; again two electrons spinning in opposite directions can have this wavelength. So we go on, filling up places in the band of wavelengths until every electron has been accommodated. The most energetic turn out to have a wavelength about equal to the distance between atoms in the lattice.

Unlikely though this idea may sound, there is good experimental evidence to uphold it. If you heat a gas, the particles it contains share the increase in energy without favour. The amount of energy needed to raise the temperature of the gas by 1°C is known as its specific heat.

Now the specific heat of a metal crystal should be made up of two parts. Some of the energy is used in vibrating the positive ions more strongly about their lattice positions. This will presumably be much the same as for a non-metallic crystal. Another part of the energy will be used in heating

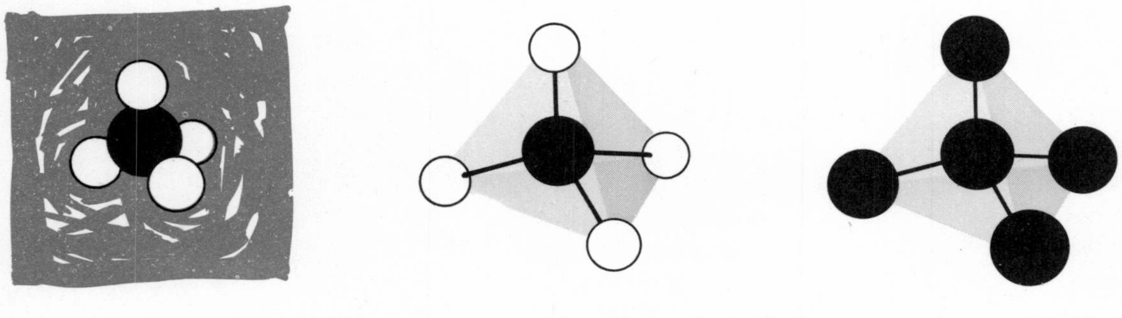

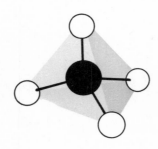

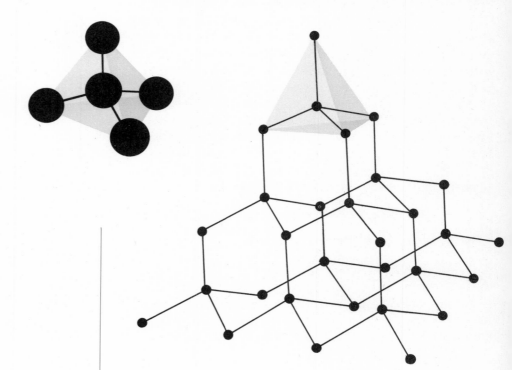

The carbon atom has four electrons in its outer shell, but the full complement is eight. In methane (main constituent of 'natural gas'), four hydrogen atoms share their single electrons with the carbon, completing, in a sense, the stable 'neon' form, and each hydrogen atom shares a carbon electron to achieve the stable 'helium' form. The carbon atom takes up its position at the centre of a regular tetrahedron, with a hydrogen atom at each vertex (left, actual packing; left centre, expanded for clarity). If we now replace each hydrogen atom with a carbon atom and link the atoms together so that each shares electrons with its nearest neighbours, we have the beautiful symmetry and powerful interlocking bonds of the diamond crystal, with its great hardness and high melting point. (10)

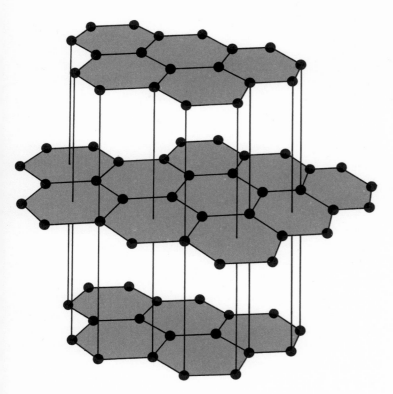

The carbon bond with carbon can also take the form shown above, in which the atoms assemble in a closed hexagonal ring. This, continued indefinitely, forms a sheet in which each carbon atom is linked with three others. Such sheets, in successive layers, are a graphite crystal. Graphite conducts electricity parallel to the sheets, but is an insulator perpendicular to them—the spare carbon electron is thought to circulate throughout the sheet, akin to what happens in a metal. The bond between the atoms within a sheet is strong, that between the sheets is extremely weak; the sheets slide easily over one another, so graphite is useful as a lubricant and for the 'lead' in pencils. (11)

the electron gas. If the electron gas were comparable with a simple 'kinetic theory' gas, it should make a major contribution to the specific heat of the metal.

In fact, the specific heat of metals is very close to that of non-metallic solids. We are forced to the conclusion that the gas has made little contribution. The reason becomes clear if we consider the band of energy levels in the metal.

The levels have been filled from the bottom to a certain height, sufficient to contain every electron. Above the surface of the filled levels are others (shown dotted) which are permitted, but vacant. Now suppose the electron gas is heated and more energy offered to the electrons. An electron close to the surface may receive enough energy to lift it into one of the unoccupied levels. But the bulk of the electrons are in lower levels and the chance that they will receive a sufficient bonus of energy to lift them clear of the surface is very small indeed. On the other hand if they are offered a smaller bonus, it is useless to them since it merely lifts them as far as a level which is already occupied. In other words, only levels at the top of the band, close to the surface are able to accept energy in this way and make any contribution to the specific heat of the metal. In fact, it is only these top-of-the-ladder electrons which are able to play an effective role in physical processes.

The importance of imperfection

The ions of a metal lattice vibrate thermally about their mean positions, the average amplitude increasing with temperature. This effect manifests itself directly by producing dimensional changes in the crystal on heating and, less directly, by producing 'fuzziness' in X-ray diffraction photographs, as described earlier.

However, the most important physical effect of the lattice vibrations is to provide the mechanism of electrical resist-

M. A. Jaswon

ance in a metal by scattering the free electrons as they move under the influence of an applied electric field. Other disturbances of the regular lattice provide additional scattering and therefore an increase in electrical resistance. These disturbances may be due to vacancies in the regular network, or to impurity atoms which have become lodged in the interstices of the lattice. Their number can be augmented in various ways: by neutron irradiation which may transform some atoms and knock others out of their regular positions; by mechanical working of the metal at low temperature; or by quenching (rapid cooling) from a high temperature, thereby preserving the equilibrium concentration of lattice defects characteristic of the high temperature. All these methods and, of course, the deliberate addition of alloying atoms may be used to increase the electrical resistance.

The importance of defects in crystals first became clear for an entirely different reason. Since the interatomic forces are fairly well understood in very simple crystals, such as sodium chloride, it ought to be possible to work out the strength of the crystal. The theoretical estimates of the compressibility of sodium chloride gave quite good agreement with the observed value. But there were serious discrepancies between theory and experiment on the force required to slide one layer of the crystal over another. Similar disagreement existed on the force needed to fracture the crystal. In both cases theory predicted that very much stronger forces (about 1000 times as great) would be needed than were actually required. Single crystals, in particular, proved to be exceptionally weak, much more so than polycrystalline materials.

This led to an investigation of the way in which the crystals shear and the planes slip over one another. These slip planes are often visible on the surface of crystals. Slip occurs only on occasional planes, separated by thousands of atomic diameters. These planes evidently slip readily over one another, while the ones in between do not.

The solution to this puzzle came in sight in 1934 when Taylor, Orowan and Polanyi suggested the idea of the edge dislocation, a particular kind of misfit that would enable the crystal plane in which it was contained to run like a laddered stocking. Although the dislocation itself is a displacement simply of a line of atoms, by viewing a line dislocation in a thin metal film almost end on it can be seen under the electron microscope. Films of the movement of dislocations, as the laddering process takes place and they move through the crystal, have demonstrated the soundness of the theory.

fig 12

fig 13

p 173
(27, 28)

p 172
(23, 24)

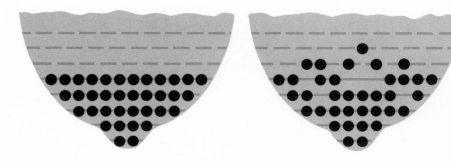

Only the electrons on the highest energy levels can play an effective role in physical processes. The electrons completely fill the available places in the lower levels until all electrons are accommodated, an increasing number being associated with the levels as the energy increases. Above them further levels are permitted, but vacant. If more energy is offered (as when the electron gas is heated), those electrons near the top may receive enough to lift them into the unoccupied levels, but it is unlikely that those lower down will receive sufficient to lift them above the surface. Anything less than this would lift them only to levels in which no place is available—i.e. they could not accept the extra energy. (12)

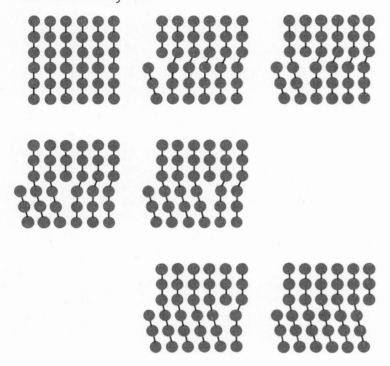

Where is the structural weakness which causes occasional atomic layers to glide over one another under much smaller stress than calculations suggested? The answer lies in edge dislocation. One row of atoms in the perfect crystal splits into two and one half is displaced. The displacement is propagated readily under very low stress atom by atom across the rows until it passes right out of the crystal. (13)

The dislocation theory has successfully explained many of the features of solid materials. For instance, polycrystalline materials are stronger than single crystals because the sudden change of orientation of the crystal planes at the boundary is a barrier to the movement of the dislocation, just as a daub of nail varnish can stop a laddered stocking from running farther. If more and more crystal boundaries are introduced into a piece of metal, by reducing the size of individual crystals through forging or alloying, its resistance to stretching and its ultimate strength will increase. Dislocations are introduced into crystals as faults in the way in which they grow. They may also be responsible for the growth of the crystal. For example, it has been shown that one type of dislocation (the screw type) acts as a kind of catalyst to the growth of crystals from vapour and makes it possible for growth to proceed at a finite rate.

The wandering holes

The other main type of lattice defect in crystals occurs at particular points. It may be the absence of an atom or ion from its proper place on the lattice—like a dropped stitch in knitted fabric—or the presence of some impurity: a foreign atom which has either substituted itself for one of the correct kind and is sitting on one of the lattice points, or has penetrated between the interstices of the lattice.

The absence of an atom from the lattice is called a vacancy. The number of vacancies depends on the temperature. At ordinary temperatures about one vacancy per 1000 sites occurs in typical crystals. These vacancies are mobile and migrate randomly through the crystal as neighbouring atoms (or ions) slip into the empty space as a result of thermal fluctuations and leave holes where they came from. In ionic crystals an electric field will make the vacancies migrate in a particular direction, giving rise to ionic conductivity.

The vacancies are also indirectly responsible for the photographic process. What happens is this. The emulsion contains ionic crystals of silver bromide. When light strikes the crystals it may release an electron from one of the bromine ions. This electron quickly gets trapped by an impurity atom in the crystal, and acts as a centre of attraction for positively charged silver ions, which make use of vacancies to swap positions and migrate towards the electron. The cluster of silver ions forms the latent image which is subsequently intensified by the developing process.

Foreign atoms may also have an important effect on the behaviour of a crystal. For instance, zinc oxide and zinc sulphide crystals are believed to contain an excess of zinc atoms which do not occupy lattice sites but are interstitial. The outer electrons of these atoms, being rather loosely bound, can sometimes be freed, either by the action of light or by thermal fluctuations. In zinc oxide thermal fluctuations release a small number of free electrons (the number increasing with the temperature). These electrons are free to move under the influence of an electric field. Thus zinc oxide conducts electricity at high temperatures, although considerably less well than a metal. The phenomenon is known as semi-conduction.

Basically, the same type of mechanism holds for all other semi-conductors, though naturally the details vary from case to case. Semi-conductors, mainly based on germanium and silicon (covalent crystals) with suitable impurities added, are now widely used in the electronics industry as they can be made to pass current in one direction only (a rectifier) or arranged so that large currents can be controlled by very small ones (a transistor).

p 176-9

fig 14, 15

p 173 (30)

p 173 (27)

p 173 (29)

n-type   p-type

n + − p

n + − p

n   p

Rectifiers, which change two-way currents to the one-way impulses necessary in receiving sets, are frequently made from silicon crystals. When pure, they are poor conductors, but if an impurity is added such as indium, whose outer electrons are less tightly bound, the silicon becomes conducting. It is called n-type, because current is carried by the negatively charged mobile electrons. Silicon can also be made a better conductor by adding an impurity such as antimony, which readily absorbs electrons from the silicon atoms, leaving 'holes' in the electron structure. The crystals are then known as p-type, because atoms with such holes are positive. Electrons from other silicon atoms can now move through the crystal by hopping from one hole to another, the holes seeming to move in the opposite direction. In the drawing (left) only the mobile electrons and holes are shown; the impurity atoms not shown have opposite charges: each crystal is neutral.

(2) If now the two crystals are joined together, one might expect n-type electrons to move across into the waiting p-type holes. But the first few electrons which diffuse across make the neutral p-type crystal negative, which then repels any further electrons and the flow stops. A barrier is set up. (3) Now apply an outside voltage, positive to the n-side, negative to the p-side; the barrier is increased and no current can flow. (4) But if the voltage is reversed, the barrier is neutralized and current flows. Only the one-way half of a two-way current passes. (14)

In zinc sulphide crystals the electrons are too strongly bound to be released by thermal vibrations, but they can be released by ultra-violet rays, or by the impact of a stream of electrons. Electrons 'lifted' into a higher energy level in one of these ways may fall back immediately to their old position, or may become trapped at some higher level owing to the influence of an impurity atom. At some later time the electron may escape from this trap and fall back to its old level, releasing as it does so a quantum of light. The effect is called phosphorescence. Phosphors which are activated by an electron stream, mainly based on zinc sulphide, are used as the coating on television screens.

p 174·5

Electrons freed from their normal orbits by the action of light can, of course, conduct electricity. This photo-conductivity depends on the amount of light falling on the crystal. It has many technological applications.

Spinning electron magnets

This survey of the behaviour of atoms in co-operation has discussed most of the observed properties of matter: the electrical and thermal conductivity of metals; the low strength of single crystals; the high strength and hardness of diamond; the behaviour of semi-conductors and photo-conductors; the reason for the large size and individual habit of ionic crystals. Only one outstanding property of the metallic state remains to be considered: ferromagnetism.

Magnetism arises from electron spin. Every electron is

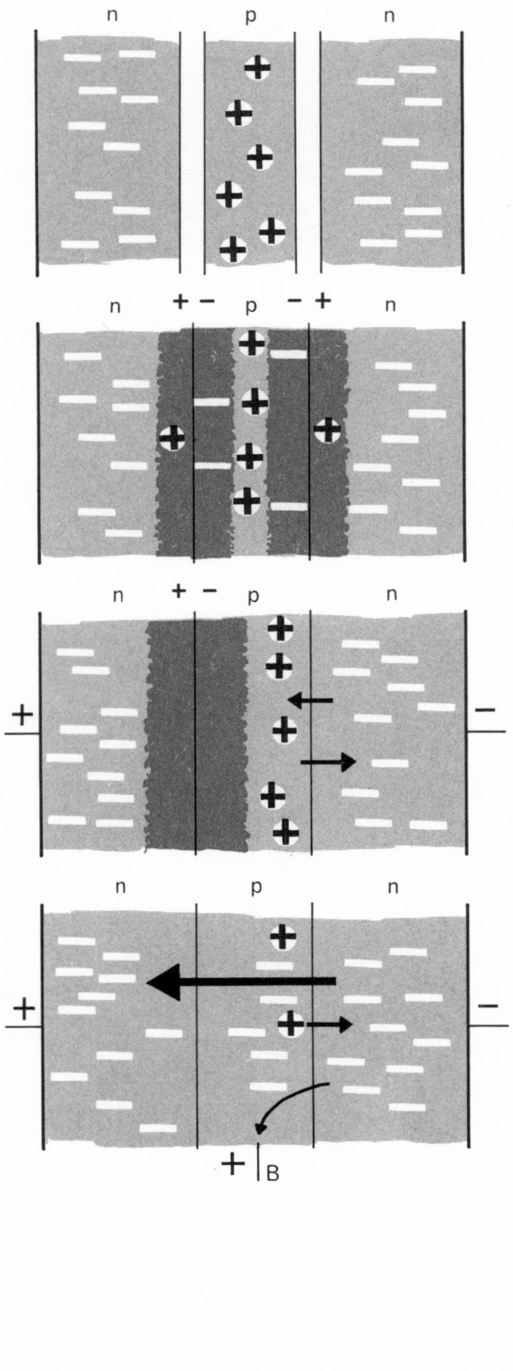

A transistor, when used to increase the strength of radio signals received, can consist of a very thin p-type crystal sandwiched between two n-type crystals. The one has 'mobile' holes, the others mobile electrons and only these are shown (right). The impurity atoms not shown have equal opposite charges and each crystal is neutral. (2) When the crystals are put together, the first electrons to diffuse across form a barrier at each junction. The two barriers work in opposite ways.

If now an outside voltage is applied (3), one of the barriers will prevent current flowing. In the drawing the n-p barrier will be increased and stop the current, although the p-n barrier would break down and allow current through. If the voltage were reversed, the effects would be interchanged, but still no current could flow. (4) But if a positive source of current B, from a rectifier or battery, were applied to the p-type crystal, the p-n barrier would break down and electrons would flow from the right-hand crystal via the p-type holes into this positive terminal. Also the new positive source has diminished the negative barrier before the left-hand n-type crystal, and if the p-type crystal is made thin enough (one-thousandth of an inch or less) some of the electrons will be attracted into the left-hand crystal and current will flow through the whole transistor. In practice, most of the current flows this way, flowing only when the B-current is flowing, closely proportional to the B-current, but much greater than the B-current alone. The transistor acts as an amplifier. (15)

fig 16

spinning and acts as a small magnet. However, since most electrons are paired, one spinning in one direction and one in the other, their magnetic effects usually cancel one another out. Only in those cases where an atom or molecule has an odd number of electrons is there any net electron spin and any appreciable magnetic effect. In most of these cases the individual magnets do not tend to line up unless they are persuaded to do so by a powerful magnetic field. These substances with atoms or molecules which behave like small magnets are said to be paramagnetic.

In one or two special cases and for a reason that is not fully understood, the small magnets are spontaneously aligned even in the absence of an external magnetic field. These crystals, mainly iron, nickel and cobalt and certain of their alloys, are said to be ferromagnetic. The interaction between the atomic magnets is closely related to the interatomic spacing. For instance, iron exhibits ferromagnetism only in the body-centred cubic form, and not in the face-centred form where the closest interatomic separation is rather less. Manganese, although not ferromagnetic itself, produces a number of ferromagnetic alloys. Again, there appears to be a critical interatomic distance at which the spins spontaneously interact and line up.

p 170 (14, 15)

As might be expected, the spin aligning forces are always opposed by the thermal agitation factor. As the temperature is increased the spontaneous magnetization decreases until it finally disappears at a temperature known as the Curie point. Above the Curie temperature the ferromagnetic material behaves like an ordinary paramagnetic.

The fact that iron is spontaneously magnetized at temperatures below the Curie temperature (770° C) raises another problem. Many pieces of iron are quite obviously not magnetized. The answer has been convincingly demonstrated as due to the splitting up of the iron crystals into zones or domains, in each of which the iron is spontaneously magnetized, but which arrange themselves in such a way that the net effect is zero or almost zero. Thus a domain in which the spins are aligned in one direction will be sandwiched between two domains in which they are aligned in the opposite direction. Along the boundary between the domains the spins gradually change over from one direction to the other.

p 180 (54, 55)

These domains are not coincident with the crystal boundaries: each crystal may contain many different domains. But the direction of magnetization in the domains is related to the crystal planes. In iron there are four preferred or 'easy' directions of magnetization in which the energy is a minimum, and the domains are magnetized in these directions. This means of course that as the crystal orientation varies from crystal to crystal in a polycrystalline specimen, so the crystal boundaries will also be domain boundaries.

When a piece of iron is magnetized, domains in which the spontaneous magnetization is generally in the right direction swell at the expense of those in which it is pointing the wrong way. The process takes place by the movement and the eventual elimination of the domain boundaries. This leaves a small number of preferred domains in which the spontaneous direction of magnetization (along an 'easy' direction in the crystal) approximates more or less with the applied field. Increasing the field still more turns the spins out of the easy direction and aligns them more closely with the field direction.

If, on removing the external field, the redevelopment of domain structure is inhibited by the presence of internal stresses, micro-cavities or foreign inclusions, the specimen

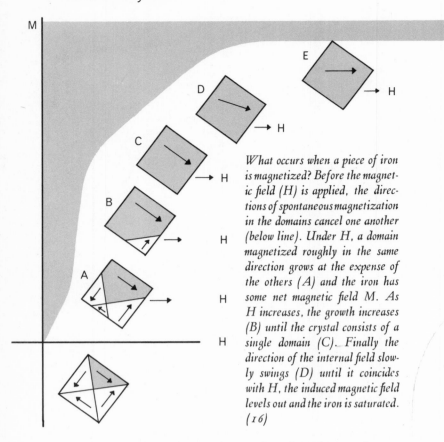

What occurs when a piece of iron is magnetized? Before the magnetic field (H) is applied, the directions of spontaneous magnetization in the domains cancel one another (below line). Under H, a domain magnetized roughly in the same direction grows at the expense of the others (A) and the iron has some net magnetic field M. As H increases, the growth increases (B) until the crystal consists of a single domain (C). Finally the direction of the internal field slowly swings (D) until it coincides with H, the induced magnetic field levels out and the iron is saturated. (16)

retains its magnetization and can therefore be used as a permanent magnet.

Although all the naturally occurring elemental ferromagnetic substances are metals, they need not necessarily be so. In recent years non-metallic magnetic materials called ferrites have been developed and have very wide applications. They are oxides of iron and other metals akin to ionic crystals, and therefore non-conductors of electricity, but capable of exhibiting spontaneous magnetization.

The strange world of absolute zero

Ferromagnetism provides a remarkable example of the way in which the fine details of the structure of complicated atoms and crystals can have a very large effect on their properties. One of the most powerful methods discovered for working out the fine details of solid structure is through the use of very low temperatures. Under these conditions the thermal fluctuations of the lattice become small and effects which would not otherwise be noticed become obvious. One of the most dramatic is superconductivity.

It was discovered by Kamerlingh Onnes in his laboratory in Leiden in 1911 when he was investigating the

p 180
(51-3)

variation of the resistance of mercury as the temperature was lowered. At first the electrical resistance decreased in a normal gradual and not very interesting way. Then suddenly, at 4.2° above absolute zero, it disappeared completely. The most accurate measurements show that it is less than 10 million millionths of what it was at a slightly higher temperature. The change occurs within one hundredth of a degree centigrade. Superconductivity occurs in many, but not all metals. Its onset takes place at the highest temperature (11.2° absolute) in the metal technetium and at 7.2° absolute in lead. Metals like copper and silver, which are the best conductors at ordinary temperatures, do not show superconductivity.

Magnetic fields destroy superconductivity, if they exceed a certain critical value. And the critical temperature and magnetic field at which it disappears vary for different isotopes of the same element, showing that the ions in the metallic lattice must have a major part to play. But the cause of superconductivity, apart from the fact that it is a large-scale quantum effect, is still far from clear.

Even so, superconductivity now appears to have a number of technological applications. A current started in a superconducting ring continues to flow indefinitely. This fact is being used in a new kind of 'memory' for electronic computers. Superconducting wire is now being made for winding electromagnets which will produce a high magnetic field with the expenditure of little electrical energy. The same wire may eventually be used instead of the grid line to distribute electricity from the major power stations.

An even more surprising low-temperature effect is the behaviour of liquefied helium when it is cooled below 2.1° absolute, a temperature known as the lambda point. At this temperature the liquid becomes a 'superfluid'. The liquid gas flows with ease through the finest capillaries and will siphon itself out of a container by flowing up hill in a film which quickly climbs over the container walls. Yet measurements of the viscosity show that it is small but still quite measurable. The present view is that the liquid helium is in fact a mixture of two liquids, one of which has no viscosity and shows this property of superfluidity. Again, the explanation is not entirely clear, but is connected with the quantum behaviour of the liquid.

Although the everyday solids and liquids with which we deal do not behave in the queer quantum-controlled ways of matter at low temperatures, their properties are, nevertheless, controlled by the new set of physical laws which are necessary to describe atomic behaviour. Advances in the understanding of the structure of solids thus rest firmly on the exciting discoveries of the atomic physicists forty years ago.

The dramatic advances of technology

during the past twenty years would not have been possible without the patient, intricate and fascinating studies of scientists on the build-up of atoms to form solid matter. From their discoveries springs the modern industry of electronics—transistors, colour television, computers, solar cells and all the tiny devices of microelectronics.

It had been known for some time, from analysis by X-rays, that most solids are crystalline—especially surprising perhaps in the case of metals. This is dramatically demonstrated by the micrographs produced by Dr Erwin Mueller. He took an extremely fine platinum needle, ending in a hemisphere sixteen millionths of an inch in diameter. This he enclosed in a tube of rarefied hydrogen, applying to it a very high positive voltage. Under such electrical pressure the hydrogen atoms, as they

'settled' on the atoms of the needle tip, were ionized and torn off as protons, streaming away from the tip in a direction almost perpendicular to the surface at every point. Others replaced them and were torn off, at the rate of 100,000 atom layers per second.

At the other end of the tube they struck a fluorescent screen, producing the picture of the needle tip, enlarged approximately 750,000 times, shown in the photograph opposite. Clearly the platinum is crystalline. Round pyramids are built up of plane upon plane of atoms in the crystal, the rims of the planes in many cases being resolved into representations on the screen of the atoms themselves. It is the nearest man has come to seeing individual atoms and the beautiful microarchitecture of the solids which make his world. (1)

The elegant symmetry of the close-packed atoms in the inert gases and the metals takes three forms. The hexagonal form is built up from seven atoms as picked out in the first layer (right). The second layer includes three atoms, which form part of a similar interlocking unit (far right). The third layer repeats the hexagon (1212). In reality the electron shells almost touch, forming the unit shown in red. In bronze the unit is expanded. (2–5)

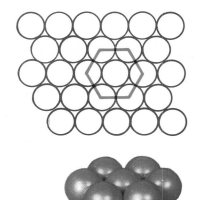

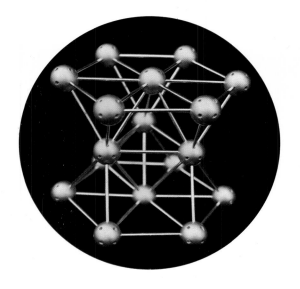

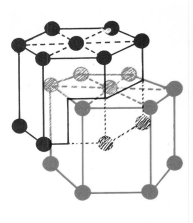

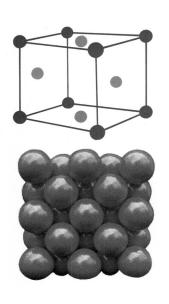

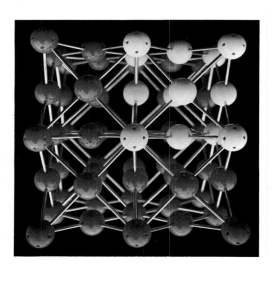

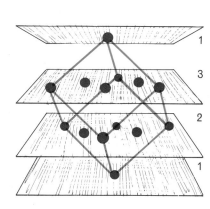

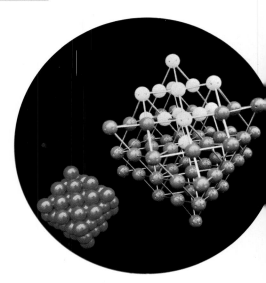

Metals such as copper form face-centred cubic units (above). Eight atoms form a cube, six settle in the centres of its faces (four only are shown). The units can be recognized in the red close-packed model, more clearly in the blue expanded form. The packing is 123123, in which the fourth layer is similar to the first, but the four packing layers in this case do not correspond with the faces of the cube, which points down through the layers. (6–10)

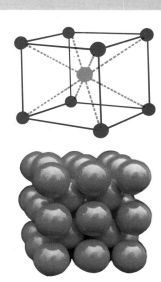

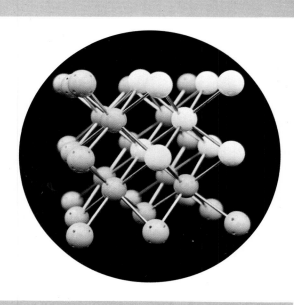

The atoms of sodium form a different kind of cubic unit, 'body-centred'. Eight atoms form a cube (left) but the ninth takes up a position in the cube's centre, an arrangement which the red close-packed model reveals with study but which is clearly visible in the expanded form. The packing is not quite so close as in the other unit-forms, where each atom has twelve near neighbours; in the body-centred unit there are only eight near neighbours, with another six at a slightly greater distance.

Which of the three forms the atoms adopt is decided by the interplay of attraction and repulsion in the complex of positive ions and negative electrons, the stable position being the one with which the least energy is associated. The atoms are not still; each is vibrating about its mean position, a movement which ceases at absolute zero. (11–13)

The crystal form can change on heating. Iron is body-centred cubic at normal temperatures (left model), but becomes face-centred cubic above 900°C (right). The closest atomic separation is then slightly less, and the iron also ceases to be magnetic. (14, 15)

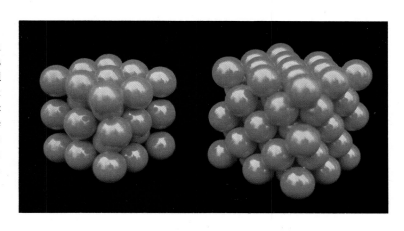

170

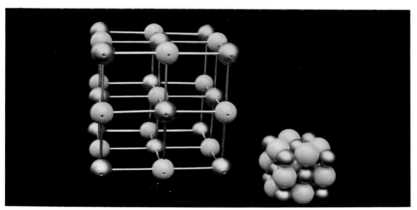

The crystal of common salt contains equal numbers of two different atoms, sodium and chlorine. New forces now affect the arrangement, the strong attraction of sodium ions for chlorine ions and the mutual repulsion of ions of the same kind. The result is a simple cubic structure (left) in which each ion surrounds itself with the largest possible number of ions of the opposite kind—and keeps away from its own kind. This 'rock-salt' structure is the simplest ionic crystal; its strong internal forces mean that single crystals can grow to large sizes, as in the natural crystal above—a cube in which the external faces correspond closely to the crystal planes of the multitude of units which make it up. (16-18)

Two different atoms in equal numbers are also present in crystals of caesium chloride (right), in which the caesium and chlorine are linked by ionic bonds similar to those of sodium chloride above. But in this case an ion of one kind is at the centre of a cube of ions of the opposite kind—eight nearest neighbours of opposite kind and six next-nearest neighbours of the same kind. In fact the caesium chloride structure can be thought of as body-centred cubic with the two different ions occupying alternate sites. (19, 20)

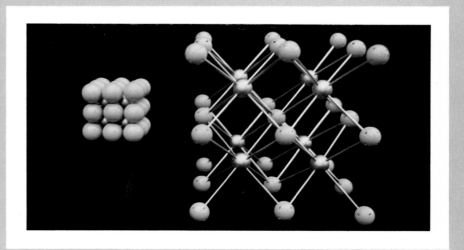

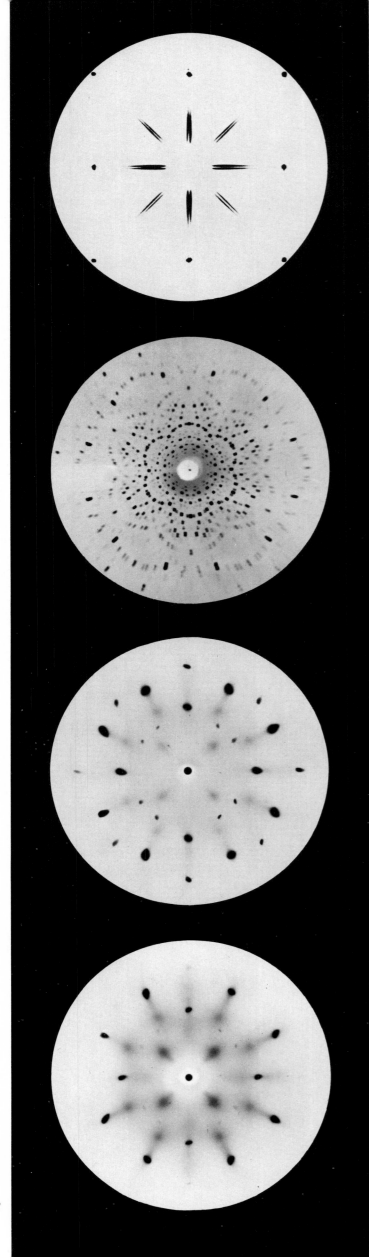

The solids which surround man are mostly crystalline. Metals, for instance, are composed of many small interlocking crystals, variously inclined to one another, a fact which helps to explain their strength. To make their structure visible, the surface is polished and then etched with acid, when the crystals are revealed, as are those of the nickel-iron alloy of the meteorite below, shown in its approximate natural size. Under the microscope, magnified 350 times, a silicon crystal grown by condensation of its vapour (above) reveals clearly the right-angled precision with which it is built up and its essentially cubic architecture. (25, 26)

The military order and symmetry of the atoms in crystals have been revealed by X-rays. The rays are diffracted by the three-dimensional lattice of atoms into patterns which can be analysed, by elegant techniques, to show the atomic positions. Above left is a diffraction pattern from a crystal of common salt, below it one from beryllium. That the atoms are not still, but vibrate increasingly with temperature, is shown by the two patterns from aluminium (left, below), at room temperature and 500°C. Streaks leading inwards from the outer spots increasingly confuse their position at the higher temperature. (21–24)

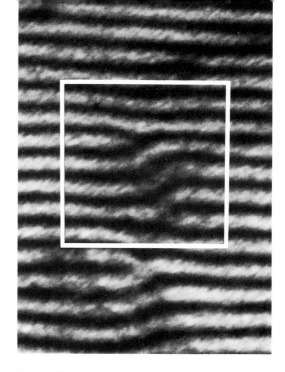

Crystals are not perfect. Dislocations in occasional lattice planes cause them to slip over one another under little stress. The beautiful spiral growth on a silicon carbide crystal (left) is assisted by a screw dislocation. Edge dislocations are revealed under the electron microscope. Thus a film of palladium deposited on to a gold film gives the moiré pattern above. Where the half-lines end (bottom right and left-centre of the marked area) are the dislocation sites. (27, 28)

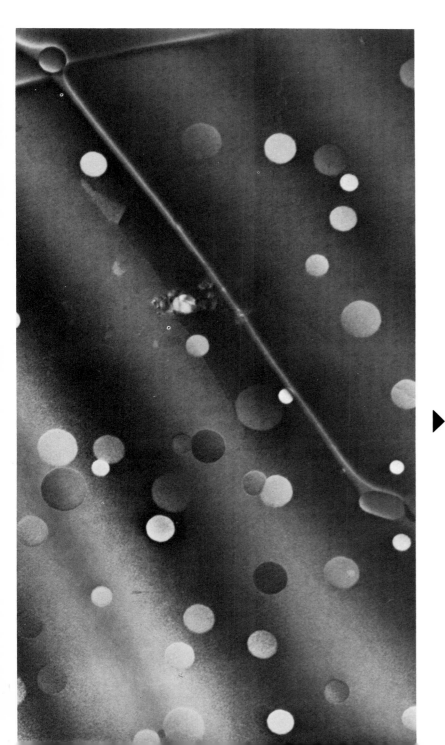

▶ **Vacancies in crystal lattices** can weaken the crystals. In nuclear reactors, neutrons at speeds up to 100,000,000 miles per hour strike the graphite rods and steel containers. They displace atoms, which form clusters, usually flat disks, one atom thick. The vacancies left behind also cluster into similar flat disks, seen (left) under the electron microscope in graphite film one hundred thousandth of an inch thick. The atom and vacancy clusters attach themselves to lines of slip between crystal planes, restricting the ease of movement under stress. Serious damage could result—the steel containers could become brittle in a few days. (29)

Brittleness in metals can also be due to traces of impurity. The heavy metal molybdenum is strong at high temperatures but breaks easily at room temperatures. Even if the metal is prepared by melting in an electric arc in a vacuum, when it is comparatively free of impurity, it is still poor in strength. This is because its component crystals are long and thin and the impurities which remain migrate to the crystal boundaries and form growths, such as those of molybdenum carbide, magnified 1000 times, above. These make the metal brittle. Processes of rolling and annealing correct this effect, by causing new and smaller crystals to grow. (30)

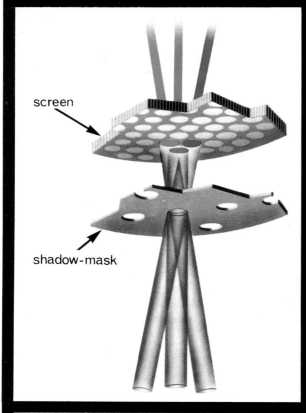

screen

shadow-mask

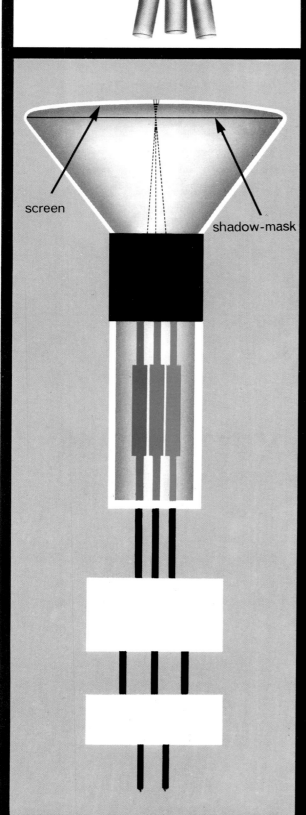

screen

shadow-mask

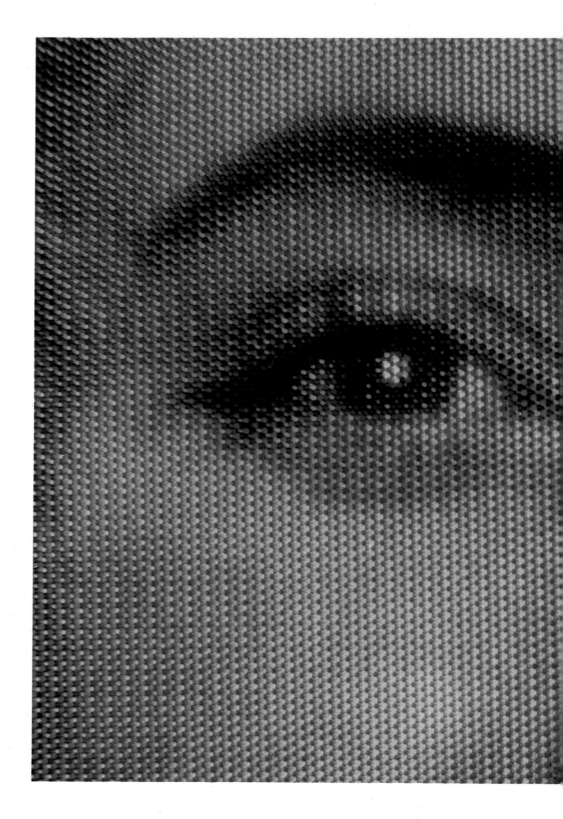

Modern television in colour makes skilful use, in its rectifiers and transistors, and the fluorescent paint of its screens, of the discoveries made in the study of crystals. The waves which reach the receiving aerial bring (bottom left) not only the sound which is to accompany the picture and the 'information' necessary for black and white receivers, but also the colour content of the scene in three different colours, blue, red and green. The various parts of the scene follow one another so quickly that the eye will be deceived into thinking them simultaneous. Each colour signal is transformed by the receiver and cathode ray tube into a stream of electrons, varying in intensity according to the original colour content.

If these three colours (which are not the same as the artist's primary colours) can be superimposed in their varying strengths, they can produce all the colours of the original scene, including white. To achieve this, the screen of the television receiver is coated with phosphor dots in blue, red and green triplets, more than a million of them on a 21-inch tube. When a stream of electrons strikes the dots, their electrons are lifted to higher energy levels, falling back after an interval and emitting photons of light; the dots glow blue, red and green.

But the stream of electrons from each colour signal must excite only dots of the same colour. To ensure this, the electron streams are focused to pass through a shadow mask (top left), which in reality is curved parallel to the face of the tube. It is a screen with something like 400,000 holes, each of which directs the three streams correctly on to the appropriate dot of a triplet. The magnetic field which focuses the streams also sweeps them rapidly to and fro across the mask and through its holes to the screen: each dot is made to glow to the appropriate brightness twenty-five or thirty times a second. The eye sees the complete picture in its correct colours.

The different systems of colour television vary, in the receiver, only in the method of sorting out the signals; the shadow mask and phosphor dots are common to all. (31, 32)

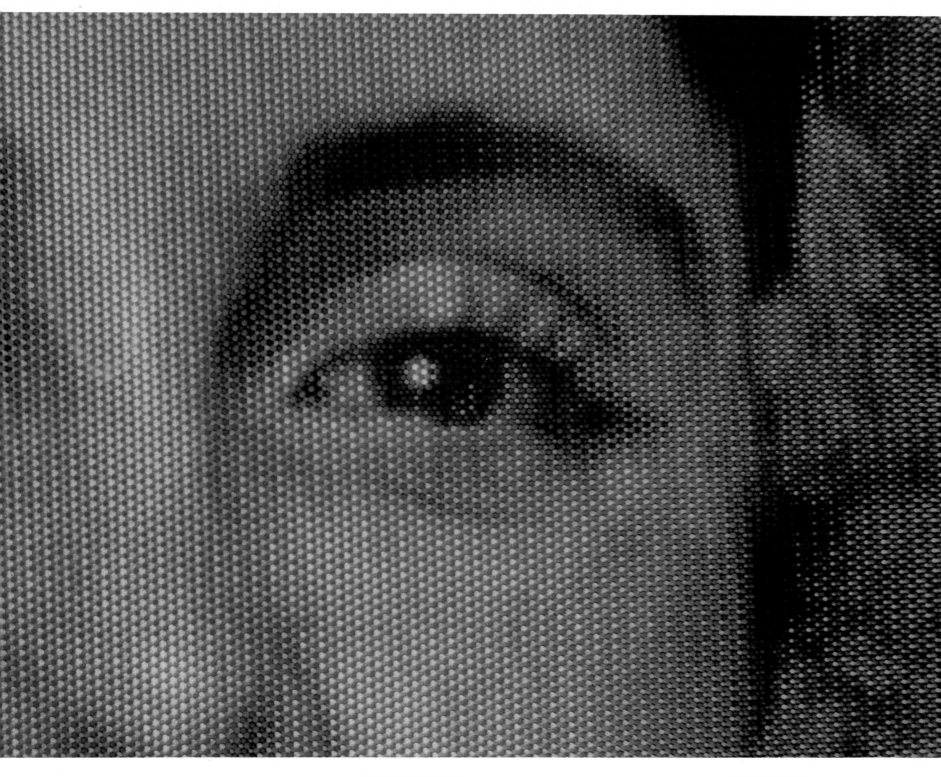

The myriad phosphor dots of the colour television screen are clearly seen in the enlargement above, from the complete picture at bottom right. Each colour signal, coming through alone, produces its own colour (they are shown here, photographed as they appear on the screen). The three combined produce the full picture. Black and white receivers simply use the accompanying separate information to produce the black and white picture on the right. (33–38)

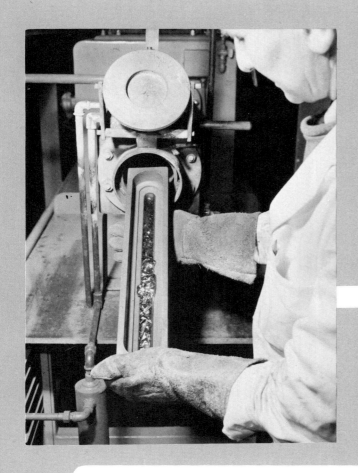

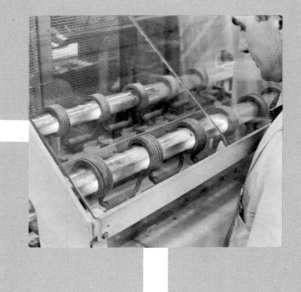

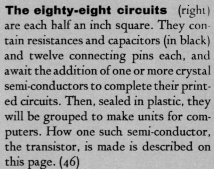

The eighty-eight circuits (right) are each half an inch square. They contain resistances and capacitors (in black) and twelve connecting pins each, and await the addition of one or more crystal semi-conductors to complete their printed circuits. Then, sealed in plastic, they will be grouped to make units for computers. How one such semi-conductor, the transistor, is made is described on this page. (46)

The huge transistor industry is engaged basically in removing the useless impurity atoms from crystals and inserting useful ones. The crystal in a germanium transistor begins with the refined ore, germanium dioxide powder, which is reduced to the metal by heating in hydrogen; it is then fused into a bar (left). To remove the impure atoms, the bar is drawn several times through a tube surrounded by radio-frequency heating coils (centre) which produce intense heat in the germanium, driving the impurities from zone to zone to the end, which is then cut off. The bar is now pure to one part in a hundred million. (39, 40)

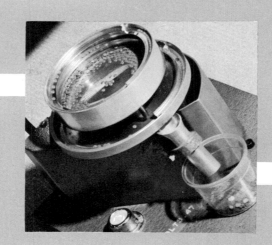

A rapidly revolving diamond wheel slices the bar into disks which are ground and polished with fine abrasive (above, left) to remove any deposited phosphorus. The disks are then diced by an ultrasonic drill into tiny wafers and sorted (centre) to reject imperfect specimens. The finished wafers are the basis of the transistor. To add the atoms of useful impurity, pellets of indium are sorted and inspected (above, right), placed on each side of the wafer and fused in place in an alloying furnace, where the atoms diffuse into the germanium crystals. Connecting wires are soldered on, under a magnifying glass (right), by means of a jet of hot gas.

Electronic devices based on semi-conductors and made by these and other methods are used as rectifiers, switches, amplifiers and detectors for TV and radio and incorporated in their thousands in computers. On the far right, small-current rectifiers (in transparent plastic) and large-current silicon-controlled rectifiers await final tests. (41–45)

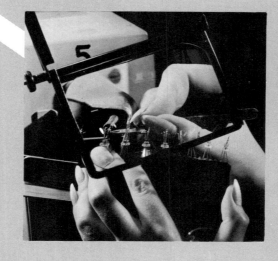

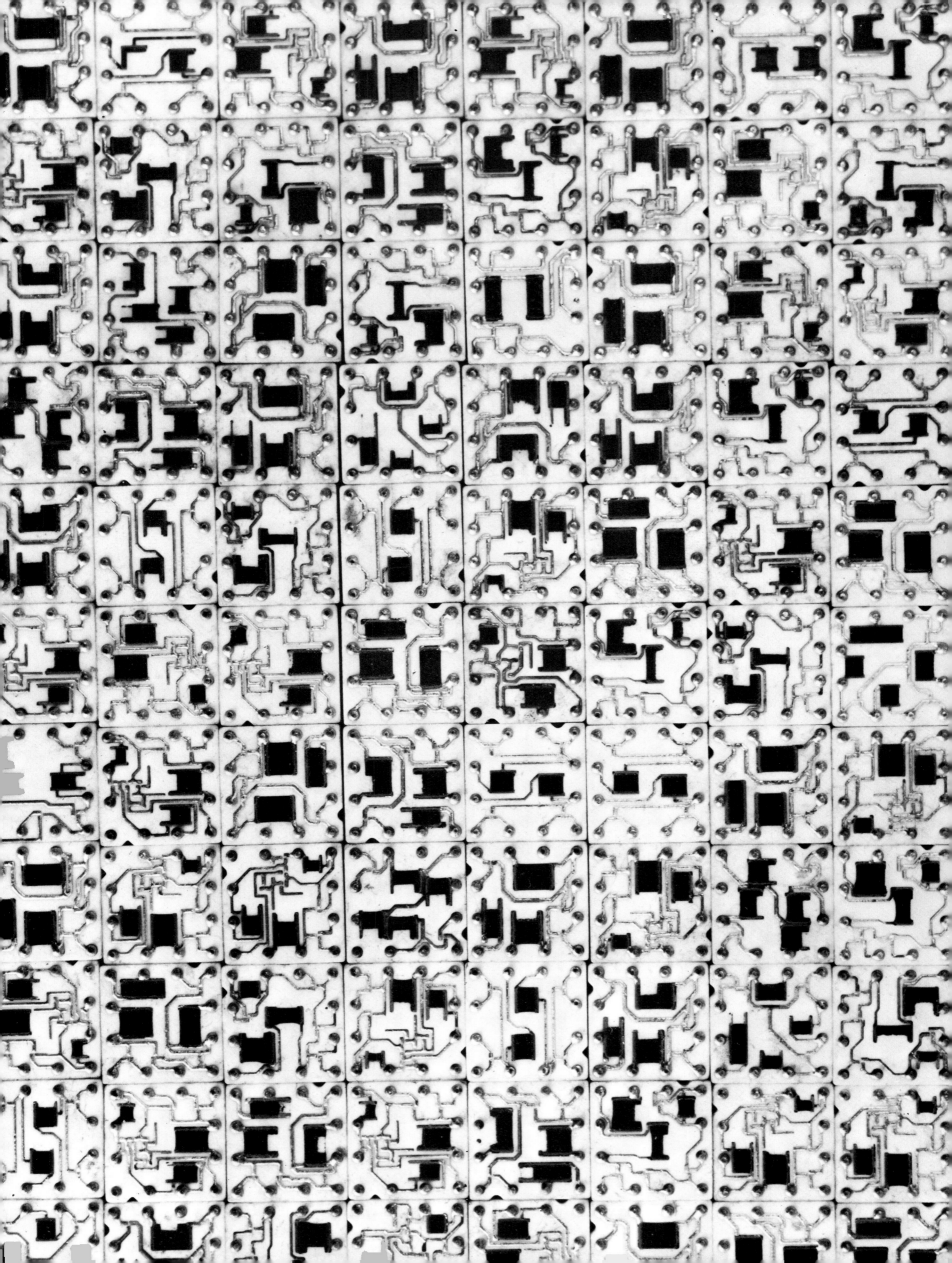

The really revolutionary invention of the electronic age, more far-reaching than the invention of the steam engine, is the computer. It springs from the discoveries of scientists on the structure of solids and on magnetism. The general principles on which it works—and the complexity of its operations—are illustrated by these pictures taken from the IBM System/360. The data on which the computer is to work can be fed into the machine by a punched card (above), the holes in which are translated into pulses of electric current. The computer knows how to deal with the data by referring to a program that will already have been written and tested, which controls its operations. (47)

The computer has a simple mind. Basically, it can distinguish only between a pulse (1) and the absence of a pulse or a negative pulse (0). All problems submitted to it must be broken down into these two units. Numbers, information in words, the readings of instruments can all be translated into them; (0) can stand for 'false' and (1) for 'true'. Once the information and instructions are expressed in this way in pulses, the control simply directs them into circuits which select, add, subtract, multiply or divide them. The operations are conducted by units (right and previous page) in groups—containing the millimetre-sized transistors and switches which sift and guide the currents. (48)

The computer also has a memory. It can retain permanent data to join with incoming information, it can hold the results of its calculations until other results are ready to combine with them and it can store the instructions for whole standard operations to save the labour of assembling them anew. One way of doing this is on stacks of magnetic disks (left), six 14-inch disks half an inch apart which are coated with a thin film of magnetizable but non-conducting ferrites. When the disks are charged with information, their tracks become chains of tiny magnets, magnetized one way to represent a (1) pulse and the other way for a (0) pulse. To tap the information, coils of wire are moved over the disk; the magnets cause faint (1) pulses or (0) pulses in the wire as the stored message dictates. These, amplified, pass into the circuits. It is the control's job to tap the parts of the memory required and to bring the pulses into the operation. (49)

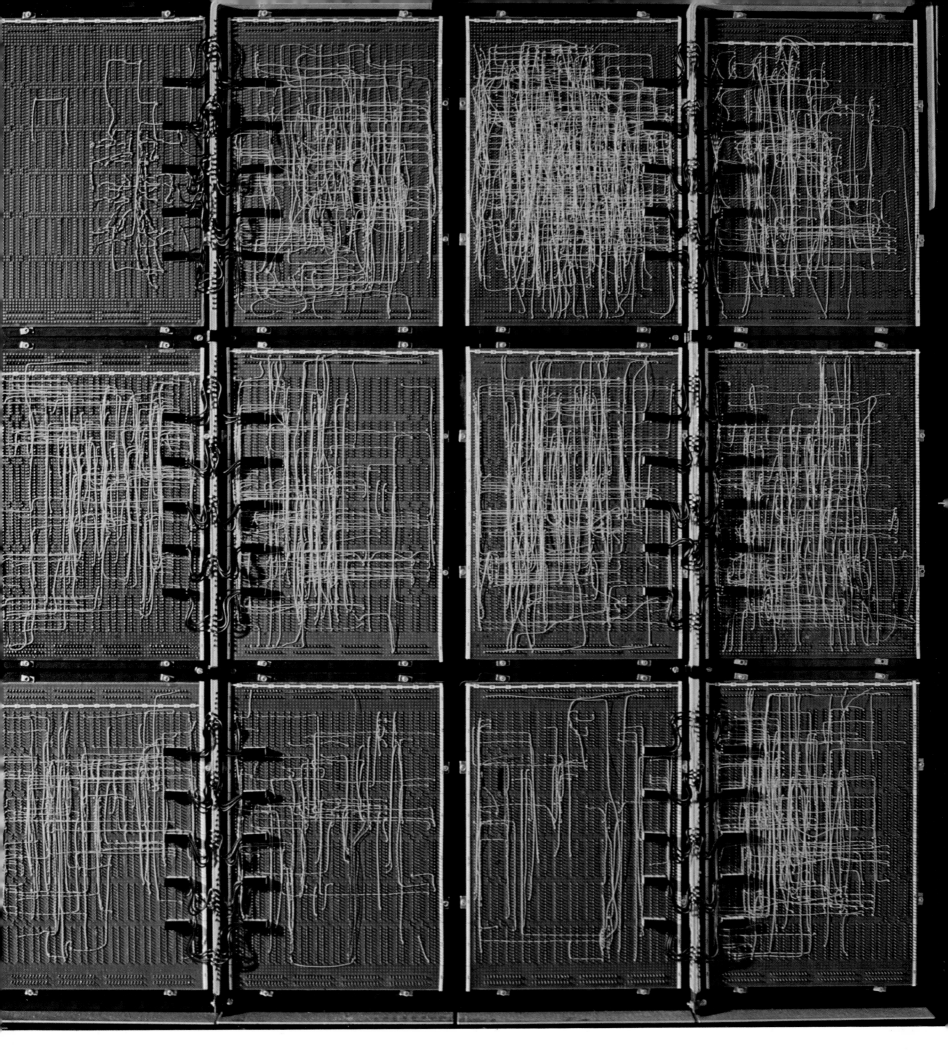

These simple but laborious methods of calculation require complex circuit-systems, providing thousands of channels along which the pulses can be directed. The tiny circuit-unit opposite must be connected to other units. It is plugged into a 'pin-board' containing a number of circuit-units with printed-circuit connections. The 'pin-boards' in turn are plugged into the panel above. Although such a panel already has twenty times less wiring than earlier computers required, it still

shows the intricate work involved in assembling the circuits and the complexity of the routes the pulses can take.

Why introduce such intricate mechanisms when the trained human mind has more direct methods? The secret lies in the lightning speed with which the computer performs its operations. The time needed to complete an operation varies between one millionth and one thousandth of a second. A calculation that would take a team of ten men a

hundred years to finish can be made in five minutes. Numbers can be read from the disk memory store at the rate of 312,000 a second. Also the simple 'yes' or 'no' decisions of the computer can be arranged in remarkable variety, including discovering and notifying its own faults and faults of the operator. The answer can take many different forms: printed documents, punched cards, magnetic tape, a spoken voice or a display on a cathode ray screen. (50)

Very low temperatures produce remarkable changes in the behaviour of solids and liquids. Many metals suddenly lose all resistance to the passage of electricity through them. If the bar magnet (left) is lowered towards a lead dish which is at the temperature of liquid helium (− 452°F), it hovers in the air, the chain slack. The magnet has induced a current in the lead; as it meets no resistance, the lead becomes a powerful electromagnet, repelling and holding the magnet above. (51–53)

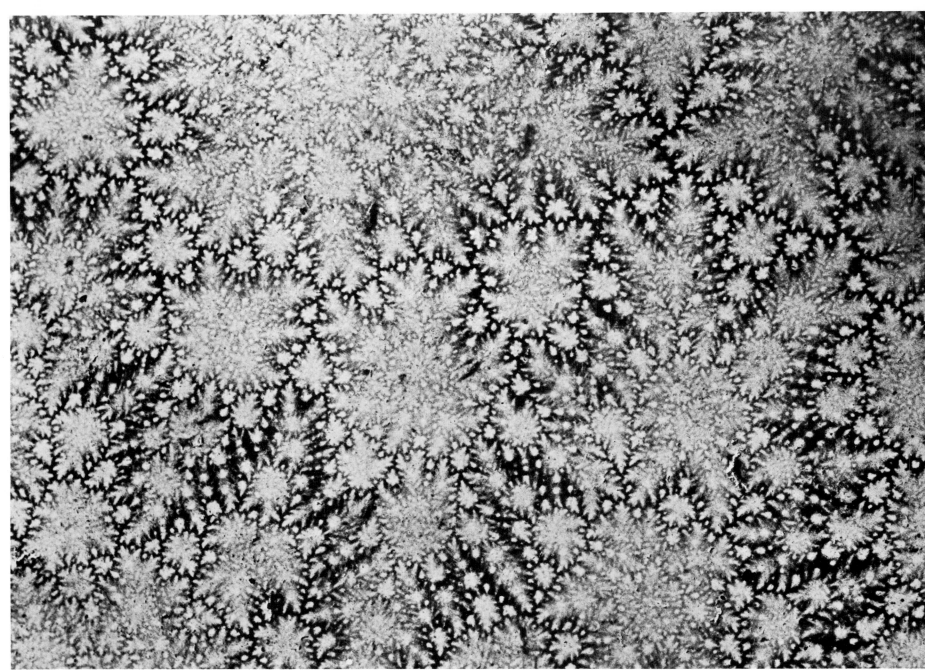

The spin of the electrons is the source of magnetism and each spinning electron is a magnet. Two electrons of opposite spin cancel one another and only those elements whose atoms contain an unpaired electron respond to a magnetic field. Only the ferromagnetic class, which includes iron, nickel and cobalt, show spontaneous magnetism, in which the spins of groups of atoms so align themselves, without outside influence, that the group develops a magnetic field. Such groups are known as *domains*. An ingenious technique developed by F. Bitter enables the domains to be seen and studied. He deposited a very fine suspension of ferromagnetic particles, each about four hundred-thousandths of an inch in diameter, on the surface of the crystals, and found that they revealed the domains. The continuous network of domains (above) is from the basal plane of a cobalt crystal, without any external magnetic field, magnified 3500 times under the electron microscope. In the single crystal of cobalt (× 80, right) the long parallel lines are domain boundaries, the heavy dark lines are slip bands caused by straining the crystal—the effect of which is to produce the dagger-shaped figures of reverse magnetization springing from the slip bands. A bar of iron is normally not magnetized. The spins in the various domains are aligned in different directions and cancel one another. When a magnetic field is applied, the spins slowly line up in its direction. (54, 55)

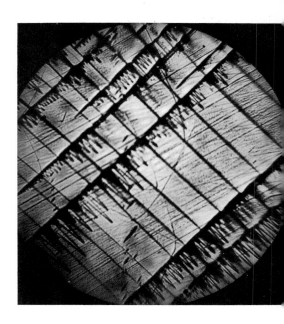

7 The chemists' dazzling bounty

G. D. Muir and Colin Bayley

The chemists' dazzling bounty

We have seen that the molecules of a substance are built up from atoms and that the bonds between the atoms can be of different kinds, influencing the properties of the substance in different ways. When a piece of yellow phosphorus (used in incendiary bombs) is exposed to the air, it bursts into flame, forming a white powder and giving out much energy in the form of light and heat. The phosphorus (P is its symbol and stands for one atom) has combined with oxygen in the air in the proportion of 2 atoms of phosphorus to 5 atoms of oxygen (O), forming one molecule of phosphoric oxide (P_2O_5). It is a very difficult matter to change this phosphoric oxide back into phosphorus and oxygen, and its properties are quite different from the two elements from which it was made.

On the other hand, the red powder mercuric oxide, which is not nearly so readily made directly from mercury (Hg) and oxygen, is easily broken down by heating into the silvery liquid, mercury and the colourless gas, oxygen. In the chemists' shorthand,

$$2\,HgO \xrightarrow{\hspace{2cm}} 2\,Hg \;+\; O_2$$
Mercuric oxide   when heated gives   mercury and oxygen

In this case, energy in the form of heat has to be applied to the mercuric oxide to break the bonds that tie the mercury and oxygen together.

Chemistry is about these simple changes, and much more complicated ones, in which bonds are made and broken and the end product or products differ quite profoundly from the starting material or materials. These changes are called chemical *reactions*, to distinguish them from the purely physical and easily reversible changes that occur, for example, when ice is changed into water by heating and by further heating into steam. Chemistry could be called the study of substances and their reactions, and has been built up by observing the properties of the materials used and produced during a reaction and measuring the quantities of these materials and the amount of energy given off or taken in. When sufficient had been learnt by this kind of experiment, chemistry developed as a theoretical as well as a practical subject, and chemists learned, and are still learning, how to predict the properties and reactions of substances before anyone has made or isolated them.

p 193
(1)

The properties the chemist seeks

The uses to which things are put depend upon their properties. The industrial chemist is therefore concerned very much with the properties of the marketable end product he is making, and is interested in the raw materials and the efficiency of the reaction that is being used mainly as a means of getting a cheap, competitive product. To him, a new chemical is a collection of potentially useful properties. Before we get on to the subject of reactions, it is worth considering these properties and looking at the illustrations which demonstrate their everyday importance:

Inflammability. It is a liquid and it burns, that is it reacts readily with the oxygen of the air with the release of energy. Will it make a good fuel for aeroplane, automobile or diesel p 194-5
(4) engines, or for domestic heating and lighting, or for rocket engines? It is a liquid and does not burn, that is it does not react readily with oxygen in the air. Will it be good for extinguishing fires, dry-cleaning clothes, dissolving things in without a risk of fire?

Texture. It is a fine, soft, inactive powder. Will it be a good covering agent in paint, suitable for cosmetics, or a p 202
(27, 28) filler for rubber or plastics? It is a thick, sticky liquid. Will it make a good adhesive or synthetic resin?

Colour. It gives a bright colour when dissolved in water. Will it be a good, fast dye for cotton, wool, or any of the artificial fibres? It is brightly coloured but does not dissolve p 194
(3) in water or other liquids. Will it be a good pigment for incorporating in paints, rubber or plastics?

Strength. It is a hard, strong solid. Will it be a good substi- p 195
(5) tute for metal or wood in making things?

Sensitivity. It explodes when suddenly heated or struck. p 194
(2) In other words, a sudden shock initiates a chemical reaction within the material which releases energy so rapidly that there is an explosion. Will it make a good explosive? It is sensitive to light, that is light initiates a chemical reaction in the material. Will it make a good photographic chemical? An ingredient of a fluorescent or luminescent paint?

Resistance to water and light. It repels water and does not change colour or crack in daylight. Will it make a paint p 195
(6, 8) film, protective enamel for metal or wood, waterproof film or surfacing material for fabrics?

Smell. Is the smell pleasant enough to be used in perfumery or unpleasant enough to be used for detecting leaks in gas mains?

Physiological action. If used in the garden, will it kill ants, greenfly, potato eelworm, blackspot on roses, daisies on the p 195
(7) lawn, weeds on the path or algae in the fishpond? Can it be used safely to relieve headache, cause sleepiness or unconsciousness, reduce fever, prevent conception or control cancerous growth?

Many other important properties could be discussed and it must be stressed that to be useful in everyday life a product of the chemical industry must possess a combination of favourable properties, a very important one being cheapness. The cost of raw materials has a great effect upon the cost of a product, but just as important is the efficiency of the reaction by which it is produced. We now return to this question of chemical change.

Making and breaking to produce something new

Why should one substance react with another to give a product with entirely different properties? We can only approach this question by considering a rather more complicated reaction than those which introduced this chapter. In this, two elements compete to combine with a third, and the reaction chosen as an illustration is the very important one that takes place in every blast furnace. Here, carbon (C) in the form of coke is depriving iron oxide, in the form of iron ore, of its oxygen and liberating iron (Fe). The chemist writes this briefly as:

p 196 (9)

$$2Fe_2O_3 + 3C \longrightarrow 4Fe + 3CO_2$$
iron oxide and coke react to give iron and carbon dioxide

which tells us that three atoms of carbon react with two molecules of iron (ferric) oxide to give four atoms of iron and three molecules of carbon dioxide gas.

This reaction can only happen if the bonds which hold iron and oxygen atoms together in the iron oxide are so disturbed (by heating in the blast furnace) that they break and new bonds are formed between carbon and oxygen. This bond disturbance is called 'activation'. The amount of energy (as heat or light) needed to disturb the bond so that a reaction is possible is called the 'activation energy' and is a precise quantity that can be measured. For any reaction a certain amount of energy is needed to enable the reaction to occur. Reactions that happen at room temperature (e.g. the spontaneous burning of phosphorus) get their energy requirements from the prevailing conditions and do not require extra heat.

In many cases, especially those involving compounds of carbon, the reaction is not as simple as it looks, but involves two separate reactions. If a compound X—Y is to react with an element Z, the first step in the reaction may be the formation of an intermediate substance X—Y—Z. At energy level I, corresponding to room temperature, no X—Y—Z is formed. To make the new compound we must raise the energy to level II by heat, or in any other way. The X—Y—Z

fig 1

that is formed then breaks down spontaneously to produce element X and the compound Y—Z.

When the unstable compound X—Y—Z breaks down, the original chemical bonds between X and Y are broken and the new bond between Y and Z is strengthened. The existence of these short-lived unstable compounds like X—Y—Z can be shown by modern methods of instrumental analysis. To get the reaction to go, an 'energy hump' has to be overcome. We can say, therefore, that to get a reaction to work and produce new substances by breaking chemical bonds, we must lift the reaction over this 'hump'.

An important reaction with far-reaching implications is the combination of nitrogen and hydrogen to form ammonia, which is used extensively in the form of its salts as a fertilizer in agriculture. When nitrogen and hydrogen are mixed together they do not react, and, in fact, have to be heated to an extremely high temperature before even a small amount of combination occurs. In other words, the 'energy hump' is too large for this method of making ammonia to be practicable, since the supply of large quantities of energy as heat is a costly business. However, if the gases are mixed and passed over finely divided iron at the comparatively low temperature of 500°C, they will combine to form ammonia. Examination of the iron after the reaction shows that it is unchanged, so that it has not itself taken part in the reaction but has lowered the activation energy to a convenient level. The effect of the iron is said to be catalytic and the iron is called a catalyst.

A catalyst will lower the activation energy needed to get a reaction started and yet does not appear to combine chemically with any of the reacting substances. Because of this property, catalysts are particularly important in industry where they allow reactions to be carried out at convenient and economic temperatures and pressures, for example, in the manufacture of chemicals and plastics from petroleum.

The reaction between the nitrogen (N) and the hydrogen (H) is written by chemists as:

p 196 (10)

fig 2

$$N_2 + 3H_2 \longrightarrow 2NH_3$$

The symbol N_2 stands for one molecule of nitrogen, made up of two atoms of nitrogen bonded together. Under normal conditions nitrogen, hydrogen, oxygen and many other elemental gases are in molecular form. The symbols above read that one molecule of nitrogen combines with

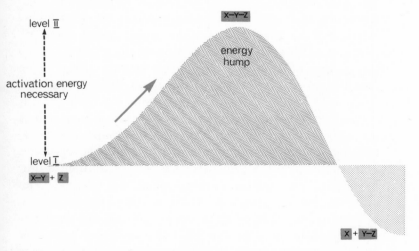

Any chemical reaction between substances requires energy to break the existing bonds and enable new ones to form. In some, extra heat (or light) is needed, to an amount which can be precisely measured—an energy 'hump' must be overcome. When sufficient energy has been applied, compound X–Y (above) combines with element Z to produce the unstable intermediate compound X–Y–Z. This then breaks down spontaneously, producing element X and compound Y–Z. (1)

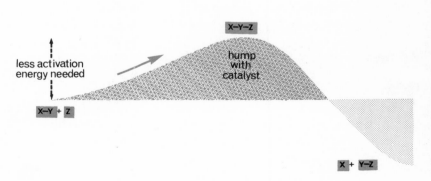

To reduce the amount of energy which must be applied (a costly item in industrial processes), some reactions are made to take place in the presence of a catalyst—a substance which, itself unchanged, reduces the energy 'hump' to be overcome and speeds the reaction. Nitrogen and hydrogen require a very high temperature before they will combine; in the presence of finely divided iron the reaction occurs as low as 500°C. (2)

three molecules of hydrogen to give two molecules of ammonia and that the ammonia molecule consists of one nitrogen atom combined with three hydrogen atoms. The manner in which the nitrogen and hydrogen atoms are bonded together to form the ammonia molecule is closely connected with the properties of the atoms themselves. The hydrogen atom consists of a nucleus with a single positive charge, and a single electron. The nitrogen atom has a larger nucleus with seven times the charge carried by the hydrogen nucleus, and seven electrons. These electrons are arranged in two shells: an inner one containing two electrons and an outer shell containing five electrons. As we have seen in a previous chapter, an element is particularly stable when the electron shells which surround its nucleus are completely filled. The maximum number of electrons the inner shell can contain is two: thus an atom of helium, which has two electrons and whose nucleus carries twice the charge on a hydrogen nucleus, is extremely stable. The number of electrons required to fill the second shell is eight: thus the neon atom (nuclear charge 10 times that of hydrogen) has both first and second shells completely filled and is also very stable.

p 160
fig 3

In the ammonia molecule the nitrogen and hydrogen atoms come to an arrangement to fill their unfilled electron shells by sharing electrons. The nitrogen atom, which lacks three electrons in its second shell to make the full complement of eight, shares an electron with each of three hydrogen atoms. And each hydrogen atom (which is one electron short of the two required to fill the inner shell) shares one electron with the nitrogen:

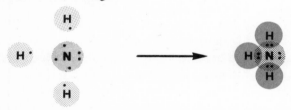

The forces acting between the nitrogen and hydrogen atoms are covalent bonds. They come about because of the electron-sharing between the atoms forming the molecule. These bonds are very stable and have different properties from the ionic bonds to be described shortly.

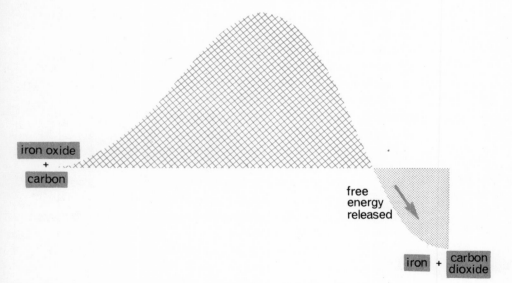

Which way will the reaction go? In such a way that less energy is locked up in the products than the original ingredients contained. When iron oxide combines with carbon in a blast furnace, energy (in the form of heat) is applied (to get over the 'hump'), but more energy is released as the reaction proceeds. Carbon dioxide is more stable, and has less energy locked up in it, than iron oxide. (3)

Which way will the reaction go?

We have seen *how* reactions occur, but the question remains —*why*? When iron is being smelted, why should carbon take the oxygen away from iron oxide, breaking the chemical bond? Why should the reaction proceed in this direction? The answer is to be found in the amount of energy locked up in the molecule. The higher the energy content the less stable the molecule is. When molecules re-arrange themselves in a chemical reaction, the tendency is always to form more stable products, and the energy difference between the less stable starting materials and more stable products is released in the form of light and heat.

When coal is burned, carbon combines with oxygen to form carbon dioxide. A great deal of energy (known as 'free energy'), which can be harnessed in a steam engine, is released in this reaction. Carbon dioxide has a low energy content and is a very stable molecule. The reaction in which atoms combine with oxygen is called oxidation. When carbon burns to form carbon dioxide, the process is one of oxidation. Iron also oxidizes, especially under damp conditions, to form iron oxide—the reaction more commonly called rusting or corrosion, which can be prevented by coating the iron or steel surface to keep the oxygen away. The oxidation of iron releases only a small amount of energy, much less than that of carbon. In other words, carbon dioxide is much more stable, and has a lower energy content, than iron oxide.

p 195
(8)

Here is the clue to the original question we asked: why, when iron is smelted, should carbon take oxygen away from iron oxide? The locked-up energy in iron oxide plus carbon is greater than that in iron plus carbon dioxide. The reaction goes 'downhill' to the lower energy state. To sum up, we have seen that for a reaction to take place, sufficient energy has to be present to make or break chemical bonds. We can measure the driving force of this reaction by finding out how much useful energy is released, or predict it from a knowledge of the free energies of formation of the participating substances.

fig 3

The breaking down of common salt

We have seen that stable *covalent bonds* are formed when the atoms in a molecule share the electrons in their outer shells. The *ionic bond* is formed (as we saw in an earlier chapter) when one atom gives up its outer electron or electrons to its partner so that both acquire stable outer shells of electrons. This transfer of electrons results in both atoms (or groups of atoms) acquiring an electric charge. For example, in the formation of the bond between sodium (Na) and chlorine (Cl) to form sodium chloride (NaCl, common salt), sodium with one electron in its outer shell gives this to chlorine, which has seven outer electrons, thereby leaving the sodium, and providing the chlorine, with stable eight-electron outer shells. The sodium atom, having lost an electron, becomes positively charged. The chlorine, having gained an electron, becomes negatively charged. These charged atoms are called ions and the bond between them the ionic bond. Thus ionic bond formation has the same purpose as covalent bond formation, the attainment of a more stable electron structure. But because it involves the giving and receiving of electrons, which are the units of electricity, the parts of an ionic molecule are separately charged and the molecule is therefore inherently less stable. We can show this in chemical shorthand as

p 163

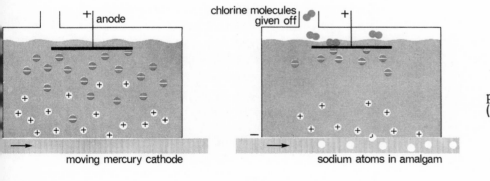

no charge   no charge   opposite charges

If sodium chloride is dissolved in water, the ionic bonds are broken (ionization) and the sodium and chlorine atoms go their own way as charged ions, shown as Na^+ and Cl^-. Then if two electrodes are placed in the solution and an electric current passed between them, the positively charged sodium ions are attracted towards the negatively charged cathode and the negatively charged chlorine ions move towards the anode (positive electrode). This process of separating ions, which revert to the uncharged atoms or groups on parting with their charges at the electrode surfaces, is called *electrolysis*. It is very important industrially; the electroplating of one metal (the teapot becomes the cathode) by another, is one example, but we shall keep to our common salt.

The way in which sodium chloride is electrolysed depends upon the products we are looking for. If the sodium chloride is melted and a current passed through it, greenish chlorine gas (important in water purification and bleaching) is given off at the anode and can be compressed into cylinders for sale; the sodium ions, on picking up electrons at the cathode, revert to metallic sodium. This silvery, inflammable metal melts at the temperature of the electrolytic cell and can be readily cast into suitable shapes for handling; it is used in heat exchangers in one type of atomic power station, and it is also widely used in the chemical industry because it is so reactive.

However, the electrolysis of sodium chloride in solution is considerably more important since it gives not only chlorine but the very important chemical, sodium hydroxide (common name, caustic soda), which is used in a great many industries. When the solution of sodium chloride in water is electrolysed in the special cells that are used, chlorine comes off at the anode as before, but in this cell the cathode is a stream of mercury which amalgamates with the sodium formed from the sodium ions. This stream of mercury-sodium amalgam is led away to vessels of water

fig 4

p 196
(11)

where the sodium reacts with the water to form sodium hydroxide, thus:

$$2Na + 2H_2O \longrightarrow 2NaOH + H_2$$
sodium   *water*   *sodium hydroxide*   *hydrogen*

Reactions can proceed in a number of ways, and their course depends to a large extent on the way in which the chemical bond between elements is broken to enable one of the partners to take part in the reaction. We have seen that the ionic bond is broken in solution, with each partner having gained or lost an electron (or electrons) to form charged ions. The covalent bond will sometimes break in such a way that each partner retains one of the electrons contributing to the bonding pair. This happens if the bond is activated with sufficient energy, and the products of this kind of bond-splitting are called *free radicals*. These are very unstable and reactive and readily attack other molecules.

Radiation of certain wavelengths, e.g. X-rays, can provide sufficient energy to break covalent bonds; thus water, H_2O, is split to some extent to give H^+ and $(OH)^-$ free radicals. The free radicals affect all kinds of body processes including the integrity of the nucleic acids which are responsible for the transmission of hereditary characteristics. Breaking the covalent bond in this way is also produced by the radiation from an atomic bomb explosion, but here the radiation is extremely energetic, greatly increasing the number of free radicals formed and, of course, the damage to nucleic acids. It is the damage caused by these free radicals that causes inherited defects; the changes produced are known as mutations.

The free radicals produced by an original reaction can cause the breakdown of a second molecule and the formation of a new free radical. This can then break down or combine with a third molecule, and the sequence continues, causing a large number of molecules to react with very little energy change—a chain reaction. Chain reactions involving free radicals occur extensively in the production of polymers, to which we shall refer later.

Isolate, identify, measure

We have said that chemistry has been built up by observing the properties of the substances used and produced during a reaction, and by measuring the quantities of these materials and the amount of energy given off or taken in. To do all this, it is obviously important to be able to isolate, identify and measure the amount of the substance formed by a reaction. The identification and measurement of the composition of substances is the primary job of the analytical chemist, and analysis has had to develop as a technique at about the same pace as the techniques used in building up (synthesizing) and breaking down (degrading) substances. Advances in analytical technique have, in fact, greatly stimulated new advances in other branches of chemistry; mutual stimulation is characteristic of relations between the branches of chemistry just as it is between the broad fields of study we call the sciences.

In this account it is only possible to touch on two general techniques used by the analyst, to help him to isolate, identify and measure substances. In recent years the trend in chemistry has been to examine molecules of increasing complexity; this has made the problems of separation and identification more difficult.

An effective method of separating mixtures is *chromatography*. This can be illustrated by considering an ink spot

p 197
(13)

+ |anode

chlorine molecules given off   +

moving mercury cathode   sodium atoms in amalgam

When sodium chloride is dissolved in water, its molecules split into two ions, carrying opposite charges: Na^+ and Cl^-. If now electrodes are inserted in the brine, and a voltage put across them, the positive sodium ions are attracted towards the negative cathode and the negative chloride ions towards the positive anode. In one industrial process for thus electrolysing brine, the anode is iron and the cathode a moving stream of mercury.

When the chloride ions reach the anode, they give up an electron and become neutral atoms, joining with another to form molecules of chlorine gas. This, drawn off, is important in bleaching and water purification. The sodium ions form an amalgam with the mercury, collecting an electron to become neutral atoms. If now the flowing amalgam is passed through water, the neutral sodium reacts with the water, forming the greatly used caustic soda (NaOH). (4)

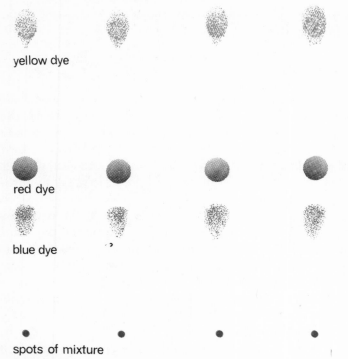

yellow dye

red dye

blue dye

spots of mixture

To identify the substances which make up a mixture it is first necessary to separate them. For this, today, the analytical chemist often uses chromatography. To produce the pattern above, three dyes, yellow, red and blue, were mixed and a small spot of the mixed solution placed on a glass plate covered with a thin layer of alumina. The plate was then placed vertically in a shallow layer of a suitable solvent. The solvent moved slowly up the layer of alumina by capillary action and the dyes went with it. But the alumina molecules held back the dye molecules, the attraction being different for each of the three dyes, and the dyes therefore mounted the plate at different speeds. After a time, the dyes are separated and can be removed from the plate and analysed. (5)

on blotting paper. Ink is a mixture of dyes and the dye molecules comprising the spot are held to the paper by their attraction for the cellulose molecules forming the fibres. If one end of the paper is put in a solvent in which the dye molecules are just soluble, and the solvent allowed to flow through the paper, the dye molecules will, of course, tend to dissolve and move with the solvent; their progress will, however, be 'braked' by the attraction of the paper.

The various dye molecules comprising the ink will be exposed to these two forces pulling in different directions and will, in fact, move with different speeds. If the paper is withdrawn, after the solvent has flowed through it for some time, and then dried, the position of the ink components can be seen by their colours. It is easy to separate them by cutting off the different coloured zones with a pair of scissors and dissolving out each component from the section of paper that contains it.

This process may be used for separating many different substances in a mixture: it is known as paper chromatography. The same principle is used when solutions of mixtures are poured through vertical glass tubes filled with absorbent powders such as aluminium oxide and charcoal; this allows for considerably more material to be absorbed and the quantities of the substances separated are larger. If the components separated in this 'column' are coloured, the absorbent can be pushed out of the tube in appropriate sections, which can then be treated with solvents to isolate the components.

This chromatographic process can be applied to substances in the vapour state as well as in solution. If a mixture of liquids is vaporized and swept along with nitrogen as a carrier gas through a tube containing an absorbent soaked in a suitable high-boiling solvent, the molecules are subject to two opposing forces, namely the attraction of the carrier

gas and that of the high-boiling liquid on the stationary absorbent. The vapours of different substances move at different speeds during this sorting-out process and emerge at the exit of the tube at intervals. These intervals allow for their separate identification or collection.

The applications of vapour phase or 'gas' chromatography have become extensive; provided a substance can be converted into a volatile form, it is separable by this technique. Its largest application at present is in oil refining, where it is possible to analyse the gases and liquids produced during the process by taking samples of vapour at various stages and analysing them by gas chromatography.

These various types of chromatography are used extensively today for separating natural products or products of a chemical reaction. Having separated them, the problem is now one of identification. The only certain way to identify a molecule is to find out its composition by detecting what elements are in it, measuring the individual amounts, and then determining, by devious and often complicated methods, how these are arranged. Fortunately chemical bonds have special characteristics, which are useful in short-circuiting this long process of 'classical' analysis. Every pair of atoms vibrates at a particular frequency, rather like a bob on a spring. The period with which it vibrates depends on the strength of the 'spring', that is the energy of the chemical bond. Different bonds have characteristic vibrations which can be used to distinguish them. These vibrations mostly fall in the same range of frequencies as infra-red, visible or ultra-violet light. If light of the appropriate frequency shines onto the bond, it sets it vibrating strongly, and this light is absorbed. Light which does not start the bonds vibrating passes through the substance unabsorbed. So, by measuring the absorption of light at different frequencies (or wavelengths) we get a picture of the kind shown. Each of the 'humps' corresponds to absorption by a bond of a certain energy. It is the presence of absorption humps in the visible light region that makes some chemical substances coloured and useful, perhaps, as dyes. Conversely, transparent substances such as glass or water have no bonds which vibrate at the same frequency as visible light, although both absorb ultra-violet and infra-red light.

These graphs or 'spectra' are obtained by using instruments called *spectrophotometers*, which pass light of known wavelengths (in either the ultra-violet or infra-red parts of the spectrum) through a solution of a substance and measure the amount absorbed at each wavelength. A series of peaks are shown up on a chart produced by the instrument which serve as the 'fingerprints' of the substance for the chemist. By examining and cataloguing the charts of a very large number of known substances, an unknown substance can be identified by comparison.

The astonishing carbon: backbone of abundance

Although there are over ninety known elements, their significance in everyday life ranges from nil to overwhelming importance. Here we can only select a few features of a very few elements to show what chemistry is, and how chemists reason. The majority of the elements, including the familiar metals, form molecules by one atom combining with a number of atoms of other elements. The number of atoms involved remains small, and a single central atom provides the basis of the molecule. However, a few elements—notably

p 197 (12)

fig 6

fig 5

carbon—readily bond to themselves to form chains on which other elements can bond using this central 'backbone'.

The atom of carbon has certain special features which make it behave in this way. It has two electrons in the inner shell and four in the partly filled outer shell. Because the electrons are close to the nucleus of the atom, they are held rather firmly, so carbon does not form ionic bonds. Instead the atom clings tenaciously to its outer four electrons, but is prepared to enter into covalent bonds in which these electrons are shared with other atoms to make up a full complement of 8 (shared) electrons in the outer shell. These bonds give carbon compounds great stability. The shared electrons may be borrowed from atoms of other kinds. For example, one carbon atom may share electrons with four hydrogen atoms. Or it may link up with atoms of its own kind to make complicated chains or rings. This is why carbon atoms are the 'vertebrae' of the substances we find in living matter, and why 'organic' or carbon chemistry has grown to an enormous subject about which more has been written than about all the other elements put together.

The forming of fossil fuels, oil and coal, by geological pressure on dead organic matter was mentioned in an earlier chapter. The burning of these and other carbon-containing materials such as wood, peat and natural gas, has provided man with virtually all the heat energy he has used during his fire-conscious history. The low-temperature 'burning' in the body of foodstuffs, all of which have the essential carbon backbone, is, in fact, the means whereby he keeps warm and finds the energy to work.

Hydrogen is the other most common element present in living matter and the fossil fuels, and burning is essentially

p 163

p 202 (29)

p 36

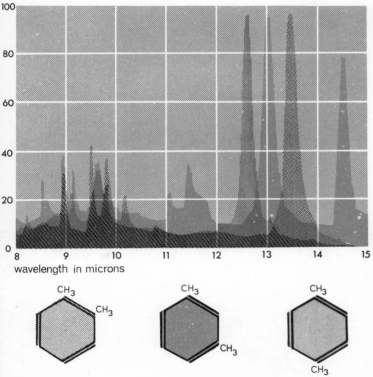

In chemical bonds, different pairs of atoms vibrate at different frequencies, each pair with its own precise, characteristic period. If light-rays (or infra-red or ultra-violet rays) of the same frequency fall on the pair, it is set vibrating strongly and the light is absorbed, whereas light of other frequencies passes through. This absorption is used to identify substances. To obtain the drawing above, infra-red light was passed in turn through three kinds of xylene, differing only in the point at which the –CH₃ group was attached to the benzene ring. The wavelengths of maximum absorption appear as 'humps' in the curve and when the curves are superimposed (above) the characteristic wavelengths are clearly seen to differ for each. If the xylenes are mixed, as they are in the products of coal distillation, a new set of curves results, but from it the expert is able to detect one xylene in the presence of the others. (6)

the reactions of carbon and hydrogen in the fuel or food with oxygen from the air; energy is released and carbon dioxide and water are formed. In the reaction between an atom of carbon and two atoms of oxygen, two pairs of covalent bonds (two double bonds) are formed and carbon acquires a share in a pair of electrons from each oxygen atom; in so doing it makes up the stable eight-electron outer shell of the oxygen atoms by sharing with them its four outer electrons, thus:

Carbon dioxide, formed when oil and coal burn and when animals breathe, is an essential food for all plant life.

The simplest compound of carbon with hydrogen (hydrocarbon) is methane, CH_4:

(The chemist often shows covalent bonds as single lines connecting the atoms instead of putting in the pairs of shared electrons.) Methane is the main component of natural gas and the first member of a great series of hydrocarbons of ever-increasing chain length and complexity; these occur in crude oil, and because they boil at different temperatures they can be separated from one another by the process called distillation. These hydrocarbons are often referred to confusingly as 'paraffins'. Other simple but important compounds of carbon contain oxygen, chlorine and nitrogen as well as hydrogen.

p 197 (12)

Because the hydrocarbons containing about eight carbon atoms are the most suitable as petrol and because of the growing importance of the chemicals-from-petroleum (petrochemicals) industry, much petroleum is 'cracked'; that is, the long chains of the less volatile liquid and wax hydrocarbons present are split into fragments consisting of simpler hydrocarbons by heating under pressure and using catalysts. Looking at one end of a long, straight-chain hydrocarbon that is being cracked, the following kind of bond-breaking can occur:

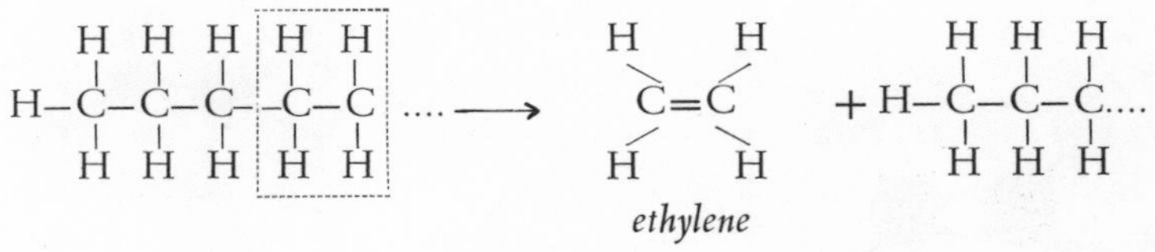

ethylene

fig 8

The ethylene, and other 'olefines' containing a double bond, that are formed during cracking are said to be 'unsaturated'. That is, instead of neighbouring carbon atoms sharing two electrons as in the 'saturated' hydrocarbon, ethane,

ethane   *ethylene*

four electrons are shared between the atoms (as they were in carbon dioxide), the formation of the double bond compensating for the two hydrogen atoms that have been lost. This double bond is of higher energy than the single covalent bond and makes ethylene and other unsaturated products of petroleum cracking, such as propylene ($CH_3—CH=CH_2$) much more reactive than ethane and propane. (Notice in

fig 7

p 198-9 (17)

The chemists' dazzling bounty

The abundance which carbon has given us is readily seen from a glance at the three great series of compounds based upon methane, ethylene and benzene. Examples from them are shown on these two pages, together with some of the vast range of products which chemists have made from them and which are in constant use in all aspects of modern life. Each series grows by the addition of the unit $-CH_2-$, a carbon atom linked to two hydrogens. The new unit can bond itself in various ways to the previous member of the series, but always the unit is the same. The series based on methane (the 'paraffins') advances from gases at normal temperatures to liquids, oils, waxes and solids, the boiling point rising with each increase in the length of the molecular chain. The formula for ethane, C_2H_6, results from the addition of $-CH_2-$ to methane, CH_4 (marsh gas), both of them ingredients of natural gas. A further $-CH_2-$ results in propane, C_3H_8, the first of the 'bottled' gases. The atoms, it should be remembered, arrange themselves in three dimensions.

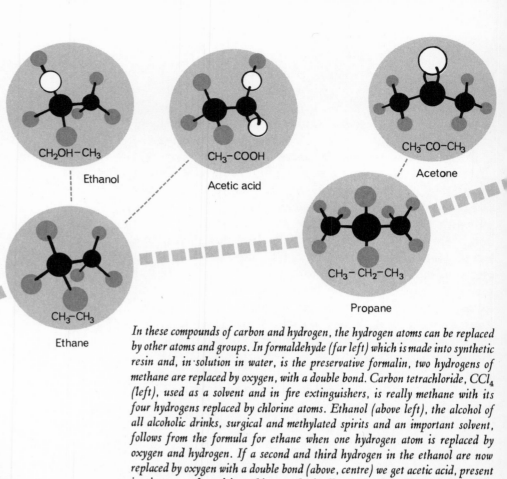

CH₂OH–CH₃
Ethanol

CH₃–COOH
Acetic acid

CH₃–CO–CH₃
Acetone

CH₃–CH₃
Ethane

CH₃–CH₂–CH₃
Propane

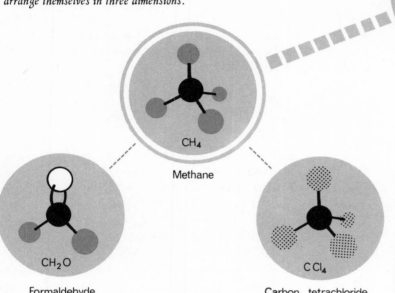

CH₄
Methane

CH₂O
Formaldehyde

C Cl₄
Carbon tetrachloride

In these compounds of carbon and hydrogen, the hydrogen atoms can be replaced by other atoms and groups. In formaldehyde (far left) which is made into synthetic resin and, in solution in water, is the preservative formalin, two hydrogens of methane are replaced by oxygen, with a double bond. Carbon tetrachloride, CCl_4 (left), used as a solvent and in fire extinguishers, is really methane with its four hydrogens replaced by chlorine atoms. Ethanol (above left), the alcohol of all alcoholic drinks, surgical and methylated spirits and an important solvent, follows from the formula for ethane when one hydrogen atom is replaced by oxygen and hydrogen. If a second and third hydrogen in the ethanol are now replaced by oxygen with a double bond (above, centre) we get acetic acid, present in vinegar and used in making synthetic fibres, plastics, flavours and scents, while acetone (above right), important as a solvent and in several chemical processes, is propane with two hydrogens replaced by oxygen. In actual manufacture, it may be more convenient to base it on members of another series, as with acetic acid and acetone below.

Ethylene, C_2H_4, is the first of the series which, adding various numbers of the unit $-CH_2-$, includes propylene, C_3H_6, butene, C_4H_8 and octene, C_8H_{16}. The double bond between the carbons is of higher energy and this 'unsaturated' series is therefore more reactive. In the table below, some of the products derived from the series are shown, from cosmetics to detergents to dynamite, with the chemical processes which are used to produce them at the various stages, and the atomic and group substitutions in which the processes result. Both the methane and ethylene series are composed of atoms and groups arranged in continuous chains, building up in three dimensions. (8)

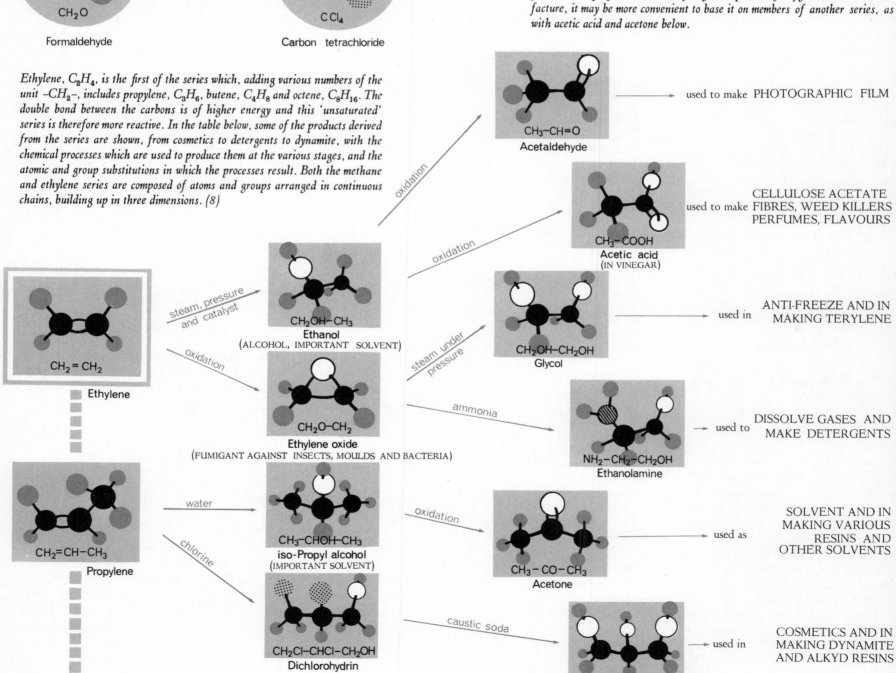

CH₃–CH=O
Acetaldehyde
→ used to make PHOTOGRAPHIC FILM

CH₃–COOH
Acetic acid
(IN VINEGAR)
used to make CELLULOSE ACETATE FIBRES, WEED KILLERS PERFUMES, FLAVOURS

CH₂OH–CH₂OH
Glycol
→ used in ANTI-FREEZE AND IN MAKING TERYLENE

NH₂–CH₂–CH₂OH
Ethanolamine
→ used to DISSOLVE GASES AND MAKE DETERGENTS

CH₃–CO–CH₃
Acetone
→ used as SOLVENT AND IN MAKING VARIOUS RESINS AND OTHER SOLVENTS

CH₂OH–CHOH–CH₂OH
Glycerin
→ used in COSMETICS AND IN MAKING DYNAMITE AND ALKYD RESINS

CH₂ = CH₂
Ethylene

steam, pressure and catalyst →
CH₂OH–CH₃
Ethanol
(ALCOHOL, IMPORTANT SOLVENT)

oxidation →
CH₂O–CH₂
Ethylene oxide
(FUMIGANT AGAINST INSECTS, MOULDS AND BACTERIA)

CH₂=CH–CH₃
Propylene

water →
CH₃–CHOH–CH₃
iso-Propyl alcohol
(IMPORTANT SOLVENT)

chlorine →
CH₂Cl–CHCl–CH₂OH
Dichlorohydrin

oxidation
oxidation
steam under pressure
ammonia
oxidation
caustic soda

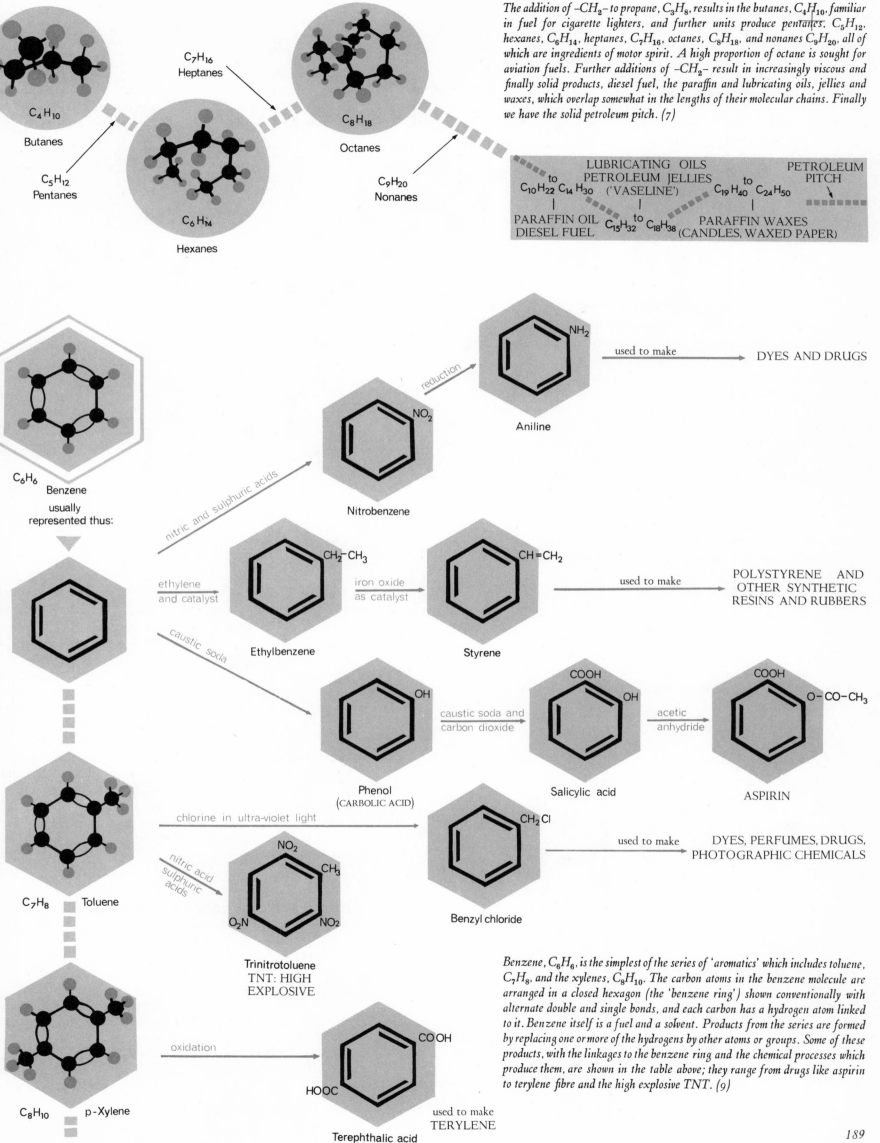

G D Muir and Colin Bayley

The addition of –CH₂– to propane, C₃H₈, results in the butanes, C₄H₁₀, familiar in fuel for cigarette lighters, and further units produce pentanes, C₅H₁₂, hexanes, C₆H₁₄, heptanes, C₇H₁₆, octanes, C₈H₁₈, and nonanes C₉H₂₀, all of which are ingredients of motor spirit. A high proportion of octane is sought for aviation fuels. Further additions of –CH₂– result in increasingly viscous and finally solid products, diesel fuel, the paraffin and lubricating oils, jellies and waxes, which overlap somewhat in the lengths of their molecular chains. Finally we have the solid petroleum pitch. (7)

C₄H₁₀
Butanes

C₅H₁₂
Pentanes

C₆H₁₄
Hexanes

C₇H₁₆
Heptanes

C₈H₁₈
Octanes

C₉H₂₀
Nonanes

C₁₀H₂₂ to C₁₄H₃₀
LUBRICATING OILS
PETROLEUM JELLIES
('VASELINE')

C₁₉H₄₀ to C₂₄H₅₀

PETROLEUM PITCH

PARAFFIN OIL
DIESEL FUEL
C₁₅H₃₂ to C₁₈H₃₈
PARAFFIN WAXES
(CANDLES, WAXED PAPER)

C₆H₆
Benzene
usually represented thus:

nitric and sulphuric acids → Nitrobenzene (NO₂)
reduction → Aniline (NH₂) → used to make → DYES AND DRUGS

ethylene and catalyst → Ethylbenzene (CH₂–CH₃)
iron oxide as catalyst → Styrene (CH=CH₂) → used to make → POLYSTYRENE AND OTHER SYNTHETIC RESINS AND RUBBERS

caustic soda → Phenol (OH) (CARBOLIC ACID)
caustic soda and carbon dioxide → Salicylic acid (COOH, OH)
acetic anhydride → ASPIRIN (COOH, O–CO–CH₃)

C₇H₈ Toluene

chlorine in ultra-violet light → Benzyl chloride (CH₂Cl) → used to make → DYES, PERFUMES, DRUGS, PHOTOGRAPHIC CHEMICALS

nitric acid sulphuric acids → Trinitrotoluene (NO₂, CH₃, O₂N, NO₂) TNT: HIGH EXPLOSIVE

C₈H₁₀ p-Xylene

oxidation → Terephthalic acid (COOH, HOOC) used to make TERYLENE

Benzene, C₆H₆, is the simplest of the series of 'aromatics' which includes toluene, C₇H₈, and the xylenes, C₈H₁₀. The carbon atoms in the benzene molecule are arranged in a closed hexagon (the 'benzene ring') shown conventionally with alternate double and single bonds, and each carbon has a hydrogen atom linked to it. Benzene itself is a fuel and a solvent. Products from the series are formed by replacing one or more of the hydrogens by other atoms or groups. Some of these products, with the linkages to the benzene ring and the chemical processes which produce them, are shown in the table above; they range from drugs like aspirin to terylene fibre and the high explosive TNT. (9)

this shorthand the bonds between the hydrogen and carbon atoms, which are always of the same type, are omitted. The lines refer to the link between carbon atoms.)

The great carbon chains

The reactivity of these double bonds in ethylene, propylene and a large number of other carbon chemicals is vital to the great industries now producing synthetic resins, rubbers and plastics. The popular plastic, polyethylene ('polythene') was first made by causing hundreds of molecules of ethylene to unite in a long chain (polymerize) by putting the gas under very high pressure:

p 198-
204
p 200
(20, 21)

···· + CH$_2$=CH$_2$ + CH$_2$=CH$_2$ + CH$_2$=CH$_2$ + CH$_2$=CH$_2$ + ····

↓

···· −CH$_2$−CH$_2$−CH$_2$−CH$_2$−CH$_2$−CH$_2$−CH$_2$−CH$_2$− ····

In 1953, new catalysts were announced that brought about this polymerization at much lower pressures, enabling polythene to be made more cheaply; the length of the polymer chain, which affects the hardness and other properties of the plastic, can also be controlled more easily.

The early development of both the chemical and plastics industries came from coal distillation, the first object of which was to produce coal gas for lighting and heating purposes. Coal gas contains both methane and ethylene, but the oils and tar that come over with the gas during the distillation are rich in 'aromatic' hydrocarbons, chemicals such as benzene, toluene, xylene, phenol, naphthalene and anthracene, all of which have their carbon atom 'vertebrae' in ring rather than chain form. These, and other chemicals originating in the coal, were the principal raw materials from which synthetic dyes and drugs were being made at the beginning of this century, and are still of great importance though some of them are now being made from oil more cheaply.

p 202
(29)
fig 9

It was from phenol, a coal tar product, and formaldehyde, that the first commercially successful synthetic polymer, Bakelite, was made. In this case, the polymer was formed by the loss of water from alternating molecules of phenol and formaldehyde:

p 202
(27, 30)

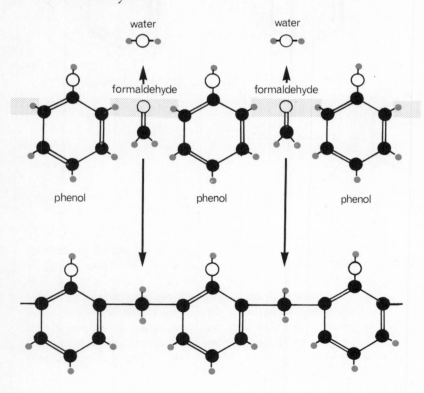

This is only the first stage in the polymerization, for it is possible to melt the single-chain intermediate polymer shown above and to dissolve it in alcohol. Further reaction of this with formaldehyde results in 'cross-linking' of the single chains, to form a kind of three-dimensional trellis work. When this cross-linking takes place the reaction mixture sets to the hard resin, Bakelite, which is unaffected by heat and alcohol. The structure is now something like this:

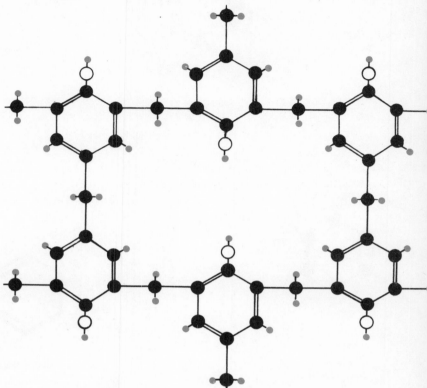

This cross-linking process is used in quite a different application to produce a 'permanent wave' in straight hair. The long protein molecules in the hair are cross-linked with a suitable reagent. The same method is used for hardening rubber by vulcanizing it.

The number of synthetic polymers with useful properties for different everyday purposes is large and continues to grow. Nylon and Terylene (made from petroleum and coal chemicals) are best known as textile fibres, but their special properties make them suitable for many other purposes. Vinyl polymers (PVA and PVC) are not suitable for synthetic textiles; their rubbery properties make them useful for making flexible hosepipe, water-proof sheeting, emulsion paints, adhesives etc. Polyurethane and polystyrene foams, Perspex and epoxide resins have all found their important niches in modern living; their special properties are decided by the way their 'backbones' are built up, and it is becoming possible to tailor-make synthetic resins, rubbers and plastics to do specific jobs.

p 204
(41)
p 199
(19)
p 200-1
(23, 26)
p 203
(32)
p 198-9
(14-18)
p 201
(24, 25)
p 202
(28)
p 203
(31, 32)

Awkward and aggressive: fluorine

Until World War II and the urgency of the atom bomb programme, the awkward, aggressive element fluorine was largely neglected by chemists because it was so difficult to handle. However, to win the active uranium isotope U$_{235}$ (needed for the bomb) from natural uranium, it was found useful to convert the uranium into a volatile compound, the hexafluoride UF$_6$. The uranium-235 hexafluoride was then separated from the slightly heavier uranium-238 hexafluoride by a process of diffusion. This meant that the problem of making fluorine cheaply had to be overcome and in the course of this difficult work much was learnt about the chemistry of its compounds.

The chemistry of carbon-fluorine compounds is largely new, but it has already given us some important products such as the refrigerant dichlorodifluormethane (CCl_2F_2) and the general anaesthetic Fluothane, which contains bromine as well as chlorine and fluorine. In these compounds the fluorine takes the place normally occupied by hydrogen. The bond between carbon and fluorine is very stable indeed, and this is shown particularly well in the polymer, poly-tetrafluoroethylene, obtained by polymerizing fluoroethylene ($CF_2 = CF_2$) under pressure with the aid of a catalyst. This is a white, tough solid with a waxy feel, which cannot be dissolved in any solvents, is extremely resistant to attack by practically every aggressive chemical and is a remarkably good insulator for electrical equipment. Its waxy nature makes it repel water and it is used as a dry non-friction bearing material, and, for example, for coating frying pans so that food does not stick to them. Virtually all substances containing carbon and hydrogen can be 'copied' with carbon and fluorine, although only relatively few have yet found commercial application.

Another 'under-developed' element of considerable promise is silicon (Si). Like carbon, it has a capacity for forming very long chains, but it does so in partnership with oxygen with which it alternates in the polymers called silicones. For example:

$$\begin{array}{cccccc} CH_3 & CH_3 & CH_3 & CH_3 & CH_3 & CH_3 \\ | & | & | & | & | & | \\ -Si-O-Si-O-Si-O-Si-O-Si-O-Si-O- \\ | & | & | & | & | & | \\ CH_3 & CH_3 & CH_3 & CH_3 & CH_3 & CH_3 \end{array}$$

These are familiar now as ingredients of car and furniture polishes and are also used for lubrication and water-proofing of fabrics.

p 195 (6)

No mention has been made so far of the important element sulphur (S), which is the raw material used to make sulphuric acid (H_2SO_4). Sulphuric acid is so fundamentally important to the chemical industry that the annual production figures have long been used as an index of its prosperity. The reaction of sulphuric acid with many organic compounds (sulphonation) results in the formation of a carbon-to-sulphur bond, a hydrogen atom in the carbon compound being replaced by the sulphonic acid group, $-SO_3H$. The great importance of this group is that the hydrogen is linked to an oxygen atom by an *ionic* bond, which has the effect of making molecules that were insoluble in water before sulphonation dissolve quite readily in it after they have reacted with the sulphuric acid. Many coloured molecules cannot be used as dyestuffs because they do not dissolve in water, but replacement of one or more of their hydrogen atoms by these sulphonic acid groups may make them useful for this purpose.

This same sulphonic acid group is the active part of the ordinary household detergent. Detergents are necessary because grease and fat stains are not soluble in water. One way of overcoming this problem is to wash in a fluid in which grease dissolves. This is the approach of the drycleaner. The other way is to use a detergent, normally a long-chain molecule structurally related to the grease, to one end of which an ionized sulphonic group is attached. The detergent molecule is thus 'double-headed'. One end, with the sulphonic group, is strongly attracted to water. The other end, the hydrocarbon end, has an affinity for grease. The detergent molecule acts as a bridge between the water and the grease, making it possible to disperse the grease.

p 203 (33-7) fig 10

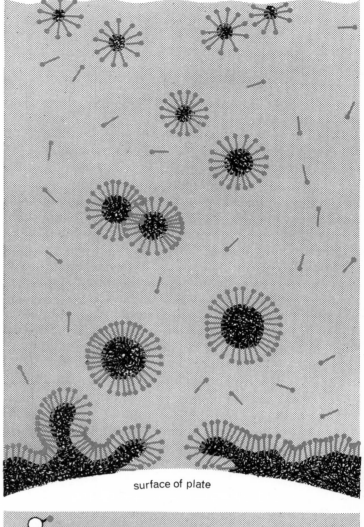

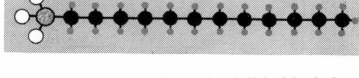

surface of plate

Detergents remove grease because they contain a 'double-headed' molecule, one example of which is shown above. To a long chain of $-CH_2-$ units is added a sulphonic group $-SO_3H$, an atom of sulphur bonded to three oxygen atoms, to one of which a hydrogen atom is linked by an ionic bond, which is broken when the compound dissolves in water. This group has a strong affinity for water, whereas the chain has a strong affinity for grease and is like it chemically. The chains of a large number of molecules attach themselves to molecules of grease (as on the surface of a plate) and, pulled by the attraction of the water for the other ends of the molecules, break up the grease into small globules and float with them in the water. (10)

The growing chains of nature

Another type of ionic group which can replace hydrogen in carbon-chain compounds is an oxidized form of phosphorus, the phosphate group, $-PO_3^{---}$ This group plays a most important part in nature in building up polymers which have important work to do as structural materials and as energy reservoirs. The structural function of cellulose in plants and trees and of protein to form muscle are familiar examples of the former. Starch provides the energy reserve in plants, and glycogen carries out a similar function in animals.

In the same way that a synthetic polymer like polyethylene is made by joining together a large number of readily available 'building blocks' (molecules of ethylene), natural polymers are constructed from units occurring in the organism, e.g. starch and cellulose from glucose and proteins from amino acids. They can only be built using

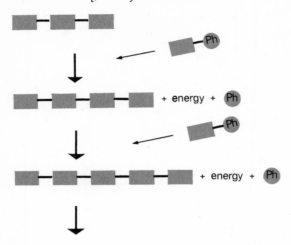

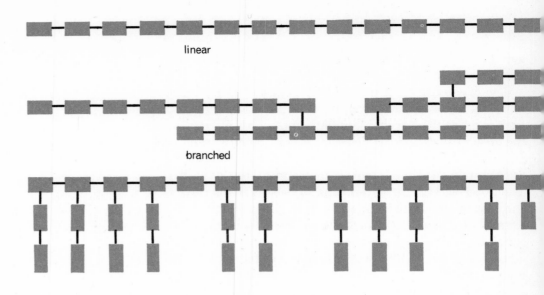

linear

branched

Polymers which occur in nature, such as cellulose and protein, cannot be built up with the help of high temperatures or pressure. Nature therefore uses its own catalysts called enzymes, in the presence of which the polymer chain can be built up step by step. Each new unit to be added is made reactive by combining it with a phosphate group, $-PO_3$. The energy available from this bond is then sufficient to add the unit to the polymer, when energy is given off and the phosphate is left free to act again, when it has been reconverted to its active form. (11)

the mild biological conditions tolerated by living things; the high temperature and pressures needed to construct synthetic polymers are obviously out of place. This is overcome by the use of extremely effective natural catalysts called *enzymes* which lead to the chain being built up stepwise. Before each unit is added to the growing chain, it is converted to a reactive form by combination with a phosphate group. This reactive combination allows an extra unit to be added to the chain using comparatively little energy. The manner in which the polymers are built up is illustrated above (left).

When energy is required from reserves, it is obtained by the release of energy originally used to build up the chains: it comes from the stepwise breakdown of the polymers which is catalysed by the enzymes.

A natural polymer of great industrial importance is rubber, which is built up from a very large number of isoprene molecules joined head to tail:

The long polymers of nature can be built up in many ways—in long linear chains (top), or in branched linkages. (12)

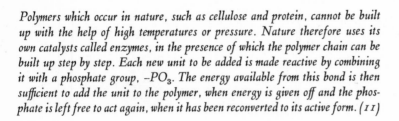

$$CH_2 = \overset{\overset{\displaystyle CH_3}{|}}{C} - CH = CH_2$$

isoprene

$$-CH_2 - \overset{\overset{\displaystyle CH_3}{|}}{C} = CH - CH_2 - CH_2 - \overset{\overset{\displaystyle CH_3}{|}}{C} = CH - CH_2 - CH_2 - \overset{\overset{\displaystyle CH_3}{|}}{C} = CH -$$

rubber

p 204 (38-42)

Synthetic rubbers are built up from molecules similar to isoprene which give them properties different from natural rubber, some of which are advantageous for special purposes, for example, resistance to oil and petrol. Recently rubber with a structure identical with that of the natural material has been built up from isoprene, and it has all the required properties of natural rubber. It is interesting to note that rubber is formed in the rubber tree in the same fashion as that described for other natural polymers, i.e. by the stepwise addition of units made active by combination with phosphate groups.

The simple union of phosphorus and oxygen with which we started this chapter has led us through to the much more complicated chemistry of living things—also involving phosphorus—which is the concern of the biological sciences.

One of the most far-reaching revolutions

of science in this century is the growth and all-pervading spread of chemistry in the service of man. Paints, plastics, synthetic fibres, new drugs and antibiotics, fertilizers for growing crops, preservatives for the harvest—all these are the work of chemists. Just over ninety different elements are the chemist's raw material; two hundred years of observation and experiment are the foundations of his work.

Chemistry is the science, and the art, of breaking and re-making the bonds between atoms and molecules, of making one substance react with another in such a way that the end compound is quite different from the starting materials. In one such reaction, under study by the chemist in the picture opposite, hundreds, if not thousands, of identical groups of atoms have been joined together to make a polymer. The length of the polymer molecule—the number of 'building blocks' in it—affects the properties of the finished product, so it is important to understand how the groups stop linking up.

The chemist opposite is studying this in polymers of acrylonitrile (better known in fibre form as Courtelle, Acrilan or Orlon), of which the 'building blocks' are made up of ethylene in which one hydrogen atom has been replaced by a nitrile (—CN) group ($CH_2 = CH - CN$). He has prepared a polymer, starting the linking with special active groups which have been 'labelled' by using the radioactive form, car-

bon-14. The linking stops; to find how it happened he has to discover what proportion of the carbon atoms in the completed polymer are radioactive. To do this, he must separate the carbon atoms in the form of carbon dioxide. He heats a small quantity of the polymer in the flask (bottom centre), treating it with oxidizing acids from the vessel above. The result is carbon dioxide, nitrogen, oxygen, nitrogen oxides and water vapour. The water is frozen out by surrounding the gases with liquid carbon dioxide in the metal cylinder above the chemist's right hand. The nitrogen oxides are then reduced to nitrogen by passing the gases over heated copper filings in the small furnace top centre. Next the carbon dioxide is frozen out by surrounding it with liquid nitrogen in the metal cylinder left centre. It can then be allowed to vaporize into the vacuum flasks at top right, where a known volume, at a known pressure, can be collected in the smaller flask and allowed to assume the temperature of the room (stabilized by the long glass tube with thermometer on the left). This fixed quantity of carbon dioxide (in which the number of molecules is known) is then drawn into a Geiger counter (off the picture to the left), where the intensity of the radiation can be measured, and compared with the intensity from a known number of carbon-14 atoms. This complex operation is an example of the laboratory work that lies behind the abundance of industrial chemistry. (1)

'What will it do?' is the first question the chemist asks about a new product. It may be sensitive to shock, like ammonium nitrate, in which the detonation of a primer sets up a violent chemical reaction (above). In a fraction of a second, with an enormous release of energy, the main explosive is converted to many thousand times its own volume of gas—and anything that stands in the way of this expansion is destroyed. In this case 1230 tons of explosive went up in the biggest ever man-made non-nuclear blast, lifting 700,000 tons of rock and water and removing a dangerous menace from a British Columbia shipping lane. (2)

The product may burn, reacting with oxygen to release energy, and may be a useful fuel. Kerosene, a petroleum product, burns quietly in the domestic paraffin stove but combines with liquid oxygen (right) in a roar of flame to lift the Nimbus weather satellite off its launching pad. (3)

The most useful property may be colour. The phthalocyanine blue being emptied out of a kneader (below) is, to the chemist, a complex molecule based on four benzene rings linked by nitrogen. It is a bright blue pigment, insoluble in water, used to colour paints and plastics. (4)

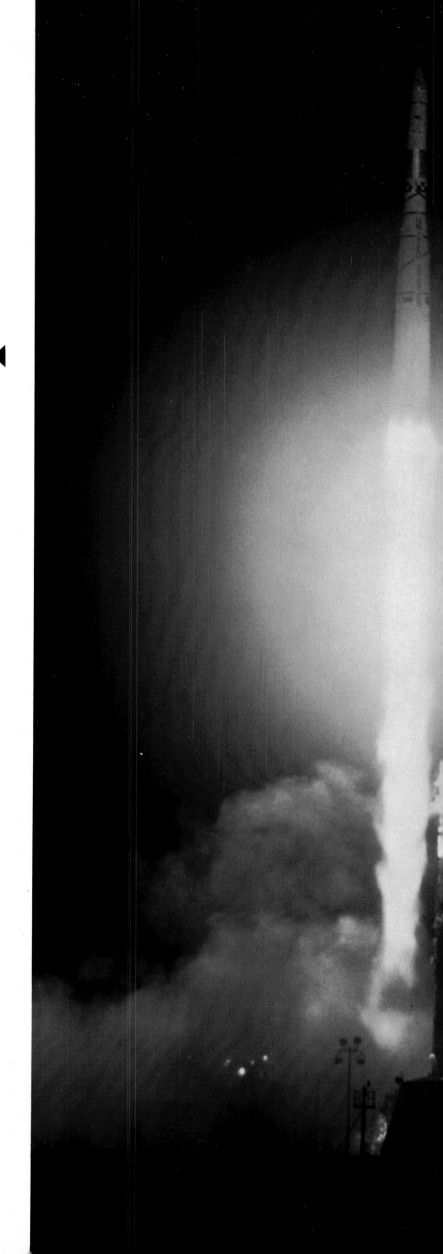

Solids that are hard are sought by the chemists. Diamond, a three-dimensional network of carbon, is the hardest known. If carbon in a metallic solvent is subjected to very high pressure (90,000 atmospheres) and a temperature of 3000°C, small diamonds are formed, making useful industrial abrasives. Those shown above are 70 times actual size. (5)

▶ **Will it repel water?** The nylon mesh (left) does, because the fibres have been treated with silicone, a chain of alternating silicon and oxygen atoms with attached $-CH_3$ groups. These groups are chemically like grease, with which water will not mix. The water forms drops and can be shaken off, but air passes through freely. (6)

Bacteria and fungi are destroyed by dichlorophen (right, under the microscope), a compound based on phenol, or carbolic acid, and much used for slime and mould control in industry. (7)

Resistance to rust is achieved by painting steel girders with red lead. When moisture settles on iron, tiny electric currents are set up, resulting in the combination of iron with oxygen to form red-brown iron oxides. Red lead, not so corroded, protects the iron. (8)

Breaking bonds and making new ones is the essence of any chemical reaction. In a blast furnace (left) a simple reaction takes place on a large scale. Iron oxide (Fe_2O_3) in the form of iron ore is brought together with carbon (C) in the form of coke. The heat necessary to keep the end contents molten is enough to break the bonds holding the iron and oxygen together. The atoms rearrange themselves as molten iron (Fe) and carbon dioxide (CO_2), a more stable arrangement, and locked-up energy is released, assisting the reaction. (9)

A difficult reaction, of great industrial importance, was the direct combination of nitrogen and hydrogen to make ammonia. To get it started, far more heat was required than was commercially possible and even then it was very slow. The problem was solved by using a catalyst. The massive vessels of foot-thick steel (left, below) contain layers of fine iron grains, over which, at 500 °C and a pressure 1000 times that of the atmosphere, mixed nitrogen and hydrogen is passed. The iron is unchanged, but in its presence the reaction is so greatly speeded as to become self-sustaining. Ammonia, thus cheaply from the nitrogen of the air and hydrogen from steam or natural gas, is the starting product not only for fertilizers and explosives, but also for drugs, plastics, fibres and a host of nitrogen compounds. (10)

Caustic soda from common salt is a frequent industrial process. We have seen how salt, dissolved in water, splits into sodium and chlorine ions. These, under a voltage, collect at opposite electrodes and the sodium, forming an amalgam with flowing mercury, is run off into a water bath, where it combines with the water to form caustic soda. In the photograph below, a huge battery of such cells is operating, the brine bath above and the water bath below. The mercury, unaffected, is pumped up to start again. (11)

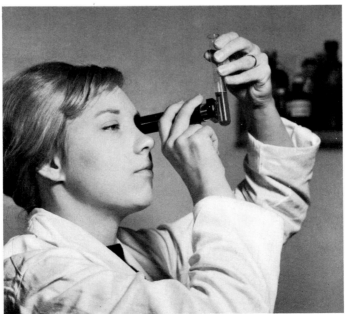

The bounty of nature, the chemist's prime source, must be adapted to human needs. In the refinery above, at Tyler, Texas, working round the clock, the wealth that is in oil is being extracted in the form of high-grade motor spirit and many by-products. Three men in the foreground control the operations. Round the corner on the left, one faces instruments and dials which regulate the volume and rate of flow in a plant where crude oil is split into petroleum fractions. The plant similarly controlled from the centre is converting some of these fractions (members of the series based on methane and ethylene), with the aid of sulphuric acid as catalyst, into high-octane motor spirit for aviation. On the right a third plant is controlled which increases, over a platinum catalyst, the octane proportion in motor spirit. The purity of the different fractions, and the precision of separation, is tested in the laboratory, in part by chromatography, from samples drawn off. (12)

The products of a reaction must be analyzed and identified. The pathologist on the left is studying a sample of human blood. She views daylight through it, and the light, as it passes through a prism in her spectroscope, is split into a band of colours—except for that which, absorbed by the blood, appears as dark lines in the spectrum, precisely characteristic of the constituents of the blood. Her test is for poisoning by carbon monoxide. If any of the gas has been inhaled, it will have combined with the haemoglobin molecules of the blood and the lines characteristic of the combination will appear in the spectrum. Carbon monoxide, absorbed by the blood thirty times more readily than oxygen, starves the tissues of the oxygen which it replaces. (13)

197

Giant molecules are big business. Designed by chemists and made by industry, they serve an enormous and ever-growing range of needs. In one process, in the making of PVC, a hydrogen furnace (above) 'cracked' butane, one of the methane series and a petroleum product, to produce hydrogen. This was caused to react with chlorine to make hydrochloric acid; hydrochloric acid and acetylene (a tricky mixture, to be handled with care) combined to make vinyl chloride gas, $CH_2 = CHCl$, which is ethylene $(CH_2 = CH_2)$ in which one of the hydrogen atoms has been replaced by a chlorine atom. Compressed into a liquid, this is stored in massive steel spheres (right). Vinyl chloride is the building-block from which the polymer, the long chain of polyvinyl chloride, is made. At the right temperature and pressure, with the aid of a catalyst, the double carbon bond is broken and block joins to block in a chain that may be 1000 or more links long—the fine, white powder of raw PVC. (14, 15)

One of the most versatile materials invented by man, PVC can be flexible and rubbery or rigid and tough, depending on the length to which the giant molecules are allowed to grow. Generally speaking, the longer the chain the greater the strength and rigidity; the shorter the chain the more flexible the finished product. The final stage in the transmutation of the white powder into material for a raincoat or a floor tile is the addition of any pigments, fillers or plasticizers that may be needed, and heating of the mixture to 325 °F to make a workable 'dough'. The chemist's work is done; it is now simply a fabrication problem. To make flooring, for instance (left), the warm, still doughy plastic is made to pass over stainless steel rollers and rolled out to the right thickness; any surplus width is sliced off and sent back to be melted down again.

PVC is tough and flexible, can be sterilized, stored without becoming stiff and sticky, and is disposable, so it is ideal for certain kinds of surgical equipment (right). Destructive agents attacking cancer must be inserted into the blood stream without reaching other parts of the body. The affected part is isolated and its circulation completed outside the body. Venous blood is pumped from the diseased area and enters the PVC unit on the left, where oxygen is passed through to revitalize it. Bubbles are removed by the sponge at the top and the blood is filtered. Then it descends slowly down the helix, allowing any remaining trapped oxygen to rise away. At bottom right the surgeon adds the destructive agent and the blood carries it through the cancerous area. (16, 18)

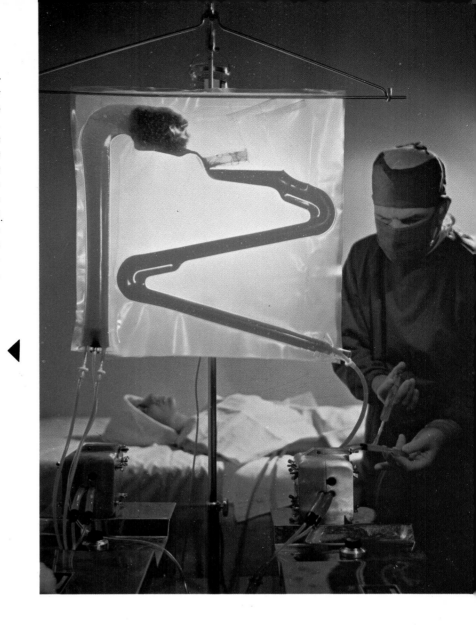

The long chains can be formed simply by adding identical groups. Molecules of propylene ($CH_3-CH=CH_2$), a gas of the ethylene series derived from petroleum, have a double bond between two of the carbon atoms. With the right catalyst and under the right conditions, half the double bond will break, leaving two links ready to occupy the broken bonds of similar groups. The chain emerges from the reaction chamber as warm, viscous ribbons of polypropylene (left) which then travel through cold water, harden, and are chopped into pellets for re-melting and forming. Perlon (similar to nylon), on the other hand, is built up from two different ingredients. When they come together they squeeze out two atoms of hydrogen and one of oxygen—in other words, water—at each join, and thus they polymerize by condensation. The molten mass of polymer is then cooled, broken into glass-like chips, re-melted and extruded through spinnerets (below) to make gossamer-fine thread. (17, 19)

199

Why are plastics strong? For some are known to be partly crystalline, including polyethylene (polythene) a sheet of which resists the pull of four Irishmen (right) as they stretch it over stacks of new-cut peat. Polyethylene (and other so-called 'strong plastics' such as nylon and polypropylene) are composed of crystals embedded in an amorphous mass of the polymer. Recently the first direcs observation (in the picture below) hat been obtained of the existence of links between the crystals. Polythene at the molten stage was blended with a 32-carbon paraffin, similar to polyethylene but with a shorter chain to its molecule.

When both had cooled, the paraffin—which separates the areas of crystal—was dissolved out. Under the electron microscope the crystal masses were seen to be connected by 'bridges'. They are magnified here 36,000 times; in actual size they are up to 60 millionths of an inch long and between a ten-millionth and one-millionth of an inch thick. Each is composed of several hydrocarbon chains. Folded up originally in the crystals themselves, they remained attached as the crystals separated, binding them together in all directions through the mass of uncrystallized polymer between. (20, 21)

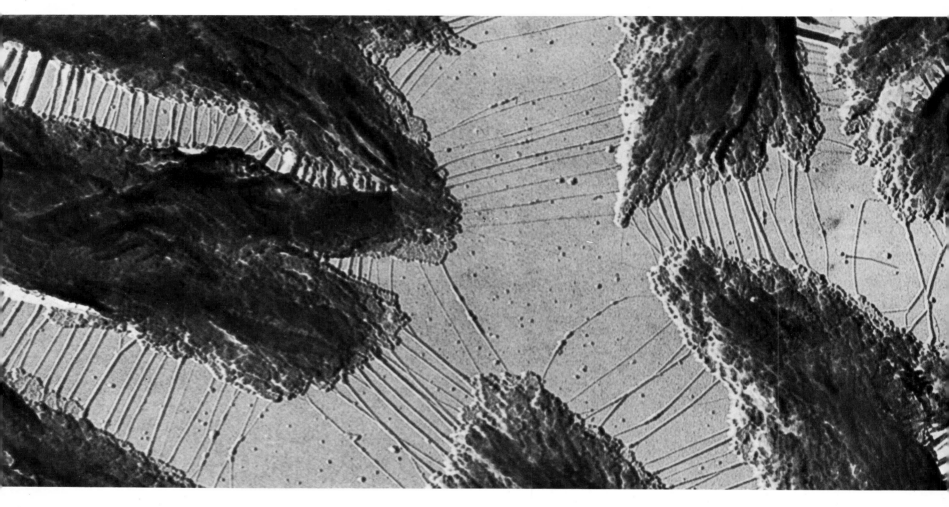

Human spare parts are among the most exciting new applications of plastics. Chemically inert, flexible, almost everlasting, with a smooth surface which prevents blood-clotting, they are the ideal replacement for worn-out flesh. Artificial heart valves (left) are made in flexible polypropylene, with a knitted ring of the same plastic in a groove round the rim to take the 24 sutures that fix it in place. This is the mitral valve, 2-3 cms. across, which passes arterial blood from the left atrium into the left ventricle. When the ventricle—the main pump chamber—contracts and pumps blood through the aorta and round the body, the mitral valve prevents backflow. The two hinged flaps of the natural valve are simplified into a round plastic plate, secured on the 'upstream' or atrium side by three tiny hooks. (22)

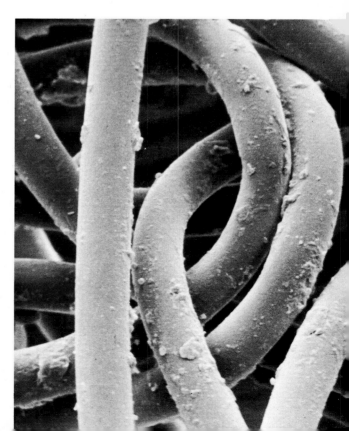

The man with the spray gun (left) is making an insulating material out of an on-the-spot chemical reaction. Three snaking hose-pipes meet at the nozzle of his gun. One carries a polyol, a short hydro-carbon chain in which oxygen-hydrogen pairs have taken the places of two, three or more of the attached hydrogens. Another carries an isocyanate, a compound related to hydrocyanic acid, HCNO. The third conveys water. The two chemicals interact to make the polymer polyurethane, used in hard-wearing paints. Excess isocyanate reacts with the water to make carbon dioxide gas, frothing the polymer into a foam which sets within seconds. A close look at the result (below, magnified 7.5 times) shows that it is light, being mostly air, but it can be soft and spongy, for stuffing car-seats, or rigid, according to the proportions of the ingredients. The man in the photograph, protected by other plastics, is experimenting with polyurethane foam as a heat and sound insulator in buildings. In mines, it seals and preserves crumbling rock faces, and being non-inflammable it inhibits the spread of fire; not even a blow-torch can do more than char it. (24, 25)

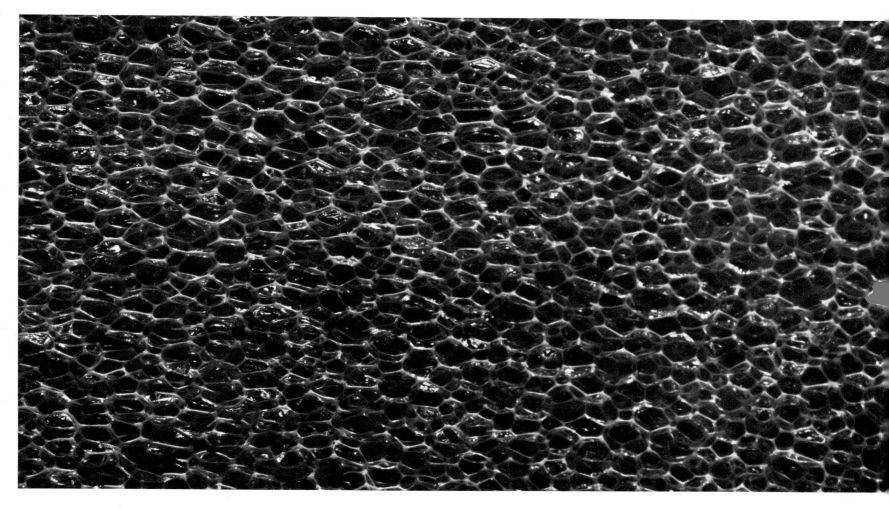

▶ **Polyhexamethyleneadipamide** (left) is better known, and more pronounceable, as nylon. Two and a half square millimetres of a warp-knitted, double-lock stitched nylon stocking are magnified 375 times by a new scanning electron microscope which gives a three-dimensional effect to the picture. The fibres are rounded and regular as a garden hose: natural fibres, cotton for instance, look as ragged and irregu-lar as a tree-trunk. But those nylon fibres, in spite of their size (about 0.07 mm. thick), are strong. A nylon hawser can hold a liner. A nylon parachute streaming from the tail of an aircraft (right) acts as a powerful brake, the fabric and the nylon cords resisting a strain measured in tons. When nylon is first squeezed out through the spinnerets (pl. 19, p. 199) it is highly crystalline. If the filaments are put under stress, the molecular chains tend to align themselves along the thread, allowing the filament to stretch and giving it more strength. The filaments are therefore cooled and then drawn between systems of rollers to impart the desired balance of stretch and strength. Nylon is made to a given thickness and woven into cloth or twisted into rope like any other fibre. (23, 26)

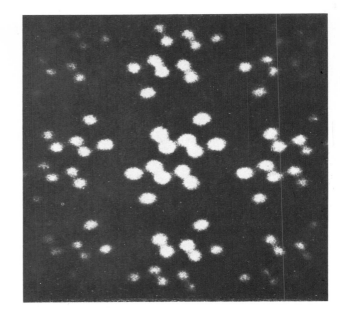

The most famous shape in chemistry is six carbon atoms in a ring, each with one hydrogen attached—the benzene ring, basis of a large number of important compounds. This hexagonal arrangement, worked out by theory, can now be actually seen (above): the contours made by X-ray diffraction through a crystal of a benzene compound are translated, with the aid of a special 'fly's eye' lens, into a pattern of spots corresponding to the actual arrangement of atoms in the molecule.

The first truly synthetic giant molecule made by man—Bakelite—is formed, we have seen, from phenol, which has the benzene ring shape, and formaldehyde. In the first stage, they join together, releasing water, and, alternating links on a long chain, pour down on to the cooling floor (left, top). Fillers and colours are added, and the second stage proceeds, cross-linking in all three dimensions. Once set, Bakelite cannot be melted, so the final stages take place in moulds to give it the required shapes. Sandwiched with paper and copper foil in powerful presses, it is used as an insulating base for printed circuits in TV sets (below). The epoxide resins are a large group of plastics which do not melt under heat: one of their two ingredients has two of the ring-shaped phenol groups in its molecule. A 13,000-ton tanker (left, below) receives a protective coat of epoxide-based paint. Not only does this give a tough, lasting, fireproof protection to hull and superstructure, but being resistant to chemical action it is also used to protect the inside of the oil tanks. Epoxide resin reinforced with glass fibres forms an immensely strong material used everywhere from gay translucent roof panels at the World's Fair (right, above) to the hulls of racing yachts (right, below). The yacht's sails, of course, are Terylene—yet another polymer with benzene rings in it. Terephthalic acid (a benzene ring with two —COOH groups attached to it) joins up with ethylene glycol (used in anti-freeze) to make a long-chain polymer with unique properties, perhaps the most generally useful of all the synthetic fibres. (27-32)

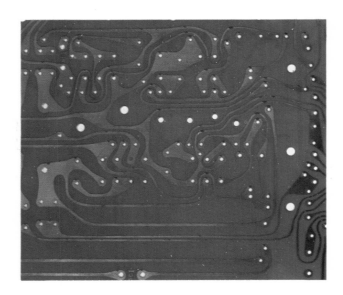

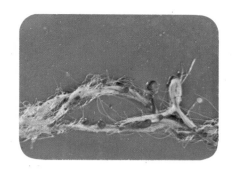

An attack on grease at the kitchen sink is caught in close-up in this film sequence. As we have seen, a detergent is a beautiful example of a molecule made to order. Carbon will make a bond with sulphur and advantage is taken of this to attach a sulphonic acid group, $-SO_3H$, to one end of a long, straight hydrocarbon chain. The group is strongly attracted to water; the chain is equally strongly attracted to grease, to which it is chemically akin.

In the pictures, water in which a detergent is dissolved surrounds fibres impregnated with grease. The invisible chains in great numbers attach themselves to the grease, their other ends pulled away by the water molecules. Tiny lumps of grease begin to break off, forming into globules since they will not mix with the water. Several are almost detached; one rises away on a longer and longer thread; a third is detached completely. All will continue to be attacked until the globules are broken up into a fine emulsion which will be washed away with the water. Other chemicals are usually added to the detergent to help it break the surface cohesion of the grease and to make the characteristic luxuriant foam.

The hydrogen atom in the sulphonic acid group is linked by the electrical attraction of the ionic bond, which means that water breaks it away and may dissolve molecules which are combined with the group. Molecules which were coloured but do not dissolve in water may therefore be converted into useful dyes after reaction with sulphuric acid. (33-37)

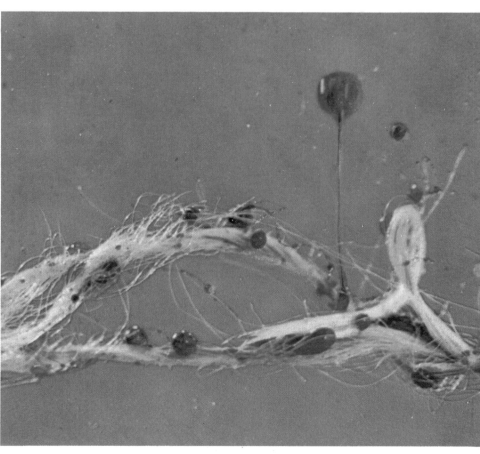

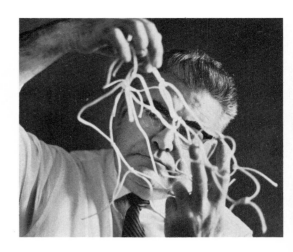

A major triumph of chemistry was the creation of synthetic rubber. In the rubber tree, nature polymerizes isoprene, C_5H_8 (and even this polymer has been copied by the chemist, to make an artificial product which is exactly the same as natural rubber). Man-made rubbers, however, are more resistant to oil or petrol, stand up better to heat or cold, or have other desirable properties built into them. Butyl rubber, for instance, is one more in the great family of synthetics-from-oil. It is made from iso-butylene, C_4H_8, a gas of the ethylene series derived from naphtha, with about 3% of isoprene. At a chill 140°F below zero, these two will polymerize into something which is recognizably rubber, but is not yet usable. It emerges first as 'crumb' (top left) in a water slurry; this is drained and dried, and compressed into an endless rope of still tacky rubber (left, centre). Compressed again, and drier, a long, thick block of raw rubber moves slowly under a guillotine, which, actuated by the interruption of a light beam, chops it into bales (bottom left).

This rubber is still not fully elastic; the molecular chains are not connected to one another and when they are straightened out by stretching, slide past each other and cannot spring back all the way. A ball made of this rubber would not bounce. The next step is vulcanization—heating with sulphur. Sulphur atoms form cross-links between the rubber chains, fixing their positions relatively to each other so that, though they will stretch under tension, they return when released. The principle can be demonstrated (above) with a simple model of knotted string: the knots represent the sulphur cross-links.

In the finished butyl rubber the cross-linked molecules are packed closely together: this makes it particularly impervious to gases, and thus the ideal material for inner tubes. The main undercarriage bogey of a Boeing 707 (below) has four tyres with butyl inner tubes to take the weight of the 150-ton aircraft. (38-42)

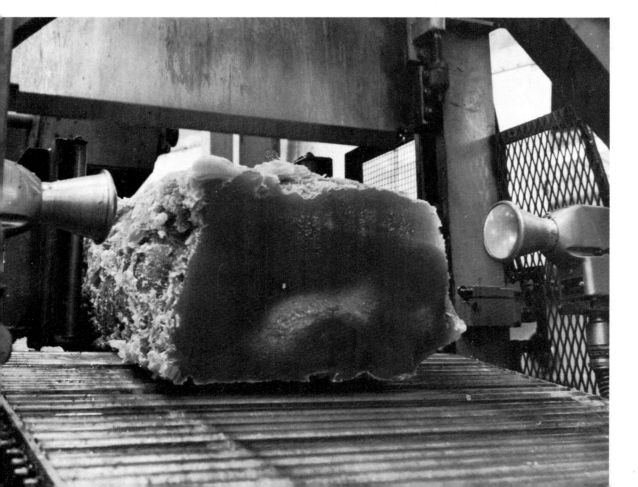

Select bibliography

The physical universe

Isaac Asimov: *The Intelligent Man's Guide to Science*. 2 vols.; New York, 1964
Alan Isaacs: *Introducing Science*. London & New York, 1963
S. D. Beck: *The Simplicity of Science*. London & New York, 1962
James R. Newman (ed.): *The Harper Encyclopedia of Science*. New York, 1963. Also published in London in 1965, revised and with new material, as *The International Encyclopedia of Science*

1. Time and the shape of space

G.J.Whitrow: *The Natural Philosophy of Time*. London & New York, 1961
Norman Feather: *Mass, Length and Time*. London & New York, 1964
Martin Gardner: *The Ambidexterous Universe*. New York, 1965
H. Alan Lloyd: *Some Outstanding Clocks over 700 Years, 1250–1950*. London, 1958; New York, 1962
A. Einstein: *Relativity: the Special and the General Theory*. 15th ed., revised, Princeton & London 1955; London, 1960
James Coleman: *Relativity for the Layman*. New York, 1958; London, 1961
H. Bondi: *Relativity and Common Sense*. London & New York, 1965
Martin Gardner: *Relativity for the Million*. New York & London, 1962

2. The empire of the sun

G. Abetti: *The Sun* (transl. J. B. Sidgwick). London, 1957
P. M. Hurley (ed.): *Advances in Earth Science*. Cambridge, Mass., 1965
L. Bertin: *Larousse Encyclopedia of the Earth*. London, 1961
Walter Sullivan: *Assault on the Unknown: the International Geophysical Year*. New York, 1961; London, 1962
G. E. R. Deacon (ed.): *Oceans*. London, 1962
T. F. Gaskell: *Under the Deep Oceans*. London, 1960
J. H. Hodgson: *Earthquakes and Earth Structure*. Englewood Cliffs, N.J., 1965
Arthur Holmes: *Principles of Physical Geology*. 2nd ed., London, 1964; New York, 1965
Z. Kopal: *The Moon: our nearest celestial neighbour*. 2nd ed., London & New York, 1963

3. The range of radiant energy

Norman Feather: *Vibrations and Waves*. London & New York, 1964
S. Tolansky: *An Introduction to Interferometry*. London & New York, 1955
Curiosities of Light Rays and Light Waves. London, 1964; New York, 1965
Banesh Hoffman: *The Strange Story of the Quantum*. London, 1963
Stanley Leinwoll: *Understanding Lasers and Masers*. New York, 1965; London, 1966

4. Into the depths of space

David Bergamini: *The Universe* (*Life* Nature Library). New York, 1962
A. C. B. and J. Lovell: *Discovering the Universe*. London, 1963; New York, 1964
A. C. B. Lovell: *The Exploration of Outer Space*. London, 1962; New York, 1963
L. Rudeaux and G. de Vaucouleurs: *The Larousse Encyclopedia of Astronomy*. London, 1959
F. Hoyle: *Galaxies, Nuclei and Quasars*. London & New York, 1965
Patrick Moore (ed.): *Handbook of Practical Astronomy*. New York, 1964
R. H. Brown and A. C. B. Lovell: *The Exploration of Space by Radio*. London, 1962

5. The assault on the atom

G. K. T. Conn and D. H. Turner: *The Evolution of the Nuclear Atom, 1897–1913*. London, 1965
G. O. Jones, J. Rotblat, G. J.Whitrow: *Atoms and the Universe*. 2nd ed., London, 1962
G. Gamow: *Mr. Tompkins in Paperback*. Cambridge and New York, 1966
A. Romer: *The Restless Atom*. London, 1962
K.W. Ford: *The World of Elementary Particles*. New York, 1965
C. N. Yang: *Elementary Particles*. Princeton, N. J., 1961

6. The architecture of matter

T. J. Lewis and P. E. Secker: *The Science of Materials*. London & New York, 1965
Alan Holden and Phyllis Singer: *Crystals and Crystal Growing*. London & New York, 1961
L. W. Marrison: *Crystals, Diamonds and Transistors*. London, 1966
R. Benrey: *Understanding Digital Computers*. New York, 1964; London, 1966
S. H. Hollingdale and G. C. Toothill: *Electronic Computers*. London & New York, 1965
W. A. Holm: *Colour Television Explained*. London, 1965
E. W. Lee: *Magnetism*. London, 1963; New York, 1965

7. The chemists' dazzling bounty

Louis C. Vaczek: *The Enjoyment of Chemistry*. New York, 1964; London, 1966
F. W. Gibbs: *Organic Chemistry To-day*. London & New York, 1961
Kenneth Hutton: *Chemistry: the Conquest of Materials*. Revised ed., London & New York, 1965
G. Porter: *Chemistry for the Modern World*. London, 1962; New York, 1963
L. P. Lessing: *Understanding Chemistry*. New York, 1959; London, 1961
H. Melville: *Big Molecules*. London, 1956; New York, 1958
W. Alexander and A. C. Street: *Metals in the Service of Man*. London & New York, 1962
Herman F. Mark: *Giant Molecules* (*Life* Science Library). New York, 1966

List and sources of illustrations

The page on which an illustration appears is shown by the first set of numerals, its plate or figure number by the second set. The publishers acknowledge gratefully the co-operation of the many people, organizations and learned bodies (indicated in italics) who have supplied pictures.

Contributing artists indicated by abbreviation are: BE, Barry Evans; CT, Clive Tunnicliffe; DC, David Cox; DTH, Deh-ta Hsiung; EP, Edward Powers; GC, Gordon Cramp; GD, Gordon Davies; JH, John Hardy; JW, Jon Wilsher; LA, Laszlo Acs; LW, Len Wightman; RG, Ruth Gardiner; SG, Sharon Goad; SP, Shirley Parfitt; TB, Tony Birks

1 Time and the shape of space

2 The empire of the sun

3 The range of radiant energy

4 Into the depths of space

5 The assault on the atom

acting as a brake chute on a Handley Page Victor. *British Nylon Spinners Ltd.* (photo Cyril Peckham)

202 27. Condensation product of a phenol and an aldehyde falls into the cooling tray: a stage in the production of Bakelite. *Bakelite Ltd.* (photo Maurice Broomfield, FIBP, FRPS)

28. S.S. *Cinulia*, a 13,000-ton tanker, receiving a protective coat of epoxy-resin-based paint. *Shell Chemicals Ltd.*

29. Atoms in benzene rings shown optically from X-ray analysis. *Physics Department, Manchester College of Science and Technology* (A. W. Hanson and C. A. Taylor)

30. Printed circuit for TV set, with Bakelite base. *Bakelite Ltd.*

203 31. Translucent Fiberglass roof panels of the New York State Pavilion, World's Fair. *Owens-Corning Fiberglass*

32. The 'Nicholson 32' class yacht *Can-Can*: terylene sails and glass-fibre hull. Photo *Eileen Ramsay*

33–7. The action of a synthetic detergent in removing grease from a textile fiber. From the Unilever film 'Outline of Detergency'. *Unilever Ltd.*

204 38. Particles of freshly formed crumb butyl rubber being transported by conveyor belt to the drying plant. *Esso photograph* (photo Hans Wild)

39. Butyl rubber, dried and compressed into rope during the finishing process. *An Esso photograph*

40. Finished slab of raw butyl rubber being guillotined into bales. *An Esso photograph* (photo Hans Wild)

41. Simple model of the cross-linking between molecules, resulting from vulcanization of rubber. *An Esso photograph*

42. Main undercarriage bogeys of a Boeing 707, just before touchdown. *Firestone Rubber Co. Ltd.*

General index